THE BEER STEIN BOOK
THIRD EDITION
A 400 YEAR HISTORY

ILLUSTRATED CATALOG
CURRENT PRICES
COLLECTOR'S INFORMATION

BY GARY KIRSNER

EDITOR: REGINA KELLETER

GLENTIQUES, LTD., CORAL SPRINGS, FLORIDA

Publisher's Cataloging-in-Publication
(Provided by Quality Books, Inc.)

Kirsner, Gary, 1945-
    The beer stein book : a 400 year history,
illustrated catalog, current prices, collector's
information / by Gary Kirsner ; editor: Regina
Kelleter. -- 3rd ed.
        p. cm.
    Includes bibliographical references and index.
    ISBN: 1-889591-00-9

    1. Steins--Germany--Collectors and collecting--
Catalogs.   I. Kelleter, Regina. II. Kirsner,
Gary, 1945- Stein book. III. Title

NK8647.K49 1999   730'.0943'075
                    QB199-1292

First Printing, 1999

Printed in the United States of America
Published by Glentiques, Ltd.
P.O. Box 8807
Coral Springs, FL 33075

Telephone: (954) 344-9856
FAX: (954) 344-4421

CONTENTS

Preface 5
1. Stein History 7
2. Production of Steins & Marks 15
3. Early Stoneware & Earthenware 25
4. Faience 43
5. Pewter 69
6. Glass 79
7. Unusual Materials 109
8. Porcelain 125
9. Pottery & Stoneware 147
10. Art Nouveau 185
    Color Photographs 193
11. Mettlach 225
12. Other Etched Ceramics 241
13. Occupational 267
14. Regimental 273
15. Military 297
16. Character 303
17. Brewery 323
18. Modern Brewery 339
19. Modern Era 353
20. Bibliography and References 365
    Appendices 369
    Glossary 375
    Index 379

Preface

When *The Stein Book* and *The Beer Stein Book* were being written, a number of decisions had to be made to limit the size of the books. Many changes in collecting trends have occurred since these books were written. Chapters covering Art Nouveau and modern brewery steins are included in this book due to the tremendous increase in interest by collectors of these particular specialties. In addition, coverage of steins in numerous other areas has been vastly strengthened.

The Beer Stein Book, Third Edition still had to be selective. The breadth of the topic has forced the making of some really tough decisions about what to include. Nevertheless, it is hoped that even stein experts will find exciting pictures and new important information about their individual specialties.

During the writing, and right after the release of *The Stein Book* and *The Mettlach Book*, the same question was repeatedly asked: "Why would you want to publish information about steins that a few advanced collectors, museums, and dealers know are worth three or four times the price for which they can often be purchased?" It has been suggested that publishing this kind of *inside information* would be bad for the stein dealers' businesses. Again, in preparing this book, the aforementioned question has come up, and the answer is the same as before. When a hobby begins to slip under the control of those who have *inside information*, it breeds mistrust, suspicion, and disappointment among the majority of collectors. The publication of *real* prices in previous books has proved that the resulting trust, openness and enthusiasm are great for the hobby, as well as for dealers.

This book attempts to answer the most common questions about steins:

· How and why did they originate?

· What do the different types look like?

· Which ones are most valuable?

· How old are various types?

· What effect does condition have on what collectors will pay?

Before acknowledging the tremendous assistance that has been graciously contributed by many stein experts, a little personal information: Gary Kirsner studied economics and accounting at New York University and Miami University of Ohio. The business in general antiques, which he began in the early 1970s, soon focused almost exclusively on steins. Gary soon grew to be a leader in the purchase and sale of quality steins. With his wife, Karen, he lives in Coral Springs, Florida.

Gary's family offered important support to tasks involved in assembling this book. His daughters, Beth and Britt, provided help with preparing photo files and text layout.

There are also a number of other people who deserve specific thanks for having made their stein collections available for photographs: Frieder Aichele, Bob Alutin, Dan Cipriano, Jim DeMars, Bill Floyd, David Fuller, Irving Miller, Helmut Neuner, Ulrich Schneider, along with those who wish to remain anonymous. Because of the success of *The Stein Book* and *The Beer Stein Book,* there are high expectations for this book. We believe this book will:

· show the whole range of steins to collectors, so they will not need to use *trial and error* in order to discover what they like best,

· release steins from collectors who have been holding on to pieces because they didn't know their value,

· build a stronger demand for steins at every level, and

· help collectors build up a lifetime of pricing experience that will improve their confidence and knowledge.

Again, with this book, the hope is that people will see stein collecting not only as a hobby, but as an activity that combines beauty, excitement, history, and investment. Stein collecting can tell us a great deal about past generations, and perhaps something about ourselves.

Gary Kirsner
September, 1999

1. Stein History

The word *stein* is a shortened form of *Steinzeugkrug*, which is German for stoneware jug or tankard. By common usage, however, stein has come to mean any beer container—regardless of its material or size—that has a hinged lid and a handle. Tankard would be more technically appropriate than stein, but these two words are used interchangeably in this book. Be warned, however, that some people reserve the word tankard for the all-pewter or all-silver varieties of steins. One final definition: *mug* is universally used as the name for those vessels that have handles but would never have had a lid. So much for the semantics; those with a deeper interest in definitions should refer to the Glossary.

1.1 Earliest Steins 1525–1700

From about 1340 until 1380, a bubonic plague, or Black Death, killed more than 25 million Europeans! As horrible as this historic event was, it prompted tremendous progress for civilization. And, of interest here, it is also responsible for the origin of the beer stein.

Recall from above that the distinction between a mug and a stein is the hinged lid. This lid was originally conceived entirely as a sanitary measure. During the summers of the late 1400s, hoards of little flies frequently invaded Central Europe. By the early 1500s, several principalities in what is now Germany had passed laws requiring that all food and beverage containers be covered to protect consumers against these dirty insects. The common mug also had to be covered, and this was accomplished by adding a hinged lid with a thumblift. This ingenious invention was soon used to cover all German beverage containers while still allowing them to be used with one hand.

This covered-container law and several other public health laws were enthusiastically passed and vigilantly enforced as a result of public fears about a return of the Black Death. In the period from Roman times to the 1300s, sanitation had continually declined. During the years of the Black Death, it became obvious to all, with 95% of those in filthy areas dead and only 10% dead in clean surroundings, that the plague was somehow related to unsanitary conditions.

The covered-container law was only one in a whole series of sanitary regulations that were passed in Germany after the plague: pigpens could not be adjacent to streets, old or diseased meat had to be labeled as such, and beer could be brewed only from hops, cereals, yeast, and water.

Strictly enforced regulations concerning the quality and transport of beer in many of the German provinces resulted in a tremendous improvement in the taste of beer, and also had an impact on stein making. Many records show that average beer consumption increased to about two liters per day in many places. Beerhouses, city hall cellars, and taverns began to proliferate in the 1500s. There is an old saying, "The German will place great value on that which brings him his food or drink." Everyone in Germany needed a personal drinking vessel to be proud of.

Local brews in many other parts of Europe were still being made with rotten bread, cabbages, eggs, and anything else at hand. Soon the Bremen, Hamburg, and other clean northern Germany beers became famous and were exported throughout northern Europe, and even as far as the East Indies and Jerusalem. Such beers raised a new need for relatively inexpensive, but durable, large containers; the search for appropriate materials was on.

As for individual beer vessels, up to the 1400s, well-to-do Germans had pewter beakers; a few of the wealthiest had silver vessels. These metal containers, and those made of glass, remained too expensive for general use or for large containers. Some wooden beakers were used, but other than wood, porous earthenware was by far the most common material for beer beakers, mugs, and the larger containers. However, both the wood and the earthenware broke easily, which may have been a blessing because these materials absorbed beer, giving off a smell that got worse with each subsequent use.

Scientific experimentation was begun to try to improve the earthenware. The all-powerful Roman Catholic Church, long at odds with science, would previously have squelched all such scientific inquiry. During the Black Death, churches claimed prayer would end the plague and sometimes announced that Revelations had begun. In either case they lost some of their hold on the public, and more pragmatic scientific views began to prevail. The subsequent rise of science and its marriage with art has been credited with starting the Renaissance.

The obvious earthenware experiments involved raising the firing temperature past the usual level of 500°C (900°). Higher temperatures, however, could not be achieved merely by throwing more wood into the furnace; they required new furnace designs. One such invention, which produced temperatures up to 1200°C (2200°F), had a furnace on the lower floor, and above it, through some slats, a ceramic firing chamber entirely enclosed in brick, except for small flues. At these extreme temperatures, not only was all the moisture driven out of the clay—as in earthenware production—but also the clay vitrified, or partially melted, into a solid stone-like material, hence the name stoneware.

Stoneware required days of firing and dozens of cords of wood, but the product proved to be far superior to earthenware. It is resistant to chipping and cracking, and is not porous, resulting in a much more sanitary container.

The high cost of stoneware steins, especially after the covered-beverage-container law required lids, made steins worthy of some fine decorative ceramic art. Renaissance artists supplied many designs for applied and carved stein decorations, and colored glazes complemented these designs nicely. A clear saltglaze had been invented about 1400, and a blue glaze from cobalt oxide was also known at that time. A chocolate saltglaze was invented in the 1600s, and a manganese oxide purple glaze was invented around 1650.

Tankards were soon decorated with shields and historical, allegorical, and biblical scenes. Beer drinking had now also become a pleasure for the eyes! And the landless day laborers, the masses that had survived the Black Death, were in a position to command higher wages for their services. This meant they could afford a few modest luxuries, and the personal tankard became an important status symbol and display piece for these Germans.

Once again, consider the historical situation. The guild system was well in place in the 1500s and guild representatives held powerful positions on the city councils. Although no records of it exist, the Pewter Guild was no doubt an important sponsor of the covered-container law that prompted creation of the beer stein. The Potters' Guilds are known to have continually pushed up minimum standards for the quality of both the decorations and the stoneware, thus making steins increasingly attractive.

The Black Death, by depleting the population, had created a surplus of food, especially grains. Much of this surplus grain made its way into local beers, making a fine, pure beverage really worthy of celebration. Eventually, large quantities of surplus grains made their way to the breweries in the north. (There were only a few cloister brewers in the south at that time.) In the 1500s, Hamburg had 600 breweries, producing 25 million liters of beer and directly or indirectly employing half of the population of that city.

Initially, a few glass bottles were made in Delft to be used for shipping some of that northern beer. But soon the fine clay of the Cologne area was used to make large stoneware jugs. The shipping industry was rejuvenated, and the beer export and stein-making businesses boomed, producing some extremely wealthy merchants.

Such wealth did not go uncontested, and the resultant Thirty Years' War had changed many things by its conclusion in the 1640s. It was a war fought with fire. Virtually all of the northern breweries were destroyed, and most of the southern vineyards as well. A few southern breweries in cloisters survived and, more or less by default, Bavaria became Central Europe's beer land. Beer soon replaced cider and wine as the beverage of choice throughout Germany.

An expanded new market for beer steins developed, and the stoneware industry from the areas of Köln and Koblenz responded. Pewter, silver, and glass luxury steins were also available, but the Chinese connection for the luxurious Ming porcelain mugs had been disrupted by rebellions in China in the middle 1600s. No one in Europe knew how to make porcelain, but several German potters were quick to jump in with a porcelain substitute: faience.

Faience is earthenware with a porcelain-like white glaze made from tin oxide. German faience was not as durable as the Chinese porcelain, but it was far less expensive and had two aesthetic advantages. First, the motifs on German faience were popular late-Renaissance and early-Baroque designs, not foreign-looking Chinese figures. And second, the cobalt oxide of China was contaminated with purple manganese oxide, and the Persian cobalt oxide that the Chinese artists sparingly mixed in would often diffuse badly. The purer German cobalt oxide supplies were bright blue and allowed for crisp lines. So by the time the Chinese porcelain supply was re-established, German faience had gained a firm hold on the stein market.

1.2 Transition Period 1700–1850

Throughout the 1700s, the Pewter Guilds maintained their tight hold on the covered-container law. It seems certain that this involvement was responsible for keeping the lidded design of the stein from disappearing since there has always been a tendency to return to beakers and a master stein, or to find some other way of getting around the expense of an individually hinged lid. Yet by the end of the 1800s, when the covered-container law was apparently no longer in force, over 300 years of conditioning had taught Germans to view a stein as incomplete without a lid. Thus, steins with lids are here to stay.

Many of the trends that were in place just before 1700 continued to strengthen thereafter. For example, by 1750 there were over 4000 breweries in Bavaria. And the art and production of stoneware and faience steins increased substantially, all the way into the late 1700s.

European porcelain was invented in 1709 but did not begin to have a noticeable impact on stein making until the 1720s. Several porcelain factories were started in the 1700s, but their products were very expensive. Only the wealthiest Germans were drinking beer from porcelain or glass vessels at that time.

The quality and taste of beer—the flowing bread—continued to improve. Besides offering taste and fellowship, beer was considered to be important for the constitution, with the ability to induce strength, health, and relaxation. From the earliest times right up into the 1800s, many considered beer to be the most effective medicine known: the drink from the gods.

Although glass beer beakers were used in Roman times, the Church viewed glassmaking as heathenish and suppressed its production during the Middle Ages. The art of making and enameling glass was not relearned by the Germans until the late 1500s. These early enameled items were mainly beakers and pokals.

A few engraved glass steins began to be used in the 1700s. However, partly because of their fragility and partly because their costliness limited the number produced, not many of these early glass steins still exist. The color of this glass was almost always clear, which required some special efforts to achieve because the usual *Waldglas* of the time was partially made with wood ashes that caused a definite greenish tinge. The use of clear glass would seem to support the theory that an important feature of the early glass stein was to show off the rare clarity and color of the costliest beers that were brought from some distance.

Toward the end of the Baroque period, around 1800, pewter and silver tankards were still uncommon in Germany. However, the English, and to some extent the Scandinavians, had by now adopted the finished look of a lidded mug. And except for a few ceramic factories, they were making pewter and silver steins exclusively.

The Scandinavians had also perfected a method of making a nice all-wooden tankard, complete with a wooden hinge. The few German wooden steins from this period generally have pewter mountings and pewter overlaid designs, and even these were no longer being made by 1800.

Horn drinking vessels, so popular in Roman times, did not adapt well to the covered-container law and became rare. Ivory steins were made only for the exceptionally wealthy.

In the 1600s, it was rather easy to determine a stein's origin; every small region had considerable pride in its own typical form. The Bohemian, Austrian, and other southern tankards were wide and sturdy; sleek and tall drinking vessels were preferred in the northern areas. The western steins were gray stoneware with blue decoration; the eastern steins were brown-glazed stoneware.

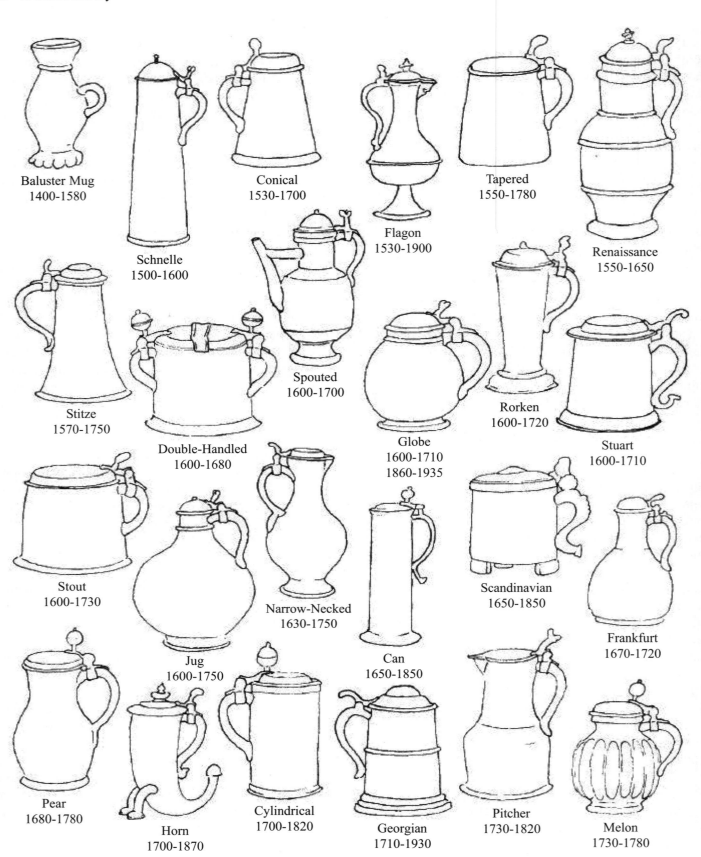

Baluster Mug
1400-1580

Schnelle
1500-1600

Conical
1530-1700

Flagon
1530-1900

Tapered
1550-1780

Renaissance
1550-1650

Stitze
1570-1750

Double-Handled
1600-1680

Spouted
1600-1700

Globe
1600-1710
1860-1935

Rorken
1600-1720

Stuart
1600-1710

Stout
1600-1730

Jug
1600-1750

Narrow-Necked
1630-1750

Can
1650-1850

Scandinavian
1650-1850

Frankfurt
1670-1720

Pear
1680-1780

Horn
1700-1870

Cylindrical
1700-1820

Georgian
1710-1930

Pitcher
1730-1820

Melon
1730-1780

Some of the typical shapes of early steins, their most common names and the period when they were most popular.

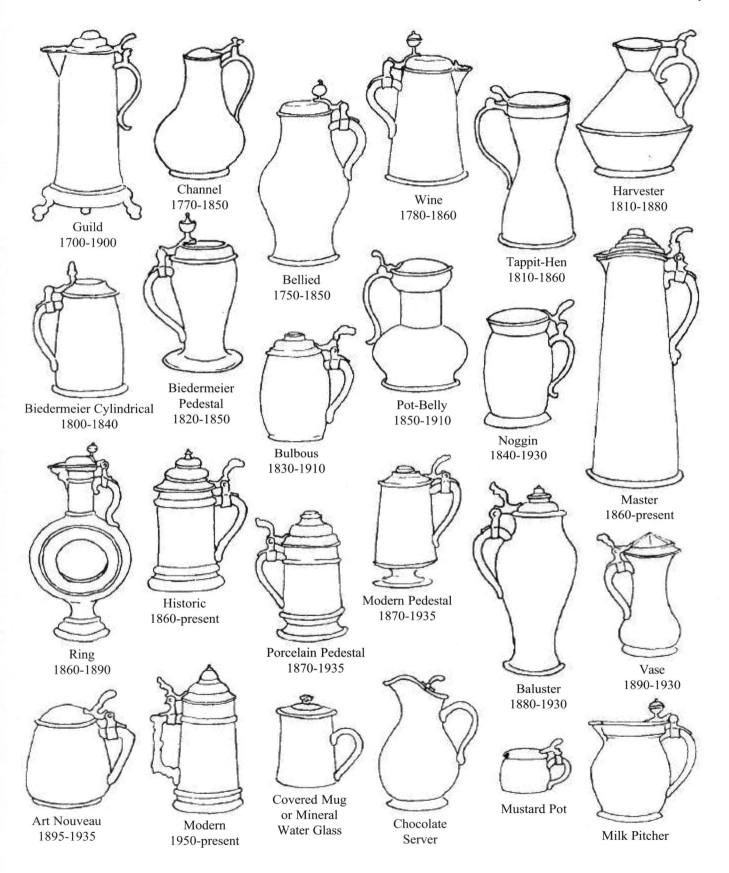

Guild
1700-1900

Channel
1770-1850

Bellied
1750-1850

Wine
1780-1860

Tappit-Hen
1810-1860

Harvester
1810-1880

Biedermeier Cylindrical
1800-1840

Biedermeier
Pedestal
1820-1850

Bulbous
1830-1910

Pot-Belly
1850-1910

Noggin
1840-1930

Master
1860-present

Ring
1860-1890

Historic
1860-present

Porcelain Pedestal
1870-1935

Modern Pedestal
1870-1935

Baluster
1880-1930

Vase
1890-1930

Art Nouveau
1895-1935

Modern
1950-present

Covered Mug
or Mineral
Water Glass

Chocolate
Server

Mustard Pot

Milk Pitcher

Some typical shapes of later steins, as well as a few of the covered containers that are closest to the stein shape.

During the 1700s, shape became less important. The faience steins predominantly assumed a pleasing cylindrical shape about twice as high as wide. Stoneware, glass, porcelain, pewter, and other steins soon followed suit. Regional differences of shape and size were replaced by differences in materials and motifs.

Soon after 1800, another transition began that was as significant and unpredictable as that which brought on the Renaissance. The Napoleonic war and other rebellions of the time so diminished the aristocrats' wealth and power that the newly monied middle class became the most important market for steins and other artistic products. This middle class cast off the Baroque extravagances, preferring instead a sturdy, functional folk art. This era is known as the Biedermeier period.

Also around 1800, secularization had resulted in the closing of many monasteries, but there were enough private breweries to assure that cloudless beer, without dregs, would still be available to the masses. And perhaps pride in the appearance of the clear beer led, in part, to a major influx of glass steins into the marketplace soon after 1800. These glass steins usually carried enameled folk art designs.

The straight-sided, cylindrical pewter tankards also became very popular at this time. Engraved or stamped designs were common, especially those using the same type of folk art motifs. Occasionally, pewter steins with remnants of painted decorations are found from this period. Considering that paint applied to pewter is not durable, this type of decoration must have been quite common to still be visible on any surviving examples.

Porcelain and silver steins continued to be made in the early 1800s, always with the Renaissance and Baroque designs that still appealed to the wealthy.

In the early 1800s, the preference of the masses was so clearly for glass and pewter that nearly all of the faience workshops were permanently closed. Most stoneware manufacturers stopped making steins and turned to everyday items such as bowls, jars, and wide-mouthed jugs.

The Villeroy & Boch firm of Mettlach was established at this time. Although the family was wealthy, the von Bochs' plates and other utilitarian items had to appeal to common tastes in order for the company to stay in business. However, as the Biedermeier period was drawing to a close in 1850, the Mettlach factory, with its aristocratic owners and classically trained artists, was ready to respond to the upcoming change in artistic tastes.

During the early 1800s, many archaeological expeditions had uncovered outstanding examples of Greek, Roman, and Renaissance art. By about 1850, the public had been so captivated by the beauty of these finds that they were ready to forsake the mundane, functional styles of the Biedermeier period.

1.3 The Golden Era 1850–1910

By 1850, art instruction consisted entirely of having students copy the forms and designs of the archaeological finds from the Renaissance and Classical periods. The new style that resulted has been called neo-Renaissance and neo-Classical or, more commonly, Historicism. As for beer steins, the white clays of the Köln area were again used to make stoneware steins with Renaissance allegorical motifs. These steins have gray saltglazed relief decorations and often have inlaid porcelain lids.

In later years, a major resurgence of interest in stoneware steins resulted when Reinhold Hanke of the Westerwald region made blue and purple saltglazed Historicism pieces. Molds were used to avoid the manufacturing expense encountered with the labor-intensive originals. The molded products were no longer unique steins; they were mass-produced, as their seams clearly attest. But there was an artistic advantage to using molds, and Hanke, Dümler, and other stoneware manufacturers exploited this to the fullest. The advantage was that molds could be used to quickly reproduce painstakingly carved, elaborate reliefwork on hundreds of steins.

In the second half of the 1800s, glassmaking techniques had progressed enough to allow molds to also be used to mass-produce glass steins. The surprising sturdiness of the thick molded glass steins no doubt helped to increase their popularity. Other glassmakers' tricks were also applied to glass stein production. Multicolored glass overlays, acid etchings, staining, and pewter overlays were used to make some rather spectacular glass steins.

Advances in the use of moisture-absorbing plaster molds helped the porcelain stein manufacturers. These molds allowed novel shapes to be produced, making the so-called character steins much more common. Also, due to the variation in the thickness and thus the translucence of the porcelain, molds could be used to create the lithophane scenes that are visible in the bottom of many porcelain steins.

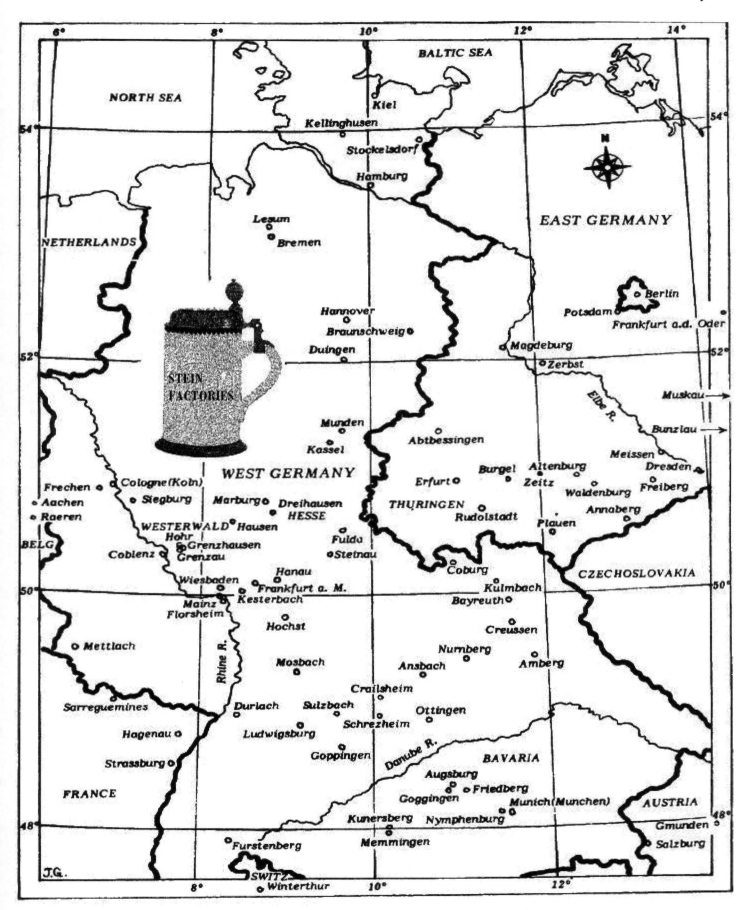

NORTH SEA

BALTIC SEA

Kiel

Kellinghusen

Stockelsdorf

Hamburg

NETHERLANDS

EAST GERMANY

Legum

Bremen

Berlin

Potsdam

Frankfurt a.d. Oder

Hannover

Magdeburg

Braunschweig

Zerbst

Duingen

STEIN-
FACTORIES

Muskau

Elbe R.

Bunzlau

Munden

Abtbessingen

Meissen

Kassel

Dresden

WEST GERMANY

Burgel

Altenburg

Freiberg

Frechen

Cologne (Koln)

Erfurt

Zeitz

Waldenburg

Aachen

Siegburg

Marburg

Dreihausen

THURINGEN

Annaberg

Raeren

WESTERWALD

Hausen

HESSE

Rudolstadt

Plauen

BELG

Hohr

Grenzhausen

Fulda

Coblenz

Grenzau

Steinau

Coburg

CZECHOSLOVAKIA

Wiesbaden

Hanau

Kulmbach

Frankfurt a. M.

Mainz

Kesterbach

Bayreuth

Florsheim

Hochst

Creussen

Mettlach

Mosbach

Nurnberg

Ansbach

Amberg

Rhine R.

Sarreguemines

Durlach

Sulzbach

Crailsheim

Hagenau

Ludwigsburg

Schrezheim

Ottingen

Strassburg

Goppingen

Danube R.

BAVARIA

FRANCE

Augsburg

Friedberg

Goggingen

Munich (Munchen)

AUSTRIA

Kunersberg

Nymphenburg

Gmunden

Furstenberg

Memmingen

Salzburg

J.G.

SWITZ.

Winterthur

The Mettlach factory, with its classically trained artists, was quick to introduce the Renaissance motifs into its new line of relief steins. Experiments with glazes and clays led to some new, brightly colored Mettlach steins of the mosaic and etched types. These were popular enough that many laborers were willing to spend a week's pay on one of these beautiful steins.

By the 1900s, the designs and motifs of Historicism had begun to lose favor and to be replaced by town scenes, occupational emblems, common social scenes, and commemoratives, particularly of military service. To meet these diverse new demands, many potters entered the market with stoneware or glazed pottery steins.

A new art style, Art Nouveau, was gaining limited popularity when, around 1910, political and economic turmoil threw the stein industry into a tremendous slowdown. With the subsequent outbreak of World War I, the materials and labor needed by the pewter industry were converted to use for munitions production, and stein making virtually ceased.

1.4 The Modern Period From 1920

Production of stoneware, glass, and porcelain steins, especially character steins, increased during the 1920s. Except for slowdowns during economic and political disturbances, notably during the early 1930s and the early 1940s, substantial quantities of steins have continued to be manufactured.

The modern period owes a great debt to Historicism and its reverence for Classical and Renaissance art. It was during the Historicism period, from 1840 to 1900, that most of the great public museums were started. The general public, not just the art intellectuals, now wanted to see artistic masterworks, including Renaissance steins. This appreciation for antique steins led to museum and public collecting of steins.

Antique stein collecting has been a major force shaping stein manufacturing in the modern period. First in about 1900, then again in the 1920s, good quality reproductions of antique steins were made, particularly in faience and pewter. Many of these early reproductions are clearly marked and are obviously not intended to fool antique stein collectors. The exceptions to this are some unmarked reproductions of Renaissance stoneware, early pewter, and some rare faience pieces that had reached remarkably high prices in the marketplace, even at the turn of the century. These are the steins that require the closest scrutiny to determine authenticity. It has really only been since the 1960s or 1970s that most types of antique steins have attained a value high enough to consider reproducing steins for the purpose of deception.

One major new direction in stein production in the Modern period, especially since World War II, has been the introduction of tremendous numbers of relief pottery steins.

The last forty years have seen many changes, with economics playing a key role. America has been the primary market for new beer steins of most types, especially the limited editions. Some companies have been very successful, while others failed to cope with the competition and have stopped producing steins.

In the early 1970s, Ceramarte of Brazil entered the stein-producing business and has rapidly become one of the dominant producers. Post-World War II production by this and other companies is discussed in more detail in Sections 18 and 19.

2. Production of Steins & Marks

Since steins in various sections of this book were often produced in similar ways, the common elements are discussed here. For example, several of the sections include steins made from ceramic materials; their common method of production is covered in this section.

2.1 Pewter Mountings

Pewter can contain as much as 90% tin, with the remainder of the alloy made up of copper, zinc, bismuth, antimony, and, occasionally, small quantities of lead. Pewter is a very workable metallic alloy that melts at a relatively low temperature, thus imposing few requirements on the pewter workshop or the pewter craftsman.

In fact, its undemanding nature is rivaled only by lead, which melts at an even lower temperature than pewter. Nevertheless, ever since the inception of the covered-container law, pewter has been the material most commonly chosen for stein mountings. One reason for this is that lead has a tendency to get very dark and to powder, pit, and scale. And an even more important reason why pewter is almost always used for stein mountings is that, since the Middle Ages, it has been known that lead is toxic to humans and, therefore, unacceptable for holding food or drink.

The various parts of a stein's mounting are shown on page 17, though generally one stein will not contain all the elements shown in the illustration.

Because of the low melting temperature of pewter, mountings of this material can be fastened to most steins with little risk of damaging the already completed body of the stein, whether it is ceramic or glass. Fastening the pewter mounting to the handle of the stein is generally accomplished in one of two ways. The most common method has been to wrap a leather strap around the handle, cover it with clay, and then pull the strap out to leave a mold for the melted pewter. Occasionally, wax has been used, covered with clay, then burned out by the molten pewter, hence the so-called lost-wax process.

The purpose of the footring has always been to protect the bottom of the stein from chipping, cracking, or other damage. Because of their susceptibility to damage, virtually all faience steins, even modern replicas, have footrings. Footrings will also occasionally be found on stoneware and glass steins, even those made up to about 1900.

The changes in hinge production over the years are also interesting. Before 1860, the outside of the hinge was closed over, requiring a good deal of labor; after about 1860, the hinge was drilled and the pin set right in through all the teeth. Thus, the hinge pin of these more modern steins generally shows on the outside of the hinge.

The most common method for making lids and footrings has been to cast them, then trim away excess pewter by working the pieces on a lathe. This lathe-work will leave spinmarks on the inside, and often on the outside, of the lids and footrings. Up until about 1900, pewter had been quite expensive relative to labor costs. Lids that appear to be of an older style, but that were cast with a heavy hand and not slimmed down on the lathe, are usually reproductions.

The old types of ball thumblifts, commonly used in the 1700s, were made by soldering together two cup-shaped pieces of pewter. This saved on both

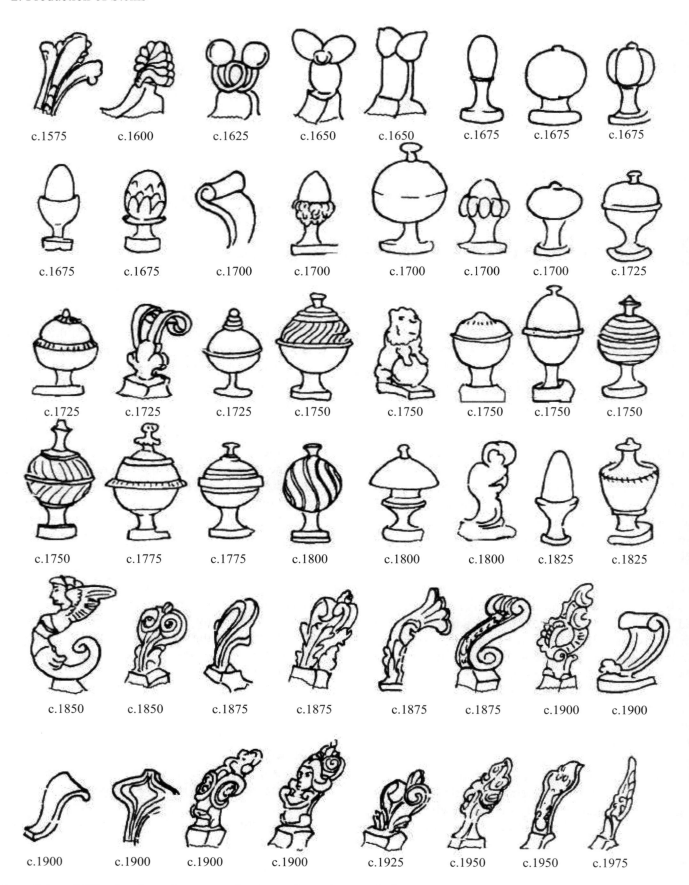

c.1575   c.1600   c.1625   c.1650   c.1650   c.1675   c.1675   c.1675

c.1675   c.1675   c.1700   c.1700   c.1700   c.1700   c.1700   c.1725

c.1725   c.1725   c.1725   c.1750   c.1750   c.1750   c.1750   c.1750

c.1750   c.1775   c.1775   c.1800   c.1800   c.1800   c.1825   c.1825

c.1850   c.1850   c.1875   c.1875   c.1875   c.1875   c.1900   c.1900

c.1900   c.1900   c.1900   c.1900   c.1925   c.1950   c.1950   c.1975

Styles of thumblifts that have been popular in various time periods.

weight and expense. Earlier types of thumblifts, from the 1600s, were generally solid, small figurals, most often shells or single or double acorns. Thumblifts of the early 1800s ran the whole range from hollow vase-like devices to small solid balls and figurals. Toward the end of the 1800s, the thumblifts were commonly bas-relief-decorated tabs or figurals.

Pewter mountings and patina often convey information about steins. Patina can best be described as a visual effect that will be lost if pewter is cleaned with an abrasive material. Patina encompasses both the evidence of wear and the color that comes from aging. It gives old pewter a uniformly soft appearance, virtually impossible to reproduce exactly. A check for possible repairs on a stein should thus begin with a careful examination of the strap, the hinge, and the patina, or color, of the pewter.

Being relatively soft, pewter mountings are easily marked with stamps that may give some informa-

tion about the age and origin of a stein. On early steins, these touchmarks were the registered symbols of the master pewterers. Reference books that identify touchmarks can be studied at many museums and some libraries.

The results of such touchmark searches, however, are often disappointing, since many of the original pewter guild records have been lost. On average, it seems that the city of the pewterer may be identifiable about one-third of the time, the name of the pewterer perhaps one-tenth of the time.

Dates that are part of touchmarks and, for that matter, visible on lids, can be deceiving. Touchmark dates usually represent the date the pewter guild was founded, often 1708, or the date the master first registered his symbol.

Some of the names and symbols that occasionally occur on pewterwork of the last hundred years are discussed in Section 5.

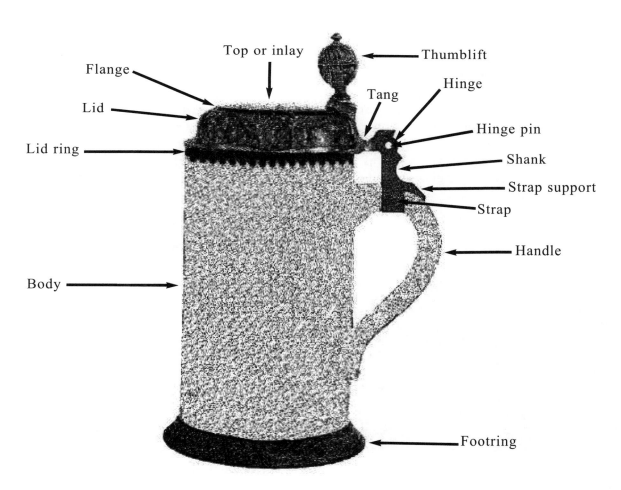

The most common names for the various parts of a stein's mountings.

2.2 Hand-Thrown Ceramics

Earthenware, Hafner ware, pottery, stoneware, *Steingut* (fine stoneware), porcelain, and other ceramics all differ in only two respects: firing temperature and recipe, that is to say, the type of clay and other additives. As far as stein production is concerned, ceramic pieces were either hand thrown or molded.

In either case, production began by making sure all ingredients were in clay or powder form, which may have required some grinding. The proportions called for in the recipe were then measured out and dumped into a vat with water. The resulting slurry was thoroughly mixed and strained to remove impurities.

In the case of the hand-thrown articles, this slurry was dried and kneaded until the hump held its shape when worked by hand. The hump was then set on a potter's wheel (for early steins these wheels were turned by apprentices) and the cavity was pushed in and the walls pulled up.

Scrapers were used to make the outside cylindrical, as well as to carve excess materials from the inside, especially the bottom corner. Templates, called ribs, were then used to produce the lip and any bands that were desired on the outside.

The hump was then cut away from the wheel by pulling a wire under it, leaving concentric whorls, or by using a knife once the wheel was stopped.

At this point, the handle was added as well as any applied work, incising, or glazing, and the mug was ready for firing.

Two different mechanisms that were used as potter's wheels.

2.3 Slip-Molded Ceramics

It is not known exactly when slip molding was invented, but it had become an important stein-making technique by the late 1800s.

The slurry was prepared in the same manner as described previously. The drying, however, was not accomplished in a mill or other separate process; instead it took place right in the mold.

The molds were made of plaster, which slowly drew the moisture out of the contingent slip, or slurry. The longer the slip was kept in the mold, the thicker the dried portion became. After a prescribed number of hours, the excess slip was poured out and the plaster mold was disassembled.

Because of the time, effort, and expense involved in making the plaster mold, slip-molded steins are generally made of finer materials such as porcelain. Because slip molding could accommodate almost any kind of shape, it helped to make possible the mass production of the oddly shaped character steins shown in Section 16.

2.4 Stein Marks

A large percentage of steins are not marked with the name of the manufacturer. There are several theories as to why this is so. It could be that, as with the earliest steins, merchants preferred that their customers not be able to contact the manufacturers directly; thus, they persuaded makers to use only an identifying mold number. It is also known that the Europeans, particularly the Germans, have always been somewhat reluctant to discuss where they purchased items. Whatever the reason, it has made it very difficult to study stein producers. In many cases, research has to begin by locating old catalogs.

Artists' names on steins are even more scarce. Except in the case of some Mettlach steins, a collector would be fortunate to locate the artist's initials somewhere in a stein's design. During the Renaissance Revival of the 1800s, artists were taught to aspire to the Classics and, as copyists, not to sign their names. Perhaps this tradition continued through to the modern era.

Aside from the Mettlach factory, which had an elaborate marking system that is described in *The Mettlach Book*, there is little that can be learned from the markings on the bottom of a stein. The accompanying pages show symbols that have been identified as those of particular manufacturers or distributors. Pertinent dates are also included.

The following list gives the meanings of some other markings that are occasionally found:

Germany, or **Made in Germany**, indicates that the stein was probably meant to be exported to the United States or elsewhere outside Germany; this mark was required after the 1891 Marking Law and was used until World War II.

West Germany is a mark used after World War II and until 1990.

MUSTERSCHUTZ means *protected against copying*.

Geschützt means *protected* or *patented*.

Gesetzlich Geschützt translates as *legally protected*.

Gegen Nachbildung Geschützt means *protected against copying*.

Reg. U.S. Pat. Off., registered at the U.S. Patent Office, was put on some items intended for sale in the United States.

Incised numbers most often denote the manufacturer's catalog number of the mold that was used.

Painted numbers usually represent the decoration number.

Steins have occasionally been found with paper labels that show prices, export information, or even the manufacturer's or distributor's name. Of course, these are uncommon and rarely help to identify antique steins.

Marks for some of the stein manufacturers.

Villeroy & Boch, Mettlach

Villeroy & Boch.	**VB**				
1836-1855	1885-1895	1893-1930	1842-c.1860	c.1852-1873	1873-1883

1883-1931 with variations	1906-1910	1874-1909

V. Zsolnay, Pec, Hungary	Werkstatt Cadinen	Maximilian von Heider	Keramische Werkstätten München-Herrsching

1878-1910	1910-	1896-	1923-1929

Jacob Scharvogel	Robert Burdack	August Sältzer	Hauber & Reuther
			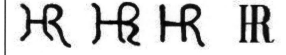
1906-1913	1900-1918	1887-	1887-c.1910

Marks for some of the stein manufacturers:

Reinhold Merkelbach

         R·MERKELBACH GRENZHAUSEN

1882-1933   c.1900   c.1900   1903-1904   1911-1916   c.1910   c.1916

1916-1945   1945-1964   1945-1964   1964-1968   1968-1971   1970s

Merkelbach & Wick

1880s-1921   c.1900-1921   c.1921

Wick-Werke

1937-1960   1960-1972   1921-1937

Reinhold Hanke

Hanke   R.Hanke HOHR   RH

1900-1938   c.1900-1930s   c.1900-1930s   early 1900s   early 1900s

      WESTERWALD ART POTTERY

early 1900s   early 1900s   c.1900-1910   c.1900-1930s

Königliche Keramische Fachschule

FACHSCHULE ·HOEHR·   early 1900s

Roßkopf & Gerz

     before 1917

Marzi & Remy

1879-1964   1964-1990s

Eckhardt & Engler

1918-   -1971

J.W. Remy

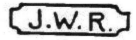   J.W.R. GERMANY   JWR

c.1900-1960s

Adolf Diesinger

D.R.G.M. 154927

1901-1918

Marks for some of the stein manufacturers.

Dümler & Breiden

early 1900s

c.1900-c.1930

c.1900-1920s

Gilles & Sohn

1903-1970s

modern

Albert Jacob Thewalt

1893-1896

1897-1918

1918-1930

1930-c.1990

1990s

1990s

Simon Peter Gerz

c.1900

1960-1990s

1977-1990s

1990s

Steinzeugindustrie (Steuler)

1917-

Joh. Ferdinand

1920-1935

Matthias Girmscheid

1880s-1970s

modern

Alphons Lötschert

1924-

Peter Willems

P. W.
before 1910

August Corzelius

late 1800s

Werner Corzelius

modern

Unknown

c.1900

Paulus & Thewalt

c.1910

Karl Merkelbach

1935-

Walter Merkelbach

Theodor Paetsch

1887-

Marks for some of the stein manufacturers.

Porcelain marks on steins copying Meissen or Royal Vienna styles.	Porzellanfabrik Rudolstadt

late 1800s

late 1800s, A. Lamm

1895-1906   1900-1906

Royal Vienna Porzellan (Austria)   **Ackerman & Fritz**   **Elbogen Porzellan**

pre-1864, frequently copied late 1800s & 1900s

1910-   1935-   1908-   1935-

Staatliche Porzellan-Manufaktur Nymphenburg   **Fürstenberger Porzellanfabrik**

1882-1920s   1896-   1896   1895-1920   -1910   1895-1930

1896-1906   1906-1918

Meissner Porzellanfabrik, Meissen   **Königliche Porzellanmanufaktur**   **F.A. Mehlem, Bonn**

1800s

1832-   1870-   late 1800s

1896-

Rosenthal Porzellan   **H. Hutschenreuther**   **Porzellanfabrik L. Hutschenreuther**

1900-

1910-

1870-1902   1916-1938

Porzellanfabrik Rauenstein   **Swaine & Co.**   **Risler&Cie**   **Porzellanfabrik Weiden**

1887-c.1930   c.1890-c.1930   -1896

c.1920

1879-

1921-

Marks for some of the stein manufacturers.

Schierholz & Sohn, Porzellan - Manufaktur Plaue

1907-　　　　1910-　　modern　　1880-1906 & 1980s-　　　　modern

Ernst Bohne Söhne

-1910　　c.1900　　c.1903　　early 1900s

Albert Stahl & Co.

modern

Bonn

Dorfner & Cie

1896-

Gebrüder Dorfner

1896-1918

Gebrüder Benedikt

1883-1932

Adolf Bauer

1887-

Ludwig Wessel

1880-c.1900

Wilhelm Krumeich

c.1900　　c.1910

Ferdinand & Kamp

c.1900

Bareuther

Adolf Schneider

1887-

Gebrüder Horn

1886-

Gebrüder Heubach

1882-

Royal Doulton, England

1902-

O'Hara Dial

early 1900s

Royal Copenhagen

c.1905-　　1929-

Ceramic Art Co. - Lenox

late 1800s-early 1900s

Royal Worcester, England

1865-1880　　1862-1875　　1876-1891

Marks for some of the stein manufacturers.

Martin Pauson (distributor)	Theodor Wieseler (distributor)	Felsenstein & Mainzer, Nürnberg
Martin Pauson München	T.W.	F&M N
early 1900s	early 1900s	early 1900s

Josef Reinemann, (distributor)	L. Ostermayr.	Stangl Pottery, New Jersey
J.REINEMANN MÜNCHEN	L.OSTERMAYR NÜRNBERG	 STANGL POTTERY MADE IN TRENTON USA
early 1900s	early 1900s	after 1926

Rastal Werk	Würfel & Müller	W. Goebel	Ceramarte (Brazil)
rastal	KING WERK	 Goebel	 Ceramarte PRODUCT OF BRAZIL
1959-present	modern	1950-1957 c.1980s	1970s-present

Hachiya Brothers, Japan	Found on modern porcelain steins.	Lindner Porzellan	Silberdistel
 HACHIYA BROTHERS c.1950s-c.1960s	modern	 Lindner Handarbeit Germany original handgemalt modern	

Dresden Art	Kaiser Porzellan	Cooper & Clements	Royal Porzellan Manufaktur
 DRESDEN ART MADE IN GERMANY	AK KAISER	 COOPER & CLEMENT INC.	R.P.M.
c.1960s		c.1960s	1950s

3. Early Stoneware & Earthenware

The early history of stoneware steins, as discussed in Section 1, is virtually the same as that for steins in general, since stoneware was for some time the only really important material used to make steins. However, there is a very short chapter in the history of stein making that does precede stoneware, and information about that follows.

3.1 Earthenware and Hafner Ware

Earthenware vessels, especially in a baluster shape, were common in the Rhineland area in the 1400s. They were made by firing clay to about 800°C (1500°F) to drive off all the moisture. The resulting pottery was not durable, and the surface was quite porous. None of these early pieces still in existence show evidence of having had a lid.

Hafner ware pieces, on the other hand, have been found with lids, that is to say, in the true beer stein form. Hafner ware is earthenware that has been covered by a lead glaze to make it nonporous and to somewhat increase its durability.

Hafner ware had long been used to make stove tiles and other useful household items. Decorative glazes have been seen on Hafner ware steins, and known examples date from the 1500s to the 1700s. Most of these are from Austria, northern Switzerland or southern Germany. They are quite uncommon, however, and do not merit further discussion in this kind of general book.

3.2 Stoneware

The most common of the stoneware steins are those from the Westerwald region. Again, some of

their history was discussed in Section 1. The remainder of this section will thus concentrate on some of the production techniques, factories and their styles, and information for collectors.

Stoneware is a product of clay heated so intensely, to about 1200°C (2200°F), causing the clay to be vitrified into stone. It is hard to scratch, even with steel, and is impervious to liquids. Thus, glazes have been added only for aesthetic reasons.

Furnaces capable of producing such heat took some time to evolve, but it is really the special clay required for stoneware that prevented earlier discovery of this product. Stoneware clay must be very plastic,

Hafner ware, .75L, relief, originally enameled with brown, red & green, interior has green & tan glaze, early 1600s, later pewter mounts, $2000-3000.

free from metallic and alkali impurities, and fired with little (5% or less) shrinkage, no warping, and no cracking. Stoneware clays, sometimes called *white gold*, were originally mined out of potholes, the sides of which were supported by saplings. These clays are still being mined today, but extensive shaft and tunneling techniques are now used.

3.3 Stoneware Factories

Although the major deposits of stoneware clays have been in the Westerwald region, these did not become important until the 1600s. Before that time, and even after the Westerwald area began production, there were several regional stein producers that had their own distinctive styles and decorative techniques. Examples from most of these factories are shown in the following pictures, so only brief characterizations of the steins produced by these factories are listed below.

3.4 Collecting Early Stoneware

Few of the early stoneware steins were artist signed. However, some of the famous Raeren and Westerwald steins from around 1590 were signed, and some of the Creussen steins were signed on the bottom with the letters of the artist's name cryptically combined into a clustered stick pattern. Occasionally, a Westerwald stein, especially one with a *GR* design (*Georgius Rex*, made for export to England), has a central applied design that came from an initialed mold. These are virtually the only identifying marks that will be found on any of these old stoneware steins. The reason, as explained previously, is that stein merchants did not want customers identifying, requesting or contacting specific stein makers.

Some collectors are interested in the area within the broad Westerwald region where certain steins were made. It is true that the vast majority of

---

Annaberg: middle 1600s to early 1700s; dark brown to grayish brown stoneware; saltglaze and various colors of enamel; squat cylindrical and pear shapes; chip carving, relief decor, and organic designs.

Altenburg: 1650s to early 1800s; gray stoneware; light brown and creamy white glazes; tall cylindrical shapes with designs often made from many applied pearls of white clay and usually depicting folk art patterns.

Bunzlau: 1700s; cream stoneware-earthenware; pear and bulbous shapes; brown glazes with occasional cream-colored applied bisque decorations, sometimes with smooth melon ribs.

Creussen: early 1600s to middle 1700s; brown stoneware; saltglaze and often many colors of enamel; chocolate background color from the combination of the clay, so-called *black salt*, and particular wood used for fuel; squat cylindrical and pear shapes; relief decor; chip carving; coats of arms, portraits, religious scenes, hunt scenes, and mythological decorations.

Duingen: 1600s to about 1800; light brown stoneware; various brown saltglazes; plain bands with an occasional coat of arms.

Freiberg: middle to late 1600s; dark brown or grayish to olive stoneware; saltglaze and enamels; cylindrical shapes with much chip carving and stamped designs, often with checkerboard types of decorations.

Köln-Frechen: early 1500s to 1600; gray stoneware; clear or leopard-speckled brown saltglazes; jug shapes, then later cylindrical; bearded man, allegorical, or smooth decor.

Muskau: late 1600s to 1700s; gray stoneware; brown, blue, and purple saltglazes; pear and cylindrical shapes with crudely scratched or stamped organic decorations.

Raeren: about 1550 to early 1600s; gray stoneware; clear and blue or brown saltglazes; jug shapes and cylindrical; chip carving (patterns of vertical creases) with allegorical scenes; then later, bands with coats of arms.

Siegburg: early 1500s to late 1500s; white stoneware; clear glaze; slender and tall styles with Renaissance relief decorations; after 1600 the style became much like that of Westerwald.

Waldenburg: middle 1500s to late 1600s; gray stoneware; brown glazes with applied decor of allegorical scenes and coats of arms.

Westerwald: 1590 to about 1700; gray stoneware; clear, blue and purple saltglazes; jug shapes with applied decorations; 1670 to about 1800, trend toward cylindrical shapes, first with applied shields and portraits; then in early 1700s with applied diamond-shaped decorated bands; later with applied relief, stamped, scratch-incised, zigzag, and chip-carved designs.

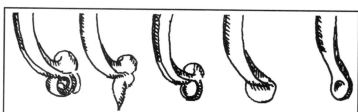

Rolled End	Tail	Thumbprint	Flat	Modern
1600-1720	1700-1780	1750-1790	1770-1870	1860-present

The potter's treatment of the lower end of the handle changed significantly over time, and can sometimes be used to help date Westerwald steins.

Westerwald steins were produced in the Höhr, Grenzhausen cluster of neighboring villages. Westerwald-type steins are also known to have been produced in Steinau, other Hessen villages, Siegburg, Raeren, and even possibly around the Frechen area. The pictures in this section identify a couple of the major style variations that are known to have come from specific villages. Examination of leaf designs, deer, ropework, checkerboarding, zigzag incising, and some floral stamps helps to identify similar steins.

There are early stoneware steins that come into the marketplace; actually more than one might at first expect. A collector should be aware of several things before considering such a purchase. Reproductions are usually easily identified, but there can be some fakes that are convincing after a cursory examination. So look at all of the parts of the stein—both inside and out—and include the pewterwork.

A second important thing to note is that there are considerable price differentials among various stoneware steins, as the information later in this section clearly shows. Note also that the value of one of these steins does not strictly follow age, aesthetic appeal, size, rarity of type, or any other immediately apparent criteria, although each of these will have some bearing. It is important to study the styles and values of the steins pictured.

Finally, it should be noted that the effect of condition on value is difficult to generalize. Damage or a repair on a stoneware stein always reduces the value. Some collectors, especially those who have previously collected mass-produced steins, are very fastidious about the condition of an old stoneware piece. On the other hand, some long-time collectors and museums tend to place more emphasis on the aesthetic and technical quality of a stein compared to others of the same type. When considering damage, keep in mind that each of these old stoneware steins is one of a kind.

There are no particularly dominant strategies for collecting old stoneware steins. Some collectors attempt to acquire examples of all of the various types. Others concentrate on those from one particular region, and this is often the Westerwald region, as products from this area are the most frequently encountered. Whatever the strategy, it is always better to concentrate on quality, since the best-made steins are the most sought after both by other collectors and museums looking to upgrade their collections.

3.5 Evaluation Information

The value range for the steins illustrated in this chapter reflects the normal price charged by a knowledgeable dealer selling to a serious collector in the United States. Prices can vary in other countries; the primary market for these steins is in Germany. Prices can and will change in the United States to reflect both price changes in Germany and other countries, as well as changes in currency exchange rates. The values reflect only steins in good to very good condition and allow for the variations that occur in decorations on hand-produced wares.

During the last ten years, the price trend for many steins in this section has been upward. However, many are almost unchanged. The Westerwald steins have a more erratic record with their prices having had a mild overall reduction, moving up then down from year to year.

Hafner ware, .5L, Drinking Bear, dark brown glaze, pewter mounts, c.1700, $5000-7500.

a. Stoneware, 1.0L, Siegburg, applied relief crests, white, saltglaze, dated 1589, $3000-4000.

b. Stoneware, 1.0L, Siegburg, applied relief panels with female vices, white, saltglaze, signed H.H. (Hans Hilgers), dated 1591, $3500-4500.

c. Stoneware, .5L, Siegburg, applied relief, white, saltglaze, signed L., dated 1589, $2500-3500.

d. Stoneware, 1.0L, Siegburg, relief, light tan, saltglaze, reproduction, Peter Lövenich workshop, c.1830, $1000-1500.

e. Stoneware, .75L, Siegburg, applied relief, orange saltglaze on white body, dated 1598 in medallion, $4000-5500.

f. Stoneware, 1.0L, Siegburg, chip carving, applied relief, red/orange glaze, late 1700s, $1500-2000.

g. Stoneware, 2.25L, Siegburg, applied relief crests, light tan, saltglaze, late 1500s, $1500-2000.

h. Stoneware, 1.0L, probably Siegburg, chip carving, applied relief, white, saltglaze, early 1700s, $1500-2000.

i. Stoneware, 1.0L, Frechen, light brown tigerware glaze, English silver mountings, early 1600s, $7000-10,000.

a. Stoneware, 1.0L, Frechen, mottled brown tigerware glaze, silver mountings, stoneware is late 1600s, silver is late 1800s, $1500-2000.
b. Stoneware, 1.0L, Köln, light brown, blue enamel on medallion, late 1600s, $2500-3500.
c. Stoneware, 4.0L, Frechen, Bartmann jug, brown glaze, early 1600s, $3000-4000.
d. Stoneware, .75L, Köln, Bartmann jug, speckled tan glaze, middle 1500s, $1000-1500.

e. Stoneware, 1.0L, Creussen, cut design, enameled, late 1600s, $4500-5500.
f. Stoneware, .5L, Creussen, relief, enameled, Christ & Apostles, dated 1703, $7000-9000.
g. Stoneware, .5L, Creussen, relief, enameled, Apostles & lamb, c.1700, $9000-12,000.

a.   Earthenware, 2.0L, Annaberg, cut design, dark brown glaze, late 1600s, $800-1000.
b.   Earthenware, 1.5L, Annaberg, applied relief, dark brown glaze, late 1600s, $3000-4000.
c.   Earthenware, .25L, Annaberg, applied relief, dark brown glaze, enameled, late 1600s, $2500-3500.
d.   Earthenware, 2.5L, Annaberg, applied relief, dark brown glaze, enameled, late 1600s, $3500-4500.

e.   Earthenware, 1.25L, Annaberg, applied relief, brown glaze, enameled, late 1600s, $5000-7000.
f.   Earthenware, .5L, Annaberg, applied relief, brown glaze, enameled, late 1600s, $4000-5000.
g.   Earthenware, 1.0L, Annaberg, applied relief & cut design, brown glaze, enameled, late 1600s, $3000-4000.

a.   Earthenware, .5L, Annaberg, applied relief, brown glaze, enameled, late 1600s, $4500-6000.
b.   Earthenware, 1.5L, Annaberg, applied relief, brown glaze, enameled, late 1600s, $2500-3500.
c.   Earthenware, 1.5L, Annaberg, applied relief, brown glaze, enameled, late 1600s, $3000-4000.
d.   Earthenware, 1.5L, Annaberg, applied relief, light blue glaze, enameled, late 1600s, $5000-7000.

e.   Earthenware, .5L, Annaberg, applied relief, blue glaze, enameled, middle 1600s, $15,000-20,000.
f.   Stoneware, 1.75L, probably Dreihausen, notch-carving, saltglazed, middle 1600s, $2000-3000.
g.   Earthenware, .5L, probably Saxon, yellow, green and brown glazes, 1600s, $3000-4000.
h.   Earthenware, .5L, Winterthur, Switzerland, applied relief, white glaze, enameled, middle 1600s, $2000-3000.

a. Stoneware, .5L, Freiberg, cut design, brown, saltglaze, late 1600s, $2000-3000.
b. Stoneware, .5L, Freiberg, applied relief and cut design, brown, saltglaze, enameled, middle 1600s, $6000-8000.
c. Stoneware, .5L, Freiberg, applied relief and cut design, gray, saltglaze, middle 1600s, $8000-10,000.
d. Earthenware, .5L, Striegau, Silesia, white terra-sigillata, beige, stamped seal on front dated 1639, $1500-2000.

e. Earthenware, 1.5L, Wetterau (Hessen), orange-red glaze, early 1700s, $2500-3500.
f. Earthenware, 1.5L, Wetterau (Hessen), orange-red glaze, sgraffito decoration, early 1700s, $4000-6000.
g. Earthenware, 2.0L, Wetterau (Hessen), orange-red glaze, sgraffito decoration, early 1700s, $5000-7000.

a. Stoneware, .75L, Raeren, applied relief coat of arms, dark brown glaze, silver lid, early 1600s, $800-1200.
b. Stoneware, .5L, Raeren, applied relief, brown-red glaze, dated 1603, $1200-1600.
c. Stoneware, .75L, Raeren, applied relief and chip carving, brown-red glaze, c.1600, $1000-1500.
d. Stoneware, 2.0L, Raeren, applied relief medallions, brown glaze, c.1600, $2500-3500.

e. Stoneware, 1.5L, Raeren, swirls, brown glaze, late 1700s, $500-750.
f. Stoneware, 2.0L, Raeren, applied relief medallion, brown glaze, early 1700s, $1200-1800.
g. Stoneware, 1.75L, Raeren, applied relief medallion, brown glaze, dated 1719, $1200-1800.
h. Stoneware, 1.0L, Raeren, light brown glaze, early 1700s, $400-600.

a. Stoneware, 2.0L, Altenburg, orange-brown saltglaze, late 1600s, $6000-10,000.
b. Stoneware, 3.0L, Altenburg, ochre-yellow saltglaze, late 1600s, $3000-5000.
c. Stoneware, 2.5L, Altenburg, white saltglaze, late 1600s, $3000-4000.

d. Stoneware, 1.5L, Altenburg, orange-brown glaze, early 1700s, $1000-1500.
e. Stoneware, 1.0L, Altenburg, orange-brown glaze, brown rosettes, late 1600s, $1200-1800.
f. Stoneware, 1.0L, Altenburg, orange-brown glaze, early 1700s, $500-700.
g. Stoneware, .75L, Altenburg, light brown glaze, early 1700s, $400-600.

a. Stoneware, 1.5L, Altenburg, orange-brown saltglaze, white & blue beading, middle 1700s, $2000-2500.
b. Stoneware, 1.0L, Altenburg, orange-brown saltglaze, white & blue beading, middle 1700s, $1500-2000.
c. Stoneware, 1.5L, Altenburg, orange-brown saltglaze, applied relief eagle, white & blue beading, middle 1700s, $2500-3000.
d. Stoneware, 1.5L, Altenburg, orange-brown saltglaze, white beading, middle 1700s, $2000-2500.

e. Stoneware, 1.5L, Altenburg, orange-brown saltglaze, white beading, middle 1700s, $3000-4000.
f. Stoneware, 1.75L, Altenburg, Occupational Bootmaker, orange-brown saltglaze, white & brown beading, middle 1700s, $2000-3000.
g. Stoneware, 1.25L, Altenburg, gray, saltglazed, blue, green & yellow beading, signed CW, middle 1700s, $5000-7000.
h. Stoneware, 1.5L, Altenburg, Saxon coat of arms, gray, saltglazed, beading, black enamel, dated 1720, $2500-3500.

a.   Stoneware, 1.5L, Altenburg, relief, double-headed eagle, white saltglaze, lid dated 1734, $2500-3000.
b.   Stoneware, 1.5L, Altenburg, gray saltglaze, early 1700s, $1400-1800.
c.   Stoneware, 1.5L, Altenburg, white saltglaze, white & blue beading, early 1700s, $2500-3500.
d.   Stoneware, 1.0L, Muskau, dark gray, cobalt blue saltglaze, early 1700s, $800-1200.

e.   Stoneware, .75L, Muskau, black saltglaze, green & white enamel design, late 1600s, $2500-3500.
f.   Stoneware, 1.0L, Muskau, applied relief, chip carving, gray body, black saltglaze, late 1600s, $2000-3000.
g.   Stoneware, 1.0L, Muskau, applied relief, chip carving, dark brown saltglaze, late 1600s, $3500-4500.
h.   Stoneware, .5L, Muskau, dark brown saltglaze, applied relief and stamped decoration, late 1600s, $1000-2000.

a.   Stoneware, 2.5L, Muskau, brown saltglaze, middle 1700s, $400-600.
b.   Stoneware, 2.0L, Muskau, brown & black saltglazes, applied relief, chip carving, late 1700s, $600-900.
c.   Stoneware, 2.0L, Muskau, brown & black glazes, applied relief, chip carving, early 1700s, $1500-2000.

d.   Stoneware, .5L, Muskau, chip carving & applied relief, brown body, black saltglaze, c.1700, $1200-1600.
e.   Stoneware, 1.0L, Muskau, chip carving & applied relief, brown body, black saltglaze, early 1700s, $1800-2400.
f.   Stoneware, 1.5L, Muskau, brown body, brown-black saltglaze on bands & circles, c.1700, $1200-1600.
g.   Stoneware, .5L, Muskau, applied relief, brown body, black saltglaze, late 1700s, $400-600.

a. Stoneware, 2.0L, Westerwald, double-headed eagles, cobalt blue & purple saltglazes, incised & applied relief, c.1700, $800-1200.
b. Stoneware, 2.0L, Westerwald, coat of arms, cobalt blue & purple saltglazes, incised & applied relief, dated 1687, $1200-1800.
c. Stoneware, 1.25L, Westerwald, cobalt blue saltglaze, incised, stamped & applied relief, dated 1598, $1200-1800.
d. Stoneware,1.75L, Westerwald, blue saltglaze, incised, stamped & applied relief, late 1700s, $700-1000.

e. Stoneware, .75L, Westerwald, blue & purple saltglazes, applied relief, early 1700s, $800-1200.
f. Stoneware, .5L, Westerwald, Hausen-style, blue & purple saltglazes, applied relief, late 1600s, $500-800.
g. Stoneware, .5L, Westerwald, blue saltglaze, incised, late 1700s, $1200-1600.
h. Stoneware, 1.0L, Westerwald, Hausen-style, blue saltglaze, incised, stamped & applied relief, c.1700, $600-800.

a. Stoneware, .5L, Westerwald, Steinau-style, blue saltglaze, cut, stamped & applied relief, late 1700s, $500-700.
b. Stoneware, .5L, Westerwald, blue saltglaze, incised, applied relief, middle 1700s, inlaid lid, $2000-3000.
c. Stoneware, 1.0L, Westerwald, Hausen-style, blue saltglaze, incised & applied relief, late 1700s, $700-1000.
d. Stoneware, .75L, Westerwald, Hausen-style, blue saltglaze, incised & stamped, late 1700s, $500-700.

e. Stoneware, .5L, Westerwald, Hausen-style, blue saltglaze, incised & stamped, early 1700s, $600-900.
f. Stoneware, .5L, Westerwald, Steinau-style, blue saltglaze, incised, late 1700s, $600-900.
g. Stoneware, .75L, Westerwald, Steinau-style, blue saltglaze, incised & stamped, dated 1788, $500-800.
h. Stoneware, .5L, Westerwald, Hausen-style, blue saltglaze, incised, late 1700s, $400-600.

a.   Earthenware, 1.5L, Saxony, glazed redware, c.1700, $2000-2500.
b.   Earthenware, .25L, Saxony, glazed redware, c.1700, $1500-2000.
c.   Earthenware, .5L, Bunzlau, brown clay slip glaze, c.1700, $800-1200.
d.   Earthenware, 2.25L, Bunzlau, brown clay slip glaze, middle 1700s, $1200-1800.

e.   Earthenware, 1.0L, Bunzlau, brown clay slip glaze, c.1700, $1200-1800.
f.   Earthenware, 1.0L, probably Bunzlau, applied relief, brown clay slip glaze, c.1700, $2000-2500.
g.   Stoneware, .5L, Duingen, dark brown, late 1700s, $300-400.
h.   Stoneware, 1.0L, Duingen, applied relief crest, brown glaze, early 1700s, $800-1200.

a. Earthenware, 3.0L, Bunzlau, applied relief, double-headed eagle, brown clay, slip glaze, middle 1700s, $1000-1500.
b. Earthenware, 2.5L, Bunzlau, applied relief, double-headed eagle, brown clay, slip glaze, middle 1700s, $1000-1500.
c. Earthenware, 2.5L, Bunzlau, applied relief, seal of Hamburg, brown clay, slip glaze, middle 1700s, $1000-1500.
d. Earthenware, .5L, Saxony, tan & reddish-brown slip glazes, middle 1700s, $400-600.

e. Stoneware, .5L, Duingen, tan & reddish-brown glazes, silver lid, late 1700s, $500-800.
f. Stoneware, .75L, Duingen, tan & reddish-brown glazes, pewter & brass mountings, late 1700s, $800-1200.
g. Earthenware, 1.0L, Saxony, tan & reddish-brown glazes, middle 1700s, $400-600.
h. Earthenware, .5L, Saxony, tan & reddish-brown glazes, middle 1700s, $350-500.

a. Earthenware, 2.0L, applied relief, reddish-orange slip glaze, 1700s, $1500-2500.
b. Stoneware, 2.0L, applied beading, slip glaze, 1700s, $1000-1500.
c. Stoneware, .5L, Malling jug, Antwerp, Belgium, speckled cobalt blue glaze, middle 1600s, $2000-3000.
d. Stoneware, .5L, speckled purple glaze, 1700s, $800-1200.

4. Faience

Antique faience pieces have Dutch, French, English, Italian, German, and all sorts of other origins, and can be found in innumerable shapes: drinking vessels, utensils, and endless numbers of purely decorative items. The study of faience is a tremendously large field. However, the focus here is on steins and thus, primarily, on the German faience factories, making this history and discussion much more manageable.

4.1 History of Faience

About the year 800 A.D., Chinese porcelain made its way to the Middle Eastern and European royal courts. Despite major efforts to produce this *white gold* outside China, it was not until 1709 that Johann Böttger and Ehrenfried von Tschirnhaus were able to produce porcelain in Meissen. The 900 or so years of searching steadily produced more attractive substitutes, of which faience was perhaps the most convincing.

Faience, as it was originally produced beginning in the fifteenth century in Faenza, Italy, was reasonably successful in imitating the white background that gave the Chinese porcelain its contrast and clarity. During the 1400s, faience spread slowly through France to the northern European countries, and gradually across the Alps into Switzerland and Austria.

Beginning in the 1600s, the then frequent Dutch Trade with East Asia brought relatively large quantities of Chinese porcelain to Europe. In the middle of the 1600s, however, revolts in the Ming Empire cut off the Chinese supply. The Dutch quickly filled this disruption in supplies with wares from its faience works. Religious changes in the Netherlands had pushed some of these potters into Germany, and in 1661 at Hanau and in 1666 at Frankfurt, German-produced faience began to supply the waiting native market.

The first of these German, so-called *porcellaine*, steins were unabashed replicas of the authentic Chinese pieces. Their decor included Oriental people in Oriental costume in the midst of Oriental landscapes. The colors were Ming blue on porcelain-like pure white. Often these steins had finely tooled silver lids, as had been made for the expensive imports.

Predictably, once European artists could control the stein decor, factories began selling blank white faience bodies to private artists, called Hausmalers, who provided decorations. Included among these craftsmen were many of the day's finest artists, who painted steins on commission or on a freelance basis, the results of which were often magnificent. Every color of glaze was used, as well as the scenes and designs most fashionable in this late Renaissance and early Baroque period.

By 1700, with Germany fragmented into hundreds of principalities, many rulers found it profitable to exclude imports and to sell licenses or franchise faience works. Thus, factories were started in almost all the locations where the clay and firewood were available.

The invention of European porcelain in 1709 slowly began to influence the faience stein market. Initially, it was almost as expensive as Chinese porcelain. However, the following major shifts began to take place by about 1725 when production began to increase and a white porcelain background became available:

(1) the best Hausmalers shifted from working on faience pieces to decorating porcelain,

(2) the silver lids, often gilded as well, were now used only on the porcelain steins,

(3) cheaper factory decorations and pewter mountings opened up the faience stein market to an eager middle class, and

(4) the larger, narrow-necked *Enghalskrug* and pear-shaped *Birnkrug* increasingly gave way to the more masculine, cylindrical *Walzenkrug* shape in individual sizes of .5 liter, 1.0 liter and 1.5 liters.

To be sure, even until about 1770, some first-rate artists remained at the faience factories. The quality of faience steins produced after 1800, however, was definitely not equal to that of earlier pieces. During the Biedermeier period, 1800 to 1850, the middle classes turned to unpretentious, sturdier materials: pewter and thick glass.

Sometime after the end of the Biedermeier period, antique faience items began to be collected by a select group. A number of crude reproductions, commonly pear-shaped, were made around 1900. In the 1920s, some excellent reference books became available, bringing the collecting of these pieces to wider attention, resulting in somewhat of a faience revival. This revival is easy to understand since faience and porcelain have always provided the stein artist with a freedom of color and a white, paper-like background unavailable elsewhere.

Another resurgence of good reference books in the 1950s seemed to sharpen the interest of museums, especially in works from their localities. Steins from the 1600s and/or from Hausmalers have largely moved from private collections into museums. Now the majority of quality faience steins that come to the marketplace are those that were made in the 1700s and decorated at the factory.

Identifying the workshop and possibly even the artist is of great interest to collectors. The fact that so many pieces are unsigned or, at best, cryptically signed, is an important part of the history of faience (as well as stoneware) steins. The guild systems, which were very strong in the 1600s and into the 1700s, afforded the few master craftsmen with the following benefits:

(1) cheap labor in the form of apprentices and journeymen,

(2) absolute control over the number of shops so the master craftsmen could remain well compensated, and

(3) quality and quantity control.

A worker who provided clay or wood to an unguilded potter could lose supplies from the other guilds such as the bakers' and butchers'. Pewterers'

Faience Factories by Region

Western German
Flörsheim 1765–1922
Frankfurt am Main 1666–1772
Fulda 1741–1758
Hanau 1661–1806
Höchst 1746–1758
Kassel 1680–1777
Kelsterbach 1758–1835
Köln 1770–1820
Wiesbaden 1770–1797

Central German
Berlin 1678–1786
Braunschweig 1707–1807
Frankfurt a.d. Oder 1763–1795
Hannoversch-Münden 1732–1854
Magdeburg 1754–1785
Potsdam 1740–1796
Wrisbergholzen 1735–1834

Eastern German
Glinitz 1767–1800
Proskau 1763-1793

Württemberg
Crailsheim 1720–1827
Göppingen 1741–1812
Ludwigsburg 1757–1824
Schrezheim 1752–1852

Baden
Durlach 1723–1840
Mosbach 1770–1828

Thüringen
Abtbessingen 1739–1791
Coburg 1739–1786
Dorotheenthal 1707–1806
Dresden 1708–1784
Erfurt 1717–1792
Zerbst 1721–1796

Upper Plains
Amberg 1759–1910
Ansbach 1710–1839
Bayreuth 1714–1835
Nürnberg 1712–1840
Sulzbach 1752–1774

Swaben
Augsburg 1678–1754
Friedberg 1754–1768
Göggingen 1748–1752
Künersberg 1745–1846
Öttingen 1735–1846
Schrattenhofen 1735–1846

Upper Rhine
Hagenau 1709–1781
Strassburg 1721–1781
Niederweiler 1735-1886

Seas
Hamburg 1625–1655
Kellinghusen 1763–1860
Kiel 1763–1787
Lesum 1756–1800
Stockelsdorf 1772–1786

Austria
Gmunden 1582–1820
Salzburg 1590–1790

guilds would attach mountings only to steins from guilded potters. And, most importantly, merchants' guilds bought steins only from potters' guilds. In return, the merchants required that the steins not be marked. They did not want buyers to know how to contact the best potters directly, so as not to cause the merchants the loss of their commissions!

Some of the cryptic bottom marks that were used are shown in this section. Also, the pictures in this chapter should help identify the styles of particular factories and painters. A number of faience books listed in Section 20 will provide additional information on glazes, styles, and colors of clays used at the different factories.

It must be noted, however, that there are few certainties in faience identification. Some artists are known to have been at three different factories in a single ten-year period. And, of course, glazes and motifs often moved with the artists. Constant experimentation with clay recipes, slightly different temperatures, and even different kinds of wood could change the color of the fired earthenware. Thus, it is often much easier to identify the region in which a stein was made rather than the specific factory responsible.

4.2 Faience Stein Production

Faience manufacturers always located themselves near woods and clay. They experimented with the clay, mixed it with some other types of earth and with sand, lime, and silicic acid, until a recipe was found that resulted in a product that was reasonably resistant to flaking, cracking, and crazing when glazed.

Once a suitable clay recipe was established, that mixture was combined with water, strained, then dried until workable. The thrower then fashioned a basic shape and let the piece dry further until leather-hard. The handle was then attached and a first firing to about 700°C drove off the water and left a hard porous, so-called bisque body.

This body was then dipped in a glaze made from tin oxide, powdered glass, and a flux. At this point, factories generally decorated the pieces with pigments that could withstand high temperatures: cobalt blue, manganese violet, antimony yellow, copper green, and sometimes iron red. The second firing, to about 1000°C, melted the tin oxide and pigments into a smooth porcelain-like finish.

Occasionally, wares were sent to the second firing with only a white glaze. Afterward, these blanks were decorated with a far greater variety of low-temperature glazes, even gold leaf, and were fired a third time to about 750°C. Often the pieces being fired a third time were set behind protective muffle bricks while other wares received the intensely hot second firing. These muffle-fired, textured decorations, as used by the Hausmalers, appear over the background glaze.

Most factories could not be bothered with the third firing; they usually accomplished all the decorations with pigments that could withstand the second firing or, occasionally (such as with some Ansbach and Schrezheim steins), just cold-painted the decorations. After much handling, such cold-painted decorations deteriorate and are often totally obliterated, leaving a plain faience stein (usually with a turquoise, white, or yellow background).

4.3 Collecting Faience

At best, faience, with its porous earthenware body, is not particularly durable. Even with the original protective lid and footring, old faience steins generally have nicks, hairline cracks, or worse damage. Of course, collectors generally have an aversion to buying a piece that has been repaired with glue. Such considerations aside, the age and aesthetic quality of a stein are more important than absolutely perfect condition.

Most reproductions can be easily spotted as the decorations are usually crudely painted. However, some better-quality reproductions have been made recently. Reproductions also generally have cast lids and thumblifts rather than carefully handspun and soldered pewterwork. Old lids can occasionally be found fastened to reproduction bodies, but the patina and file marks around the strap or shaft will almost inevitably show what has been done. See Section 19 for more information on new faience steins.

There are not many noteworthy faience collecting strategies. However, shape is often of concern in developing a collection. Those who collect steins made from different types of materials seem to prefer cylindrical faience steins, a shape that appears more compatible with the other types of steins. On the other hand, collectors who concentrate totally on faience more often relish the earlier narrow-necked and pear-shaped forms. Very few American faience stein collectors concentrate on a particular motif or factory; it is much more popular to seek diversity.

Several experts have identified the faience steins

shown on the following pages and their descriptions are reasonably accurate. Still, a substantial degree of uncertainty exists regarding the factories. For this reason, the words *possibly* and *probably* have been included in some of the descriptions.

Unless otherwise noted, the prices reflect the presumption that these steins are in reasonably good shape, although they might have a couple of faint, very short hairlines and/or some minor chipping on the handle or rim. If a stein has large pieces missing, the value drops closer to that of those with pewter mountings, perhaps to as low as $100 or $200.

4.4 Evaluation Information

Price trends for faience steins in recent years have been mixed. The early and middle 1990s saw mostly higher prices, but the late 1990s have shown weakness in prices from many factories. As is often the case, the more desirable and expensive examples have continued to move higher in price.

Abtsbessingen	Amberg	Ansbach
Baden-Baden	Bayreuth	Berlin
Bernburg	Braunschweig	Cassel
Coburg	Cöln	Crailsheim
Criseby-Eckernförde	Dirmstein	Donauwörth
Dorotheenthal	Dresden	Durlach

Erfurt	Flörsheim	Frankfurt a.d. Oder

Frankfurt a.M.	Friedberg	Fulda

Gera	Glinitz	Göggingen

Göppingen	Groß-Stieten	Halle

Hamburg	Hanau	Hannoversch-Münden

Höchst	Jever	Kellinghusen

Kelsterbach	Kiel	Königsberg

Künersberg	Lesum	Ludwigsburg

Magdeburg	**Mosbach**	**Niederweiler**
Nürnberg	**Offenbach**	**Oldesloe**
Öttingen-Schrattenhofen	**Osnabrück**	**Potsdam**
Proskau	**Rendsburg**	**Reval**
Rheinsberg	**Rudolstadt**	**Schleswig**
Schrezheim	**Schwerin**	**Stockelsdorf**
Stralsund	**Straßburg**	**Vegesack**
Wiesbaden	**Wrisbergholzen**	**Zerbst**

a.   Faience, 1.0L, Bayreuth, late 1700s, $900-1200.
b.   Faience, .75L, Bayreuth, late 1700s, $700-900.
c.   Faience, .75L, Bayreuth, late 1700s, $700-900.
d.   Faience, .5L, Bayreuth, late 1700s, $800-1100.

e.   Faience, 1.0L, Bayreuth, late 1700s, $700-900.
f.   Faience, 1.0L, Bayreuth, late 1700s, $800-1100.
g.   Faience, 1.0L, Bayreuth, late 1700s, $800-1100.
h.   Faience, .5L, probably Berlin, middle 1700s, $700-900.

a.   Faience, .75L, Schrezheim, early 1800s, $600-800.

b.   Faience, .75L, probably Schrezheim, c.1800, $500-700.

c.   Faience, .75L, Schrezheim, c.1800, $500-700.

d.   Faience, .75L, Schrezheim, middle 1700s, $800-1100.

e.   Faience, .75L, Nürnberg, late 1700s, $700-900.

f.   Faience, 1.0L, Nürnberg, middle 1700s, $1500-2000.

g.   Faience, .75L, Ottingen-Schrattenhofen, late 1700s, $1000-1300.

h.   Faience, .75L, Ottingen-Schrattenhofen, late 1700s, $1000-1300.

a. Faience, 1.0L, Thüringen region, late 1700s, $700-900.
b. Faience, 1.0L, Thüringen region, middle 1700s, $800-1000.
c. Faience, 1.0L, Thüringen region, middle 1700s, $800-1000.
d. Faience, 1.0L, Erfurt, middle 1700s, $800-1000.

e. Faience, 2.0L, Thüringen region, middle 1700s, $1500-2000.
f. Faience, .75L, Thüringen region, late 1700s, $800-1000.
g. Faience, 1.0L, Thüringen region, late 1700s, $800-1000.
h. Faience, .75L, Thüringen region, late 1700s, $800-1000.

a.   Faience, 1.0L, Ansbach, early 1700s, $1500-2000.
b.   Faience, 1.0L, Ansbach, middle 1700s, $900-1200.
c.   Faience, 1.0L, Ansbach, late 1700s, $700-900.
d.   Faience, .75L, Magdeburg, late 1700s, $700-900.

e.   Faience, 1.0L, Thüringen region, middle 1700s, $900-1200.
f.   Faience, 1.0L, Thüringen region, middle 1700s, $900-1200.
g.   Faience, 1.0L, Thüringen region, late 1700s, $800-1000.
h.   Faience, 1.0L, Thüringen region, middle 1700s, $900-1200.

a.   Faience, .5L, Thüringen region, late 1700s, $800-1000.
b.   Faience, 1.0L, Thüringen region, late 1700s, $1100-1500.
c.   Faience, 1.0L, Bayreuth, middle 1700s, $1100-1500.
d.   Faience, .4L, Magdeburg, c.1800, $500-700.

e.   Faience, .5L, Ansbach, middle 1700s, $800-1000.
f.   Faience, .5L, Ansbach, middle 1700s, $900-1200.
g.   Faience, .75L, Braunschweig, c.1800, $500-700.
h.   Faience, .5L, Berlin, late 1700s, $900-1200.

a. Faience, .5L, Ottingen-Schrattenhofen, middle 1700s, $2000-3000.
b. Faience, .75L, Berlin-Funcke factory, middle 1700s, $1800-2400.
c. Faience, .75L, Schrezheim, c.1800, $900-1200.
d. Faience, 1.0L, Schrezheim, c.1800, $900-1200.

e. Faience, .75L, possibly Thüringen region, late 1700s, $1800-2400.
f. Faience, .75L, Thüringen region, late 1700s, $1100-1400.
g. Faience, .75L, Erfurt, late 1700s, $1000-1300.
h. Faience, 1.0L, Thüringen region, middle 1700s, $1200-1600.

a. Faience, .75L, Ansbach, middle 1700s, $1800-2400.
b. Faience, .75L, Ansbach, late 1700s, $1200-1600.
c. Faience, 1.0L, Ansbach, late 1700s, $1200-1600.
d. Faience, .75L, Nürnberg, middle 1700s, $1800-2400.

e. Faience, .75L, Bayreuth, middle 1700s, $1100-1400.
f. Faience, .75L, Bayreuth, middle 1700s, $1100-1400.
g. Faience, .5L, probably Bayreuth, late 1700s, $800-1100.
h. Faience, .75L, Crailsheim, c.1800, $2500-3500.

a.   Faience, 1.0L, Thüringen region, late 1700s, $1800-2400.
b.   Faience, 1.0L, Thüringen region, late 1700s, $1100-1400.
c.   Faience, .5L, Thüringen region, late 1700s, $1000-1300.
d.   Faience, .5L, Thüringen region, late 1700s, $2000-2500.

e.   Faience, .5L, Thüringen region, late 1700s, $1400-1800.
f.   Faience, .75L, Erfurt, late 1700s, $1800-2400.
g.   Faience, .75L, Thüringen region, late 1700s, $1000-1300.
h.   Faience, .5L, Gmunden, late 1700s, $1200-1600.

a. Faience, 1.0L, Bayreuth, middle 1700s, $1500-2000.
b. Faience, 1.0L, Bayreuth, middle 1700s, $1200-1600.
c. Faience, .75L, Bayreuth, late 1700s, $1200-1600.
d. Faience, 1.0L, Bayreuth, late 1700s, $1000-1300.

e. Faience, 1.0L, Dorotheenthal, late 1700s, $900-1200.
f. Faience, .75L, Dorotheenthal, late 1700s, $900-1200.
g. Faience, .75L, Frankfurt Oder, middle 1700s, $1000-1300.
h. Faience, .75L, Crailsheim, late 1700s, $4000-5500.

a. Faience, .75L, Schrezheim, early 1800s, $700-900.

b. Faience, .75L, Schrezheim, late 1700s, $800-1100.

c. Faience, .75L, Schrezheim, early 1800s, $700-900.

d. Faience, .75L, Schrezheim, early 1800s, $1200-1600.

e. Faience, 1.0L, Magdeburg, late 1700s, $900-1200.

f. Faience, .75L, Magdeburg, c.1800, $700-900.

g. Faience, .75L, Hannoversch-Münden, late 1700s, $600-800.

h. Faience, .75L, Hannoversch-Münden, early 1800s, $500-700.

a. Faience, .4L, Magdeburg, c.1800, $700-900.
b. Faience, 1.0L, Magdeburg, c.1800, $800-1100.
c. Faience, .75L, Proskau, late 1700s, $3000-4000.
d. Faience, .75L, Proskau, late 1700s, $3000-4000.

e. Faience, 1.0L, Dorotheenthal, late 1700s, $1400-1800.
f. Faience, 1.0L, possibly Dorotheenthal, middle 1700s, $2500-3500.
g. Faience, .75L, Bayreuth, late 1700s, $1500-2000.
h. Faience, .75L, Ansbach, late 1700s, $1500-2000.

a. Faience, 1.0L, Berlin, middle 1700s, $1500-2000.
b. Faience, .75L, probably Frankfurt Oder, late 1700s, $1200-1600.
c. Faience, 1.0L, probably Thüringen region, middle 1700s, $1500-2000.
d. Faience, .75L, Thüringen region, late 1700s, $1000-1300.

e. Faience, .75L, Thüringen region, middle 1700s, $2000-2500.
f. Faience, .5L, Thüringen region, middle 1700s, $1800-2400.
g. Faience, .75L, Thüringen region, late 1700s, $1300-1600.
h. Faience, .75L, Thüringen region, late 1700s, $1300-1600.

a. Faience, .5L, probably Crailsheim, c.1800, $1100-1400.
b. Faience, 1.0L, Crailsheim, c.1800, $1100-1400.
c. Faience, 1.0L, Thüringen region, middle 1700s, $1800-2400.
d. Faience, 1.0L, Thüringen region, middle 1700s, $1800-2400.

e. Faience, .75L, Dresden, c.1800, $1300-1700.
f. Faience, .75L, Crailsheim, middle 1700s, $4500-6000.
g. Faience, .75L, Crailsheim, middle 1700s, $4500-6000.
h. Faience, .75L, Crailsheim, c.1760, $4000-5500.

a.   Faience, 1.0L, Bayreuth, middle 1700s, $1400-1800.

b.   Faience, 1.0L, Nürnberg, middle 1700s, $2500-3500.

c.   Faience, .75L, Magdeburg, late 1700s, $1000-1300.

d.   Faience, .75L, Proskau, late 1700s, $3000-4000.

e.   Faience, .75L, Crailsheim, c.1800, $1500-2000.

f.   Faience, 1.0L, Thüringen region, middle 1700s, $1800-2400.

g.   Faience, .75L, Thüringen region, middle 1700s, $2500-3500.

h.   Faience, .75L, probably Erfurt, middle 1700s, $1500-2000.

a.   Faience, .75L, Potsdam, marked P/R, late 1700s, $2000-2500.
b.   Faience, .75L, Reinsberg, late 1700s, $2000-2500.
c.   Faience, .75L, Ansbach, late 1700s, $1500-2000.
d.   Faience, .5L, Thüringen region, late 1700s, $1600-2200.

e.   Faience, .75L, Thüringen region, late 1700s, $2200-2800.
f.   Faience, 1.0L, Thüringen region, late 1700s, $2500-3500.
g.   Faience, .75L, Thüringen region, middle 1700s, $1600-2200.
h.   Faience, .75L, Thüringen region, late 1700s, $2400-3000.

a.   Faience, .75L, Erfurt, middle 1700s, $1400-1800.
b.   Faience, .75L, Erfurt, c.1800, $1600-2400.
c.   Faience, .75L, Erfurt, late 1700s, $1400-1800.
d.   Faience, .75L, Erfurt, late 1700s, $2200-2800.

e.   Faience, .75L, Nürnberg, crescent moon Madonna, by G. F. Kordenbusch, 1765, $2400-3200.
f.   Faience, .5L, Nürnberg, middle 1700s, $2000-2600.
g.   Faience, 1.0L, Nürnberg, middle 1700s, $2500-3200.
h.   Faience, .75L, Nürnberg, middle 1700s, $3000-4000.

a. Faience, .75L, Ottingen-Schrattenhofen, middle 1700s, $4000-5500.
b. Faience, .75L, Salzburg, late 1700s, $2000-3000.
c. Faience, .75L, Salzburg, late 1700s, $1800-2400.
d. Faience, .75L, Crailsheim, middle 1700s, $4500-6000.

e. Faience, .75L, possibly Durlach, early 1700s, $2500-3200.
f. Faience, 1.0L, Hannoversch-Münden, late 1700s, $350-500.
g. Faience, 1.0L, Hannoversch-Münden, late 1700s, $350-500.
h. Faience, 1.0L, Hannoversch-Münden, late 1700s, $350-500.

a.   Faience, 1.0L, Delft, early 1700s, $800-1100.
b.   Faience, 1.0L, Hanau, middle 1700s, $1000-1300.
c.   Faience, .5L, Hanau, middle 1700s, $800-1100.
d.   Faience, .25L, Hanau, middle 1700s, $700-900.

e.   Faience, .5L, possibly Ansbach, middle 1700s, $700-900.
f.   Faience, 1.75L, Nürnberg, middle 1700s, $2500-3500.
g.   Faience, 1.25L, Nürnberg, Kordenbusch Studio mark, Christ at Jacob's Well, early 1700s, $2500-3500.
h.   Faience, 1.0L, probably Hanau, muffle-fired, early 1700s, $3000-4000.

a. Faience, 1.0L, Lisbon, Portugal-Hamburg, silver mounts, early 1600s, $5000-7000.
b. Faience, .5L, Habaner faience (or Hafner ware), Moravia, dated 1691 on body, $1500-2000.
c. Faience, 1.0L, Niederweiler, late 1700s, $2000-2500.
d. Faience, 1.0L, Austrian, late 1700s, $800-1100.

e. Faience, 1.0L, Austrian, late 1700s, $800-1100.
f. Faience, 1.0L, Gmunden, c.1800, $700-1000.
g. Faience, 1.0L, Gmunden, late 1700s, $700-1000.
h. Faience, 1.0L, Gmunden, late 1700s, $1200-1600.

a.   Faience, .75L, Crailsheim, Occupational Brewer, middle 1700s, $4500-6000.
b.   Faience, .75L, Crailsheim, Occupational Miller, middle 1700s, $4500-6000.
c.   Faience, .75L, Crailsheim, Occupational Brewer, late 1700s, $4000-5500.
d.   Faience, .5L, Dresden, Occupational Tailor, late 1700s, $2500-3500.

e.   Faience, 1.0L, Schrezheim, Occupational Brewer, c.1800, $2000-3000.
f.   Faience, 1.0L, Schrezheim, cold-fired red & gold decoration on a blue body, early 1800s, $600-800.
g.   Faience, 1.0L, Schrezheim, cold-fired red & gold decoration on a blue body, early 1800s, $700-1000.

5. Pewter

Pewter history and production information can be found in Subsection 2.1, Pewter Mountings. Additional details and pictures of steins that have been made entirely of pewter are discussed here in Section 5. Unfortunately, it is not possible to include a study of the popular American and English pewter tankards. However, the many fine references in that field often include discussions of other pewter utensils, and these sources are usually available at libraries and museums.

5.1 History of Pewter Steins

For centuries, pewter was the most popular material used for making eating and drinking utensils. Pewter does not tarnish, rust, or break, and of great importance in the stein business, it does not impart a taste to beer, as do copper, silver, and iron. It was not until the 1700s that stoneware replaced pewter as the material of choice for most steins.

Shaping and decorating pewter is so easy that there have been many very different techniques used in making pewter steins. In the 1500s, pewter steins were either decorated in cast or hammered relief or by engraving or incising. The handles were relatively thin, S-shaped straps of pewter. Motifs commonly contained allegorical scenes within arcades or bands. At that time, the best relief pewter steins were produced in Saxony and Nürnberg. The quality of the engraved decorations on pewter steins made during the 1500s and 1600s usually depended on whether the pewterer did it himself or sent it to a specialist, such as a copperplate engraver.

The innovative Daubenkrug appeared in the middle 1600s. They were made by pouring hot pewter into carved-oak staves. The excess pewter was then ground off to make a smooth surface. Since these steins, mainly from Kulmbach, Thuringia, or Scandinavian areas, are primarily wood, they are pictured and described further in Section 7.

Occasionally, gilded pewter steins from the 1600s and 1700s are found. Enameling of pewter steins, however, may have been somewhat more popular, especially in the 1700s and early 1800s when pewter steins were not competing well with the more colorful faience, stoneware, and glass steins.

Around 1800, and especially in the ensuing Biedermeier period, many pewter steins were produced in the *Walzenkrug* shape: cylindrical and about twice as high as wide. Tiny zigzag, or wrigglework, engraving was quite popular in Germany and Switzerland then, and the designs are in the typical folk art style that was the fashion in that period.

After 1850, during the Historicism period, neo-Renaissance designs abounded on pewter steins: cartouches, masks, fruit bundles, garlands, and other classical devices arranged in panels or covering the stein bodies.

At the beginning of the twentieth century, pewter steins underwent their last important stylistic change to a design that often captures the sinuous lines of the Art Nouveau period.

It is probably true that the outstanding metal-working artists have always preferred silver or gold to pewter. However, pewter steins by Günther, Wiegold, Wildt, and other top artists from the 1600s are as eagerly sought as any metal tankards.

Regional differences in shape can help identify the locality in which a pewter stein was made. *Rorken*, or footed vase shapes, are more commonly from North Germany. Pear-shaped pewter steins are often from Schlesien, Bohemia, Hungary, or southern Germany. Also from southern Germany, as well as Austria and Switzerland, are the tall, tapered pewter steins.

5.2 Production and Marks

Due to the scarcity and high cost of pewter in early times, designs were often hammered into molds to save material that would be lost in casting. Lids, handles, and thumblifts also were often made in separate pieces and soldered together. Early molds were usually made from mixtures of calves' hair and clay, except for complicated molds, which were often made of stoneware. Metal molds began to be used for complicated relief pieces in the late 1500s. These molds slowly gained popularity among craftsmen until, by the 1800s, pewter steins were often made from iron molds.

Touchmarks can frequently be used to identify the origin of pewter steins made between 1600 and 1800. Not only is the master pewterer's touchmark often visible, but the town's touchmark is commonly seen on steins, especially on those from the middle 1700s. Although touchmarks are known to have been used in the 1500s, few very early steins are marked.

During the 1800s, pewterers began stamping steins with their full names, and often their city's name as well, thus removing much of the mystery from touchmark identification.

Pewter comes in three basic types, depending on the recipe. The best genuine (*Lautere*) pewter has a light color and is made from lead-free tin with small additions of copper, antimony, or bismuth. *Probezinn*, or proved pewter, occasionally called *Reichsprobe*, *Probe*, or similar names, contains about a ten-to-one ratio of tin to lead. Low (*Geringen*) pewter has a six-to-one ratio. Beginning in the 1700s, a fourth type of pewter was developed when antimony was added to pewter alloys to make a very different material—Britannia metal—some examples of which are shown in Section 7.

Steins are often stamped to identify the quality of the pewter. Sometimes *KL* is used for genuine (*klar und lauter* = clear and pure); X is for *Probezinn*. Sometimes just the ratio appears, like *10:1*. In the 1800s, it was common to see *Feinzinn* or *Englishzinn* for lead-free pewter; in the 1700s, the absence of lead was often indicated by a touchmark that showed an angel with either a sword and balance or a palm frond and trumpet.

One final mark of importance is *KAYSERZINN* or *KZ*. This is an antimony-pewter alloy used by the Kayser factory from the late 1800s to the early 1900s.

5.3 Collecting Pewter

During the Historicism period, many early styles were reproduced. These were not originally intended as fakes, but removal of the manufacturer's name at a later time has occasionally misled buyers. Most of these reproductions are cast, often in sand or gypsum/plaster molds, which are not as sharp as originals. Knowledge of marks and purity and the study of originals will greatly help the beginning collector to identify these reproductions.

Pewter can get *sick*, either with a black flaking disease or a powdering disease. In either case, the pewter may be slowly eaten away until there are actually holes in it. Leaving steins wrapped in accidentally dampened newspapers (which contain sulfur) will greatly accelerate the damage done by these diseases. Polishing (and darkening, if desired) is virtually the only way to arrest these diseases, which can, incidentally, spread to neighboring pieces.

5.4 Evaluation Information

Price trends for pewter steins in recent years have been mixed. The early and middle 1990s saw mostly steady or falling prices, but the late 1990s have shown moderate increases in prices for some pewter steins. The net result is mostly unchanged prices during the 1990s.

a. Pewter, 1.0L, Saxony, early 1800s, $200-300.
b. Pewter, 1.0L, Wasserburg, middle 1700s, $350-500.
c. Pewter, 1.5L, Salzburg, late 1700s, $300-450.
d. Pewter, 1.5L, Saxony, engraved, early 1800s, $600-900.

e. Pewter, 1.0L, Bohemia, middle 1700s, $400-600.
f. Pewter, 1.0L, Saxony, engraved, dated 1820, $300-500.
g. Pewter, 1.0L, Munich, engraved, late 1600s, $800-1200.
h. Pewter, 1.5L, engraved, marriage stein, dated 1787, $900-1200.

a.   Pewter, 1.0L, Amberg, engraved, early 1700s, $800-1200.

b.   Pewter, 1.0L, Normandy, stamped & engraved, early 1700s, $800-1200.

c.   Pewter, 1.0L, Dinkelsbühl, engraved, middle 1700s, $700-1000.

d.   Pewter, .75L, Saxony, c.1800, $300-400.

e.   Pewter, 1.5L, northern Germany, 1700s, $400-600.

f.   Pewter, 1.5L, Augsburg, c.1700, $700-1000.

g.   Pewter, 1.0L, Breslau, engraved, dated 1677, $1000-1500.

a. Pewter, 1.5L, Straßbourg, c.1800, $500-800.
b. Pewter, 1.5L, Heidenheim, middle 1700s, $600-900.
c. Pewter, 1.5L, southern Germany, engraved, early 1700s, $1000-1500.

d. Pewter, 1.5L, Bern, Switzerland, middle 1700s, $700-1000.
e. Pewter, 1.5L, Karlsruhe, middle 1700s, $700-1000.
f. Pewter, 1.5L, Bern, Switzerland, engraved, early 1800s, $600-900.
g. Pewter, 1.5L, Ludwigsburg, middle 1700s, $600-900.

a. Pewter, 1.5L, relief, late 1800s, $350-500.
b. Pewter, 1.5L, relief, Ferdinand and his dog, late 1800s, $400-550.
c. Pewter, 1.5L, relief, Occupational Tailor, late 1800s, $450-650.
d. Pewter, 1.5L, relief, Occupational Barrelmaker, late 1800s, $450-650.

e. Pewter, 1.5L, relief, Occupational Blacksmith, late 1800s, $450-650.
f. Pewter, 1.5L, relief, Occupational Baker, late 1800s, $450-650.
g. Pewter, 1.5L, relief, Occupational Carpenter, late 1800s, $450-650.
h. Pewter, 1.5L, relief, Occupational Shoemaker, late 1800s, $450-650.

a. Pewter, 1.5L, relief, knight, late 1800s, $450-600.
b. Pewter, 1.5L, relief, knight, late 1800s, $400-550.
c. Pewter, 1.5L, relief, knight, late 1800s, $400-550.
d. Pewter, 1.5L, relief, knight, late 1800s, $450-600.

e. Pewter, 2.0L, relief, marked Osiris, Art Nouveau style, c.1900, $150-250.
f. Pewter, .5L, engraved, Art Nouveau style, c.1900, $200-300.
g. Pewter, .5L, relief, devil, Art Nouveau style, late 1800s, $150-250.
h. Pewter, .5L, relief, Art Nouveau style, early 1900s, $150-250.

a.   Pewter, .5L, relief, woman sharpshooter, c.1900, $100-200.
b.   Pewter, .5L, relief, *Hamburg* souvenir, dated 1904, $100-200.
c.   Pewter, .5L, relief, dancing, c.1900, $150-250.
d.   Pewter, 1.0L, relief, forest scene, c.1900, $150-250.
e.   Pewter, .5L, relief, Germania, late 1800s, $100-200.

f.   Pewter, 1.5L, relief, courting and dancing, c.1900, $150-250.
g.   Pewter, 1.5L, relief, Imperial Eagle, c.1900, $250-350.
h.   Pewter, 1.5L, relief, knights, late 1800s, $300-500.
i.   Pewter, 1.5L, relief, Apostles, dated 1517, but made late 1800s, $300-500.

a. Pewter, .25L, relief, *St. Louis* souvenir, dated 1904, $50-100.
b. Pewter, .25L, relief, *Anaconda, Montana* souvenir, c.1900, $50-100.
c. Pewter, .25L, relief, *Santa Barbara* souvenir, c.1900, $50-100.
d. Pewter, .25L, relief, eagle, c.1900, $50-100.
e. Pewter, .2L, relief, *Winnipeg, Canada* souvenir, c.1900, $40-80.
f. Pewter, .1L, relief, *Chicago* souvenir, c.1900, $40-80.

g. Pewter, 1.0L, relief, Bacchus and revelers, late 1800s, $200-300.
h. Pewter, 1.0L, relief, mascaroons and cartouches, dated 1898, $250-350.
i. Pewter, .5L, relief, mascaroons and eagles, late 1800s, $150-250.
j. Pewter, .5L, relief, eagle, late 1800s, $100-200.
k. Pewter, 1.0L, relief, marked F.&M.N., four seasons in panels, late 1800s, $200-300.

a.   Pewter, 1.0L, relief, double-headed eagle, late 1800s, $200-300.
b.   Pewter, .75L, relief, crest, late 1800s, $200-300.
c.   Pewter, 1.0L, relief, Falstaff scene, c.1900, $100-200.
d.   Pewter, .5L, relief, marked F.&M.N., tavern scene, late 1800s, $80-120.

e.   Pewter, .5L, relief, marked F. Barth, München, The Pillow Fight, dated 1872, $700-900.
f.   Pewter, .5L, relief, marked Orivit, king, knight, maiden, late 1800s, $350-500.

6. Glass

The tremendous variety of ways in which glass has been used to produce beer steins makes it very difficult to make generalized comments and select representative pictures. Some references listed in Section 20 contain more specifics; unfortunately, these concentrate on the earliest glass steins, with little information available on glass steins made after 1850.

6.1 History of Glass Steins

The variety of ways glass has been used is certainly due to the fact that it is a material that has been known and loved for thousands of years, and thus has received the attention of many innovative craftsmen.

Glass steins dating from the 1530s and 1540s are known. A couple of examples that exist have large finials but no thumblifts. It seems possible that thumblifts, which became popular shortly thereafter, may have been finials displaced to make opening the lid easier.

It is difficult to generalize about the materials, shapes, or decorations of steins from the 1500s and 1600s because few examples from this time period are still in existence. The glass is sometimes greenish to brownish in color; sometimes it is milk glass. Some steins have applied glass *prunts*, others have enameled portraits or heraldic symbols. The enameled steins show the influence of French and Italian Renaissance designs, readily explained by the fact that the French had re-introduced the lost art of enameling to the Germans in the 1400s, with the Italian influence coming in the middle 1500s.

Enameling glass simply involves the painting of powdered, colored glass, flux, and a vehicle onto glass, then heating at a sufficient temperature to fuse the design to the glass. So-called cold-painting, done with lacquers or oil paints, is known to have been used on early glass steins. It is not durable, however, which may explain why some plain glass bodies have rather elaborate old mountings.

From the late 1600s to about 1800, milk glass was a commonly used porcelain substitute. Milk glass was made by mixing tin oxide, the same white coloring agent used in faience, into the raw materials for glass. The early decorations on milk glass steins, as on many enameled glass items of this period, are similar to those appearing on the faience steins of those times: first Chinese motifs, then the so-called Indian and German flowers, and finally genre scenes. As on faience steins, the style of these motifs changed from the Baroque to folk art by about 1800.

Also in the 1700s, some spectacular engravings were cut into clear and colored glass steins, steins that were almost always cylindrical. Common themes are floral, heraldic, hunting, portraits, celebrations, and cities; some of the earlier themes were mythological or religious.

Silver and pewter mountings were about equally popular on glass steins around 1700. Somewhat later, pewter mountings became far more common. By then, silver mountings were apparently reserved only for spectacular glass steins, such as those that were ornately engraved (often diamond-cut), or those of ruby or cranberry glass (made by using gold as the coloring agent in the glass).

During the Biedermeier period, 1800 to 1850, glass steins began changing from the cylindrical *Walzenkrug* shape into a shape tapered slightly toward the top and often pulled into a partial pedestal near the base. Enameled folk art designs were used, often featuring wedding scenes or small panels with inscriptions about weddings or commemorating other events. These were probably the most popular steins during this period.

The next period, Historicism, brought a strong interest in Renaissance enameled decorations, occasionally found on cut, and colored glass. Glass that was cut or engraved through one or more different colored layers gained in popularity through the middle 1800s. Subsection 6.2 includes information on the techniques used to make these steins, which often depict deer, forests, buildings, geometric patterns, or other folk themes. Geometric patterns created by deep cutting or mold-blown techniques were also popular in the middle 1800s.

Around 1870, elaborate pewter piercework or lattice overlays began to be constructed right over colored glass steins. Toward 1900, the pewterwork became more elaborate and extensive, often encompassing the handle so that the colored glass cup could be separately manufactured and dropped into the pewter shell.

Enamel-decorated steins continued to be popular in the late 1800s and early 1900s, but the themes changed from neo-Renaissance to those with more social significance. Also during this period, a strong interest developed in clear glass steins of every reasonable shape: cylindrical, pedestal, pear, vase, conical, spherical, and all types of combinations. Stein design sometimes included the addition of prunts, cutting, engraving, etching, enameling, or rigaree ribbons.

Such steins have continued to be popular to this day, although the handwork has generally disappeared. Occasionally, modern glass steins will carry an enameled design, which was printed or silk-screened onto a decal that was then fired onto the stein. As with stoneware, there are still a few craftsmen who are making steins using some of the old glassmaking techniques.

6.2 Production

Glass is the product of a silicic acid (often from sand) and an alkali (often from soda and ash). The combined ingredients must be brought to a temperature of about 1100°C (2000°F) in order to form a melt. Most glass houses were located in forests because when wood was used as fuel, large quantities of it were required. Some coal-fired glass furnaces were used, but these only became common in the 1800s. Sometime after 1900, electricity became the most popular energy source for glass furnaces.

The earliest glass steins were made by using a long pipe, called a punty or pontil, to remove a blob of glass from the furnace. This piece of glass was then pressed, spun, drawn, and/or blown into a cylindrical shape. The end was trimmed off, and the handle was formed and pressed into place. After some cooling took place, the mug was broken away from the pipe, leaving a pontil mark on the bottom. Even though the rough edges of this mark were often ground smooth, the mark is clearly visible on glass steins made prior to about 1870 and on the handmade steins produced in ever decreasing numbers since then.

A new mold-blown technique, which was developed around 1840, involved putting a partially blown and shaped blob of glass into a mold, then further blowing it until it touched the sides and picked up the pattern of the mold. Steins from such three-part molds, or dip molds, have soft contours, unlike sharper pressed or cut glass, and they still have pontil marks. This type of mold-blown glass stein can also be identified by hollows and patterns on the outside that to some extent correspond to patterns inside the stein. Sand spots, bubbles (or seeds), swirls, or streaks may often be seen in these steins, as in all earlier handmade glass. The sizes are usually regular, such as .25L, .5L, and 1.0L. The lids are the same as those characteristic of most steins made from about 1840 to 1880: porcelain inlaid, cut glass inlaid, or heavy steepled pewter, occasionally with faceted colored glass jewels.

In the middle of the 1800s, the demand for glass bottles and jars generated tremendous economic incentive to invent a bottle-making machine. The widespread use of coal as an abundant furnace fuel made such mass production possible. By the 1870s, automatic machinery had replaced the mold-blown processes, creating the so-called pressed glass steins. Nearly always made of clear glass, these steins are usually seen with the same types of lids as the mold-blown steins. Into the 1900s, the pewter lids became markedly less heavy and less ornate.

Colors are imparted to glass intentionally or unintentionally by the presence of metal oxides. As previously mentioned, the iron oxide in sand and other raw materials imparts a greenish blue tinge. Metallic impurities in wood ash tend to produce a grayish-green tint. Colors that may be used intentionally include:

- cobalt oxide for royal blue
- manganese oxide for violet
- chromium oxides and nickel oxides for greens
- tin oxides for milk (or white)
- gold for cranberry
- silver for gray
- copper sulfate for turquoise
- cadmium oxides for red.

Most of these colors were available in the 1200s, long before stein making started, and were subsequently refined during the Medicis' synthetic gem experiments and by other later experimentation with colored glass for stained glass windows.

Some other techniques can be used to add color to glass. If a blob of molten clear glass is touched to a blob of another color, usually red, blue, violet, green, or yellow, it will pick up a thin outer layer of that color. This layer can then be engraved, cut, or etched through to the clear glass using hydrofluoric acid. Some beautiful steins have been produced using multiple layers of this overlaid glass.

Clear or colored glass can also be stained with silver nitrate or some other products that are fired into the surface layers of the glass. These stains are always in the range from light yellow to orange-yellow, and they can be engraved, cut, or etched through to clear, in ways similar to the techniques used on overlaid glass.

Flashed glass has a thin layer of colored, translucent enamel fired onto its surface; most often the enamel is a ruby color with a slight bluish surface sheen. Flashed glass is easily cut through to clear to provide decorative effects, such as scenes of spas, buildings, or deer.

Of these three types of surface colors, the overlay is the richest, most even, and most difficult to produce. Compared to the other two techniques, it can easily be identified by its noticeable thickness at all places where it has been cut through.

As beautiful as colored glass can be, the quest for a formula for any specific color pales in comparison to the fanatical search for a perfectly clear glass. Surprisingly pure raw materials are required to make a glass of so-called superior brilliance. Even using an iron tool to stir the raw materials for glass is enough to impart to the glass that common greenish-blue tinge of iron oxide.

In the middle 1800s, it became common to mask this iron oxide tint with small quantities of manganese oxide, but this decolorizer becomes unstable in sunlight and changes to light purple. Manganese became a strategic mineral during World War I, and since it was unavailable for glass manufacture, it was replaced by the straw-colored selenium. Since the late 1920s, whenever a reasonably clear glass was desired without incurring the expense of using a crystal recipe, traces of selenium and cobalt (bluish) were mixed to yield a glass with a very light gray color. Looking into the edge of the base, or the lip, for a concentrated view of the color of the glass can help identify the period during which a clear glass stein was made.

6.3 Collecting Glass Steins

The Historicism style of the 1800s led to the reproduction of many Renaissance enameled glass pieces; however, few were steins (most were beakers and pokals, often with the Imperial Eagle motif). Streaks and seeds in the glass and the great attention to the design detail of the originals are the best ways of identifying age. Enameled names of reproduction manufacturers were frequently polished off.

The most difficult copies to detect are those that use authentic old glass bodies, originally decorated very sparsely or polished clean but later enameled using old designs. To properly bake such enamel designs onto a stein, however, requires the removal and reattachment of the mountings, a procedure that can usually be easily detected.

The same types of identification problems are encountered with reproduction engraved glass steins. And the same solutions are applicable: examining the detail of the engraving, replaced lids, and so on.

Care of glass steins is simple but important. To protect against damage from heat, they should be kept out of direct sunlight and away from fireplaces, stoves, and furnace vents when these are in use. The very old and very thin-walled steins are especially vulnerable.

Since such a great variety is available, most glass stein collectors tend to specialize in a certain type or in particular types of items, many of which can be recognized from the groupings in the following pictures. Again, the great variety means that some types do not come up for sale very often, making it difficult for collectors to fully understand the pricing structure. Therefore, this section offers a fairly comprehensive selection of pictures.

6.4 Evaluation Information

Price trends in the past ten years have been mostly upward for glass steins. Most glass steins from the 1700s and early 1800s have increased in value, some significantly. Many of the more desirable glass steins from the middle 1800s, including overlay and the better wheel-engraved steins, have increased in value throughout the last ten years. The more common transfer glass steins have been steady or are increasing only slightly.

a. Clear glass, 1.0L, wheel engraved, Occupational Butcher, inlaid glass medallion, late 1700s, pewter lid & footring, $4000-6000.

b. Clear glass, 1.0L, wheel engraved, Occupational Brewer, middle 1700s, pewter lid & footring, $2500-3500.
c. Clear glass, 1.0L, wheel engraved, early 1700s, pewter lid & footring, $4000-5000.
d. Clear glass, 1.0L, wheel engraved, Christ on cross, dated 1728 on glass, pewter lid & footring, $4000-5500.
e. Clear glass, 1.0L, wheel engraved, dated 1771, pewter lid & footring, $1500-2000.

a. Clear glass, .75L, wheel engraved, late 1700s, pewter lid, $800-1200.
b. Clear glass, 1.5L, wheel engraved, middle 1700s, pewter lid & footring, $1000-1400.
c. Clear glass, 1.0L, wheel engraved, late 1700s, pewter lid & footring, $1000-1400.
d. Clear glass, .75L, wheel engraved, Occupational Butcher, c.1800, pewter lid, $2000-2500.

e. Clear glass, .5L, wheel engraved, couple, wheel-engraved baby in base, c.1800, pewter lid & footring, $2000-2500.
f. Clear glass, .5L, wheel engraved, angel, early 1800s, pewter lid, $600-900.
g. Clear glass, .5L, wheel engraved, Occupational Butcher, early 1800s, pewter lid, $600-900.
h. Clear glass, .5L, wheel engraved, angel, early 1800s, pewter lid, $500-700.

a. Milk glass, .5L, enameled horse, c.1800, pewter lid & footring, $2000-3000.
b. Milk glass, 1.0L, enameled man, late 1700s, glass set-on lid, $1000-1400.
c. Milk glass, .5, enameled Occupational Wheelwright late 1700s, pewter lid & footring, $2000-3000.
d. Milk glass, .5L, enameled flower, dated 1795, pewter lid & footring, $1100-1500.
e. Milk glass, 1.0L, enameled flowers, late 1700s, pewter lid & footring, $1200-1600.

f. Milk glass, 1.0L, enameled flowers, late 1700s, pewter lid & footring, $1200-1600.
g. Milk glass, 1.0L, enameled flowers, late 1700s, pewter lid & footring, $1200-1600.
h. Milk glass, 1.0L, enameled heart & birds, early 1800s, pewter lid & footring, $1800-2400.
i. Milk glass, 1.0L, enameled, late 1700s, pewter lid & footring, $1000-1400.
j. Milk glass, .5L, enameled man, late 1700s, pewter lid, $2000-2500.

a. Milk glass, .5L, enameled flowers, early 1800s, pewter lid, $800-1100.
b. Milk glass, .5L, enameled flowers, early 1800s, pewter lid, $800-1100.
c. Milk glass, .5L, enameled flowers, c.1830, pewter lid, $700-1000.
d. Milk glass, 1.0L, enameled heart & birds, early 1800s, pewter lid, $800-1200.
e. Milk glass, .5L, wheel engraved & enameled design, early 1800s, pewter lid & footring, $700-1000.

f. Milk glass, .5L, wheel engraved & enameled design, early 1800s, pewter lid, $700-1000.
g. Milk glass, .5L, wheel engraved & enameled design, early 1800s, pewter lid & footring, $900-1200.
h. Milk glass, .5L, enameled children, early 1800s, pewter lid & footring, $1200-1600.
i. Milk glass, .5L, enameled flowers, early 1800s, pewter lid & footring, $900-1200.
j. Milk glass, .5L, enameled, early 1800s, pewter lid & footring, $500-700.

a.   Clear glass, 1.0L, enameled inside & outside, man, middle 1700s, pewter lid & footring, $4000-5500.
b.   Clear glass, 1.0L, enameled, horse, c.1800, pewter lid & footring, $2500-3500.
c.   Clear glass, 1.0L, enameled, birds, c.1800, pewter lid & footring, $2000-2500.
d.   Clear glass, .75L, enameled, heart & cross, early 1800s, pewter lid & footring, $2000-2500.
e.   Clear glass, 1.0L, enameled, Husaren on horse, late 1700s, pewter lid & footring, $3000-4000.

f.   Clear glass, 1.0L, enameled flowers, early 1800s, pewter lid & footring, $700-900.
g.   Clear glass, 1.0L, Saxony, enameled flowers, middle 1800s, pewter lid & footring, $700-950.
h.   Clear glass, 1.0L, Saxony, enameled flowers, middle 1800s, pewter lid, $700-950.
i.   Clear glass, 1.0L, Saxony, enameled, middle 1800s, pewter lid, $900-1200.

a. Cobalt blue glass, .5L, gold & white enamel, early 1800s, pewter lid & footring, $700-1000.

b. Cobalt blue glass, 1.0L, gold & white enamel, early 1800s, pewter lid & footring, $700-1000.

c. Orange glass, 1.0L, gold & white enamel, middle 1800s, pewter lid & footring, $700-1000.

d. Cobalt blue glass, 1.0L, gold & white enamel, middle 1800s, pewter lid, $800-1200.

e. Orange glass, 1.0L, green & white enamel, middle 1800s, glass inlaid lid & footring, $700-1000.

f. Clear glass, .5L, enameled flowers, middle 1800s, pewter lid, $350-500.

g. Clear glass, .5L, wheel engraved, middle 1800s, pewter lid, $200-300.

h. Cobalt blue glass, .5L, gold & white enamel, middle 1800s, pewter lid, $400-600.

i. Cobalt blue glass, .5L, gold & white enamel, middle 1800s, inlaid porcelain lid, $300-400.

j. Cobalt blue glass, .5L, middle 1800s, pewter lid & footring, $350-500.

a.   Overlaid glass, .5L, cut, blue & white on clear, middle 1800s, glass inlaid lid, $1000-1500.

b.   Overlaid glass, .5L, cut, blue & white on clear, middle 1800s, glass inlaid lid, $1000-1500.

c.   Overlaid glass, .5L, cut, blue & white on clear, middle 1800s, glass inlaid lid, $900-1200.

d.   Overlaid glass, .5L, cut, blue & white on clear, middle 1800s, silver-plated lid, $700-900.

e.   Overlaid glass, .5L, cut, black & white on clear, late 1800s, pewter lid, $1000-1500.

f.   Overlaid glass, .5L, cut, white on pink, middle 1800s, glass inlaid lid, $800-1100.

g.   Overlaid glass, .25L, cut, pink & white on clear, late 1800s, porcelain inlaid lid, $600-800.

h.   Overlaid glass, 1.0L, cut, blue & white on clear, gold & red enamel, middle 1800s, gilded silver lid, $4000-5000.

a. Overlaid glass, .5L, cut, blue & white on clear, middle 1800s, silver lid, $1500-2000.
b. Overlaid glass, .5L, cut, white on clear, enameled spa scenes, middle 1800s, silver lid, $800-1200.
c. Overlaid glass, .5L, cut, white on clear, enameled, middle 1800s, glass inlaid lid, $800-1200.
d. Overlaid glass, .5L, cut, blue on clear, gold enamel, middle 1800s, silver-plated lid, $600-800.

e. Overlaid glass, .5L, cut, pink & white on clear, late 1800s, porcelain inlaid lid, $1000-1400.
f. Swirl glass, 1.0L, clear & white glass, early 1800s, pewter lid, $2500-3500.
g. Swirl glass, .5L, blue & white, Venetian style, middle 1800s, glass inlaid lid, $2000-3000.
h. Swirl glass, .5L, three layers, clear, white and swirl, red, purple & white, Venetian style, middle 1800s, glass inlaid lid, $2000-3000.

a. Ruby glass, .5L, cut, deep red color, late 1800s, silver-plated lid, $600-800.
b. Ruby glass, .5L, cut, deep red color, late 1800s, silver lid with inlaid glass, $700-1000.
c. Opaline glass, .5L, blue, late 1800s, glass inlaid lid, $400-600.
d. Opaline glass, .5L, white, late 1800s, inlaid glass lid with figural satyr, $600-800.
e. Opaline glass, .5L, blue-white, late 1800s, silver lid, $700-1000.

f. Opaline glass, .5L, white, gold enamel, late 1800s, glass inlaid lid with silver rim, $1800-2400.
g. Opaline glass, .5L, pink, gold enamel, late 1800s, glass inlaid lid, $1200-1600.
h. Ruby glass, .5L, deep red, middle 1800s, gilded silver mountings & overlay, $1200-1600.
i. Overlaid glass, .5L, cut, red on clear, middle 1800s, gilded silver lid, $2500-3500.

a. Clear glass, 1.0L, wheel engraved, Bohemian, deer & mountain scene, middle 1800s, silver lid & footring set with malachite, $6000-8000.

b. Clear glass, 1.0L, wheel engraved, dog and forest scene, middle 1800s, silver lid set with semi-precious stones, $5000-7000.

c. Overlaid glass, .5L, wheel engraved, red on clear, late 1800s, glass inlaid lid, $2500-3500.

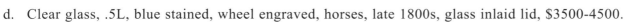

d. Clear glass, .5L, blue stained, wheel engraved, horses, late 1800s, glass inlaid lid, $3500-4500.

e. Clear glass, .5L, blue stained, wheel engraved, horses, late 1800s, glass inlaid lid, $3500-4500.

f. Clear glass, .5L, ruby stained, wheel engraved, deer, late 1800s, glass inlaid lid, $1500-2000.

g. Clear glass, .5L, ruby stained, wheel engraved, deer, late 1800s, glass inlaid lid, $1500-2000.

a. Clear glass, .5L, blown, faceted, wheel engraved, stag, late 1800s, glass inlaid lid, $350-450.
b. Clear glass, .5L, blown, faceted, wheel engraved, stag, late 1800s, glass inlaid lid, $350-450.
c. Clear glass, .5L, blown, faceted, wheel engraved, stags, late 1800s, pewter lid, $350-450.
d. Clear glass, .5L, blown, faceted, wheel engraved, stags, late 1800s, glass inlaid lid, brass mounts, $300-400.
e. Clear glass, .5L, blown, faceted, wheel engraved, stags, late 1800s, silver-plated lid, $200-300.

f. Clear glass, .5L, faceted, wheel engraved, building, late 1800s, silver-plated lid, $200-300.
g. Clear glass, .75L, faceted, wheel engraved, stag, late 1800s, pewter lid, $1200-1600.
h. Clear glass, .5L, wheel engraved, deer, late 1800s, glass inlaid lid, $300-400.
i. Clear glass, .5L, wheel engraved, deer, late 1800s, glass inlaid lid, $300-400.
j. Clear glass, .5L, ruby stained, wheel engraved, hunter in field, late 1800s, glass inlaid lid, $600-900.

a. Clear glass, .75L, cut, late 1800s, glass inlaid lid, $200-300.
b. Clear glass, .75L, faceted, wheel engraved, *Bad Reiners,* late 1800s, pewter lid, $200-300.
c. Clear glass, 1.0L, wheel engraved, stags, music box base, late 1800s, glass inlaid lid, $450-600.
d. Clear glass, 1.0L, blown, faceted, late 1800s, porcelain inlaid lid - tavern scene, pewter base, $400-550.

e. Clear glass, .3L, faceted, wheel engraved, bird, late 1800s, glass inlaid lid, $300-450.
f. Clear glass, .5L, faceted, wheel engraved, horse, late 1800s, pewter lid, $350-500.
g. Clear glass, .5L, wheel engraved, man & woman, middle 1800s, pewter lid, $600-900.
h. Clear glass, .5L, yellow stained, wheel engraved, horses, stag on other side, late 1800s, glass inlaid lid, $2000-2500.

a.   Clear glass, .5L, red flashed, wheel engraved, buildings on side panels, *Teplitz*, late 1800s, glass inlaid lid, $350-500.

b.   Overlaid glass, .5L, red over clear, middle 1800s, glass inlaid lid, $800-1100.

c.   Clear glass, 1.0L, wheel engraved, horn, dated 1876, silver lid, $1500-2000.

d.   Clear glass, .5L, wheel engraved, Zeppelin, early 1900s, glass inlaid lid, $700-1000.

e.   Clear glass, .3L, red flashed, wheel engraved, New York City, late 1800s, glass inlaid lid, $300-500.

f.   Clear glass, .5L, red flashed, wheel engraved, spas, including *Brand,* late 1800s, glass inlaid lid, $250-350.

g.   Clear glass, .5L, red flashed, wheel engraved, spas, including *Schlossburg,* late 1800s, glass inlaid lid, $250-350.

h.   Clear glass, .5L, red flashed, wheel engraved, *Kursaal zu Hamburg,* late 1800s, glass inlaid lid, $250-350.

i.   Clear glass, .5L, red flashed, wheel engraved, spas, late 1800s, glass inlaid lid, $250-350.

a. Clear glass, .5L, Art Nouveau, dated 1900, silver lid, footring & overlay, $500-750.
b. Clear glass, .5L, green prunts cut to form leaves, Art Nouveau, late 1800s, pewter lid, $350-500.
c. Clear glass, .5L, green prunts, Art Nouveau, early 1900s, pewter lid with monkey thumblift, $400-600.
d. Green glass, .5L, blue rigaree bands, late 1800s, silver-plated lid, footring & handle, $700-1000.

e. Clear glass, .5L, cut, late 1800s, pewter lid, $100-200.
f. Clear glass, .5L, cut, dated 1898, silver-plated lid, $100-200.
g. Clear glass, .5L, cut, late 1800s, pewter lid, $150-250.
h. Clear glass, .5L, cut, late 1800s, pewter lid with small porcelain inlay, $150-250.
i. Clear glass, .5L, cut, late 1800s, pewter lid, $100-200.

a.   Clear glass, .5L, cut, middle 1800s, pewter lid, $350-500.
b.   Clear glass, .5L, cut, late 1800s, pewter lid, $400-600.
c.   Clear glass, .5L, cut, late 1800s, pewter lid, $400-600.
d.   Clear glass, .5L, cut, late 1800s, pewter lid & footring, $500-750.
e.   Clear glass, .5L, cut, middle 1800s, pewter lid, $250-400.

f.   Clear glass, .5L, cut, frosted, enameled, middle 1800s, porcelain inlaid lid, $250-350.
g.   Clear glass, .5L, cut, frosted, enameled, middle 1800s, porcelain inlaid lid, $250-350.
h.   Clear glass, .5L, cut, enameled, middle 1800s, pewter lid, $250-350.
i.   Clear glass, .5L, cut, frosted, enameled, middle 1800s, porcelain inlaid lid, $250-350.

a. Clear glass, .3L, mold blown, middle 1800s, glass inlaid lid, $150-250.
b. Clear glass, .5L, mold blown, enameled, late 1800s, pewter lid, $100-200.
c. Clear glass, .5L, mold blown, hobnail pattern, late 1800s, pewter lid with bronze inlay, $100-200.
d. Clear glass, .5L, cut, c.1900, porcelain inlaid lid, $300-400.

e. Clear glass, .3L, late 1800s, silver-plated lid, brass Jäger tschako finial, $200-300.
f. Clear glass, .5L, faceted, late 1800s, pewter lid, Infantry helmet finial, $200-300.
g. Clear glass, .5L, faceted, dated 1879, silver-plated lid, Infantry helmet finial, $200-300.
h. Clear glass, .5L, faceted, silver lid, dated 1861-1911, Berlin, Husaren helmet finial, $250-350.
i. Clear glass, .5L, cut, late 1800s, metal lid with Saxon Husaren helmet finial, $200-300.

a. Turquoise glass, .5L, c.1900, pewter lid & footring, $300-450.
b. Amber glass, .5L, thumbprint pattern, c.1900, pewter lid, footring & overlay, $350-450.
c. Cranberry glass, .5L, dated 1893, pewter lid, footring & overlay, $350-450.
d. Amber glass, .5L, thumbprint pattern, c.1900, pewter lid, footring & overlay, $350-450.
e. Cranberry glass, .5L, cut, c.1900, pewter lid & footring, $400-600.

f. Cranberry glass, .5L, threaded design, c.1900, pewter lid & footring, $350-450.
g. Cranberry glass, .5L, threaded design, cranberry to clear, c.1900, pewter lid & footring, $350-450.
h. Amber glass, .5L, thumbprint pattern, c.1900, pewter lid & footring, $300-400.
i. Cranberry glass, .5L, thumbprint pattern, c.1900, pewter lid & footring, $300-400.
j. Amber glass, .5L, c.1900, pewter lid & footring, $250-350.

a. Amber glass, .5L, c.1900, pewter lid, footring & overlay, $300-400.
b. Green glass, .5L, c.1900, pewter lid, footring & overlay, $250-350.
c. Green glass, .5L, c.1900, pewter lid, base & overlay, $350-500.
d. Cranberry glass, .5L, c.1900, pewter lid, base & overlay, $400-550.
e. Cranberry glass, .5L, c.1900, gilded copper lid, footring & overlay, $500-800.

f. Cranberry glass, .5L, c.1900, pewter lid, footring & overlay, $350-500.
g. Cranberry glass, .5L, c.1900, pewter lid, footring & overlay, $350-500.
h. Amber glass, .5L, c.1900, pewter lid & pewter medallion overlay of farmer with wagon, $300-400.
i. Clear glass, .5L, green prunts, c.1900, green glass lid overlaid with pewter, pewter footring, $300-450.
j. Amber glass, .5L, green prunts, c.1900, green glass lid overlaid with pewter, pewter footring, $300-450.

a.   Green glass, 1.0L, dated 1894, pewter lid, handle, footring & overlay, $500-750.

b.   Cranberry glass, .25L, c.1900, pewter lid, handle, base & overlay, $150-250.

c.   Ruby glass, .5L, early 1900s, pewter lid, handle & overlay, $700-1000.

d.   Amber glass, .5L, green prunts, c.1900, pewter lid, $250-350.

e.   Amber glass, .5L, blue applied rigaree bands & prunts, c.1900, pewter lid, $250-350.

f.   Clear glass, .5L, cranberry flashed, cut, swirled design, c.1900, pewter lid, $350-500.

g.   Clear glass, .5L, blue prunts, late 1800s, pewter lid, $200-300.

h.   Clear glass, .75L, blue prunts, late 1800s, pewter lid, dwarf thumblift, $400-600.

i.   Clear glass, .75L, green prunts, late 1800s, glass inlaid lid, $500-700.

j.   Clear glass, .5L, yellow prunts, late 1800s, glass inlaid lid, $250-350.

a. Clear glass, .4L, enameled, c.1900, pewter lid, $200-300.
b. Clear glass, .3L, enameled, late 1800s, pewter lid, $400-600.
c. Clear glass, .3L, enameled, Occupational Glassmaker, late 1800s, pewter lid, $500-700.
d. Clear glass, .5L, enameled, c.1900, pewter lid, $200-300.
e. Clear glass, .5L, enameled, c.1900, pewter lid, $200-300.

f. Clear glass, 1.0L, enameled, c.1900, pewter lid, $450-600.
g. Clear glass, 1.0L, enameled, *v. Hindenburg, 1914,* pewter lid, $400-500.
h. Clear glass, 1.0L, enameled, c.1900, pewter lid, $500-650.
i. Clear glass, 1.0L, enameled (white), c.1900, pewter lid, $400-500.
j. Clear glass, .5L, enameled (white), c.1900, prism glass inlaid lid, $400-500.

a. Clear glass, .5L, enameled, student association, dated 1907, pewter lid, $350-500.
b. Clear glass, .5L, enameled, Infantry Regiment Nr. 160, early 1900s, pewter lid, $600-900.
c. Clear glass, .5L, enameled, *All Heil!*, early 1900s, metal lid, $250-350.
d. Clear glass, .5L, enameled, signed T.O.H., early 1900s, relief pewter lid with scene of Hofbräuhaus, $250-350.
e. Clear glass, .5L, enameled, early 1900s, prism glass inlaid lid, $200-300.

f. Clear glass, .5L, enameled, designed by Franz Ringer, early 1900s, pewter lid, $400-550.
g. Clear glass, .5L, enameled, designed by Franz Ringer, early 1900s, pewter lid, $400-550.
h. Clear glass, .5L, enameled, *Gut Heil!,* early 1900s, pewter lid, $200-300.
i. Clear glass, .5L, enameled, early 1900s, pewter lid, $150-250.
j. Clear glass, .5L, enameled, early 1900s, pewter lid, $200-300.

a. Clear glass, .5L, enameled, c.1900, pewter lid, $300-450.
b. Clear glass, .5L, enameled, hops decor, Art Nouveau, c.1900, pewter lid, $250-350.
c. Clear glass, 1.0L, enameled, flowers, Art Nouveau, c.1900, pewter lid, $350-500.
d. Clear glass, .5L, enameled, student association, dated 1907, pewter lid, $400-550.

e. Green glass, 1.0L, enameled, signed Fritz Heckert, late 1800s, pewter lid, $900-1200.
f. Overlaid glass, .5L, clear on white on clear, enameled, c.1900, metal lid, $200-300.
g. Clear glass, .5L, orange flashed, enameled (white), c.1900, prism glass inlaid lid, $300-400.
h. Clear glass, .5L, orange flashed, enameled & decorated with pieces of colored glass, *Schneekoppe,* c.1900, prism glass inlaid lid, $300-450.

a. Amber glass, .3L, enameled, c.1900, glass inlaid lid, $250-350.

b. Amber glass, .5L, enameled, prunts, c.1900, glass inlaid lid, $250-400.

c. Amber glass, .5L, transfer decoration, dice game, early 1900s, pewter lid, $150-250.

d. Amber glass, .5L, enameled, prunts, flowers, late 1800s, silver lid, $300-450.

e. Amber glass, .5L, enameled, prunts, Gmunden, late 1800s, glass inlaid lid, $350-500.

f. Amber glass, .5L, enameled, rifles & target, dated 1890, pewter lid, $250-400.

g. Amber glass, .5L, enameled, c.1900, pewter lid, $250-350.

h. Amber glass, .5L, enameled, *Gruß aus Berlin,* c.1900, pewter lid, $300-450.

i. Amber glass, .5L, enameled, c.1900, silver lid, $300-400.

j. Amber glass, .5L, enameled, flowers, late 1800s, glass inlaid lid, $350-450.

a. Green glass, .5L, enameled, student association, by Egermann, late 1800s, relief pewter lid, $500-700.
b. Green glass, .5L, enameled, blue prunts, c.1900, porcelain inlaid lid: *Garde Ulan Potsdam,* $350-500.
c. Green glass, .5L, enameled, late 1800s, glass inlaid lid, $500-750.
d. Amber glass, .5L, enameled, *Zum Wohl!,* c.1900, pewter lid & footring, $200-300.
e. Amber glass, .5L, enameled, *Dein Wohl!,* c.1900, pewter lid & footring, $200-300.

f. Amber glass, .5L, enameled, c.1900, pewter lid, $250-350.
g. Tan glass, .3L, enameled, c.1900, glass inlaid lid, $350-450.
h. Blue glass, .5L, enameled, fireman, c.1900, glass inlaid lid, $350-450.
i. Blue glass, .3L, enameled, boy, Mary Gregory type, c.1900, glass inlaid lid, $200-300.
j. Blue glass, .3L, enameled, girl, Mary Gregory type, c.1900, glass inlaid lid, $200-300.

a.   Clear glass, .5L, wheel engraved, late 1800s, handpainted porcelain inlaid lid of a girl, $200-300.
b.   Clear glass, .5L, cut, frit enameled, red beads, late 1800s, porcelain inlaid lid of Mary, $200-300.
c.   Clear glass, .5L, cut, middle 1800s, porcelain inlaid lid for Mason Occupation, $150-250.
d.   Clear glass, .5L, mold blown, hobnail pattern, late 1800s, porcelain inlaid lid of a hunter, $100-200.

e.   Clear glass, .5L, wheel engraved, middle 1800s, porcelain inlaid lid of a couple, $100-200.
f.   Clear glass, .5L, pressed, c.1900, porcelain inlaid lid for Farmer Occupation, $100-200.
g.   Clear glass, .5L, mold blown, c.1900, handpainted porcelain inlaid lid of a clown, $100-200.
h.   Clear glass, .5L, pressed, c.1900, porcelain inlaid lid for Farmer Occupation, $100-200.

a. Green glass, 1.5L, enameled, crest, late 1800s, glass inlaid lid, $600-900.
b. Amber glass, 1.5L, enameled, eagle, late 1800s, pewter lid, $450-650.
c. Clear glass, 2.0L, enameled, knight, late 1800s, pewter lid, $700-1000.
d. Clear glass, 2.0L, enameled, knight, late 1800s, pewter lid, $700-1000.
e. Amber glass, 2.0L, enameled, prunts, *Wohl bekomm's!*, c.1900, pewter lid, $300-450.

f. Green glass, 2.5L, enameled Trumpeter from Sackingen, late 1800s, pewter lid, $300-400.

g. Clear glass, 2.0L, enameled, prunts, crest, Egermann, late 1800s, glass inlaid lid, $1000-1400.

h. Amber glass, 3.0L, enameled, prunts, knights, c.1900, pewter lid, $600-800.

a. Clear glass, 2.0L, cut, Russian pattern, dated 1899, brass lid, $2000-2500.
b. Clear glass, 2.0L, cut, late 1800s, pewter lid, $250-350.
c. Clear glass, 3.0L, cut, dated 1878, pewter lid, $400-600.
d. Clear glass, 2.0L, green prunts, late 1800s, pewter lid, $500-750.
e. Amber glass, 2.0L, c.1900, pewter lid, handle, base & overlay, $400-600.

f. Amber glass, 17.5" ht., horn, c.1900, pewter mounts, $1500-2000.

g. Amber glass, 1.5L, late 1800s, bronze patina on brass mounts, $1000-1500.

7. Unusual Materials

Included in this section are steins made from silver, wood, ivory, and other miscellaneous materials. Either because of expense or because of their form, none of these materials were suitable for mass production processes. They were hand-worked, often with great detail. In the early 1800s the quality of most hand-worked steins began to decline. Each has an interesting history, but they are now encountered by collectors so infrequently that they do not warrant extensive discussions.

7.1 Silver Steins

Silver is often considered the most valuable material used regularly in stein making. Gold was very rarely used because it was expensive and so soft that it dented easily.

Early silver steins or silver mountings usually show traces of having been gilded. This was apparently not intended as a deception but rather as a means of avoiding the polishing that was made necessary by the oxidation of exposed silver. Beginning in the 1700s, gilding was no longer commonly used, as silver was appreciated for its own qualities, regardless of the polishing required.

To reduce its cost and increase its strength, silver is often alloyed, usually with copper. In the earliest days of stein making, a numeral representing the purity of the silver was stamped on a piece. This numerical figure was determined by the number of sixteenths comprising the fraction of silver in the composition, for example 11 or 12. In more recent times, this fraction has been changed to thousandths, such as 825.

Silver steins of the 1500s and early 1600s were decorated with hand-hammered relief and/or engravings. They were often tall, slim, and tapered toward the top. They were used for beer, cider, and wine, which were most often drunk warm, and sometimes even hot. With silver's high heat conductivity, it was important that thumblifts be thin and handles hollow (also reducing the cost and weight of silver steins).

In the middle 1600s, silver tankards were the first to consistently use the *Walzenkrug*, or cylindrical shape: about twice as high as wide. These steins were most often just engraved.

Toward the end of the 1600s, casting techniques provided deep and elaborate relief. However, production of this type of stein faded quickly in favor of a return to simpler engraved designs, a style that continued to be made up to the 1800s.

The 1800s began a period of revivals, especially of earlier cast pieces. In 1884, a marking rule was passed requiring that a crescent moon, crown, and purity level be stamped on all German silver steins, thus making it very helpful in identifying some of the later reproductions.

Identifying authentic early silver steins requires some understanding of styles, techniques, and marks, especially goldsmiths' marks, which should be sharp, not smooth as on many reproductions. It should also be noted that reproductions made during the late 1800s, the Historicism era, were not intended as fakes and often carried marks clearly identifying their manufacturer and the time period of production. When it appears that marks have been polished out, extra scrutiny should be used.

7.2 Wood Steins

Wood was one of the most popular materials for making beer beakers in the Middle Ages. The decline in the use of this substance, which began in the 1500s, was due to the difficulty of making a durable hinge for the lid. Occasionally, good examples of all-wooden steins are found, and when they are from the 1600s, the carving is generally very detailed and in high relief.

As mentioned in Section 5, the pewter-mounted and pewter-inlaid wooden steins were first popular from the middle 1600s to the middle 1700s. *Daubenkrug*, the name given to these steins, is derived from the wooden staves that make up the body of these steins. Natural motifs, such as plants and animals, dominate the inlaid designs on these steins.

Beginning in the early 1800s, some very nice all-wooden steins were produced in Norway and other Scandinavian countries. Existing examples are usually made from birch burl, often with feet and thumblifts in the shape of lions. Earlier examples have bodies carved with plant forms; later examples generally have smooth sides.

Around 1900, the St. Louis Silver Co. produced several types of steins made from oak staves and held together with silver-plated overlays and mountings. Also, at that time, a number of lathe-produced steins were made, often put together from separate pieces and decorated with burnt-wood designs.

7.3 Other Materials

Horn, ivory, amber, stone, coconuts, various metals such as hammered brass, and many other materials have been used to make steins. Of particular note among these are the ivory steins, which received the attention of some great craftsmen.

Production of ivory steins was not really possible until the Dutch East Indies Trade Company began to bring African ivory to Europe in the 1600s. Steins were carved in Nürnberg and the vicinity, usually in high relief. When the drilling, carving, and filling were finished, the scenes were polished with wood ashes and oil.

Cracks and discoloration have adversely affected the appearance of most ivory steins, but the workmanship is still evident. Toward the 1700s, the design subjects changed, for the most part, from cherubs and mythological scenes to hunts, battles, and city views.

Checks in the ivory are not good indicators of age as they can be purposely caused by soaking a piece in hot water and then quickly drying it. A yellowish to orange color may be a sign that a piece was torched or buried (in dung) to simulate patina. Authentic old ivory steins, however, are often as white as originals due to the bleaching action of light. Very fine workmanship on carvings and on mountings can be another good way to recognize old steins of almost any type.

7.4 Evaluation Information

Price trends for silver steins in recent years have been mixed. The early and middle 1990s saw mostly falling prices for ivory steins, but the late 1990s have shown steady increases in prices for most ivory steins. The prices for wood steins have been steady or rising in the 1990s. Silver stein price trends have been mixed. Most steins made of rarer materials have increased in price during the 1990s.

Wood, 2.0L, walnut, carved relief, silver lid, handle & base, middle 1700s, $18,000-25,000.

a.   Wood, 1.5L, Norwegian, carved, late 1600s, $10,000-15,000.
b.   Wood, 1.5L, Norwegian, carved by Samuel Fanden, c.1660, $15,000-20,000.
c.   Wood, 1.0L, German, pearwood, intricately carved, four seasons, middle 1700s, $7000-10,000.

d.   Wood, .5L, northern Germany or Swedish, carved relief, Roman scene, carved handle of Viking, inlaid lid of carved flower, pewter bands & liner, probably early 1600s, $5000-7500.
e.   Wood, 2.0L, slats, dated 1714, $1000-1500.
f.   Wood, 2.5L, Norwegian, burl, late 1700s, $1500-2000.

a.   Wood, 1.5L, Norwegian, burl, late 1700s, $1000-1500.
b.   Wood, 2.5L, Norwegian, burl, middle 1700s, $2500-3500.
c.   Wood, 1.0L, Norwegian, burl, middle 1700s, $1800-2400.

d.   Wood, .3L, Norwegian, burl, c.1770, $1000-1500.
e.   Wood, .75L, Norwegian, burl, c.1800, $700-1000.
f.   Wood, 1.0L, Norwegian, burl, middle 1800s, $600-900.

a.   Wood, 1.0L, Norwegian, painted leaves, early 1800s, $800-1100.
b.   Wood, 1.0L, *Daubenkrug* (slats), glass bottom, late 1700s, pewter lid & footring, $600-900.
c.   Wood, .75L, *Daubenkrug* (slats), engraved horse in glass bottom, c.1800, pewter lid, $700-1000.

d.   Wood, 1.0L, Norwegian, carved, c.1900, $900-1200.
e.   Wood, 1.5L, Norwegian, carved, c.1900, $800-1100.
f.   Wood, 1.5L, Norwegian, carved, c.1900, copy of earlier style, $600-900.

a.   Wood & pewter, .75L, *Daubenkrug*, Thuringia, middle 1700s, $2500-3500.
b.   Wood & pewter, .75L, *Daubenkrug*, Thuringia, early 1700s, $3000-4000.
c.   Side view of b.

d.   Wood & pewter, .5L, *Daubenkrug*, Kulmbach, by A. Haas, c.1700, $3000-4000.
e   Wood & pewter, .5L, *Daubenkrug*, Thuringia, c.1700, $2500-3500.
f.   Wood & pewter, .5L, *Daubenkrug*, Stockholm, Sweden, c.1900, $400-600.
g.   Wood & pewter, 1.0L, *Daubenkrug*, Stockholm, Sweden, c.1900, $400-600.

a. Wood & pewter, 1.5L, *Daubenkrug*, Norwegian, c.1900, $500-750.
b. Wood & pewter, 1.0L, *Daubenkrug*, German, late 1800s, $500-750.
c. Wood & pewter, 1.5L, *Daubenkrug*, probably northern Germany, late 1800s, $700-1000.

d. Wood & pewter, .5L, *Daubenkrug*, German, late 1800s, $300-400.
e. Wood & pewter, .5L, *Daubenkrug*, German, late 1800s, $400-600.
f. Wood drinking horn, .5L, carved, c.1900, $500-750.
g. Wood, .5L, carved, deer running, c.1900, $400-600.

a. Wood, 1.5L, etched, eagle, c.1900, $200-300.
b. Wood, 1.0L, etched, man drinking, c.1900, $100-200.
c. Wood, 1.0L, tree trunk style, early 1900s, $200-300.
d. Wood, .5L, barrel, silver lid and straps, early 1900s, $100-200.

e. Wood, 1.5L, marked St. Louis Silver Co., c.1900, silver-plated mountings, $250-400.
f. Wood, 1.0L, marked St. Louis Silver Co., c.1900, silver-plated mountings, $200-350.
g. Wood, .5L, marked St. Louis Silver Co., c.1900, silver-plated mountings, $125-200.
h. Wood, 2.0L, marked St. Louis Silver Co., c.1900, silver-plated mountings, $300-450.

a. Ivory, 9.5" ht., carved, 1800s, $2000-3000.
b. Ivory, 9" ht., carved, late 1700s, $3500-4500.
c. Ivory, 11" ht., carved, gilded silver lid & base, late 1700s, $5000-7000.

d. Ivory, 15" ht., carved, late 1800s, $3500-5000.
e. Ivory, 16" ht., carved, silver lid & base, gilded interior, late 1800s, $6000-8000.
f. Ivory, 17" ht., carved, late 1800s, $7000-9000.

a.   Ostrich egg, 1.0L, Augsburg, Soldier character, silver mounts, carved wood handle, late 1700s, $8000-11,000.
b.   Ostrich egg, 1.0L, late 1800s, pewter mounts, $1800-2400.
c.   Horn, .5L, English, silver lid & base, late 1800s, $1000-1400.
d.   Marble, .3L, German, silver base, inlaid lid with silver rim, late 1800s, $2500-3500.

e.   Serpentine, 1.0L, German, gray/green, faceted, pewter mounts, early 1700s, $3000-4000.
f.   Serpentine, .4L, German, dark green, silver mounts, middle 1600s, $5000-7500.
g.   Serpentine, 1.0L, German, green, pewter mounts, late 1600s, $3000-4000.
h.   Serpentine, .5L, German, dark green, silver mounts, 1800s, $2000-3000.

a.   Enamel on silver, 1.0L, Austrian, silver mounts by Hermann Böhm, late 1800s, $12,000-16,000.
b.   Enamel on copper, .5L, Austrian, middle 1800s, $3000-4000.
c.   Enamel on silver, .5L, blue & white enamel, gold & silver threading & mounts, middle 1800s, $3000-4000.
d.   Lapis, .2L, Austrian, gilded silver, semi-precious stones and enamel on lid and base, late 1800s, $4000-5000.

e.   Woven reed, 1.5L, Torgau, Saxony, pewter mounts, lined with pitch, middle 1700s, $5000-7500.
f.   Leather, 1.0L, enameled birds, pewter lid dated 1769, $4500-6500.
g.   Leather, 2.0L, inscription: Oliver Cromwell granted the right to protect England & the crown, dated 1655, silver lid, base & crest, $8000-12,000.

a. Silver, .75L, Norwegian, coin on lid, late 1800s, $1200-1800.
b. Silver, 1.0L, Norwegian, dated 1815, $1500-2000.
c. Silver, 1.0L, gilded interior, late 1800s, $1000-1400.
d. Silver, 1.0L, Scottish, George IV, repoussé, commemorates retirement of sheriff in 1623, $7000-10,000.

e. Silver, 1.0L, German, Augsburg, repoussé, cherubs, late 1600s, $5000-7500.
f. Silver, 1.0L, marked Whiting, New York, inscribed Larchmont Yacht Club Regatta, July 4, 1895, $700-1000.
g. Silver, .5L, English, late 1800s, $600-900.
h. Silver, .5L, Nürnberg, late 1700s, $2500-3500.

a. Silver, .5L, Russian, St. Petersburg, repoussé & chased, gilded, late 1800s, $2000-3000.
b. Silver, .5L, Russian, repoussé & chased, by Wilhelm Fredrich Sengbush, St. Petersburg, 1856, $1400-1800.
c. Silver, .5L, Russian, engraved, dated 1861, $2500-3500.
d. Silver, .5L, Russian, gilded interior, shape of Estonian wood tankard, dated 1841, $1500-2000.

e. Silver, 1.0L, English, repoussé, cherubs, 1800s, $1400-1800.
f. Silver, 1.5L, Russian, repoussé, by Vasily Bojzov, St. Petersburg, late 1800s, $3500-5000.
g. Silver, 1.5L, German, Augsburg, coins, late 1700s, $3500-4500.

a. Silver, 18" ht., Continental, repoussé, late 1800s, $3500-4500.
b. Silver, 18" ht., repoussé, Cain & Abel, late 1800s, $3000-4000.
c. Silver-plated, 17" ht., coin design, late 1800s, $700-1000.

d. Silver, 1.5L, German, repoussé, late 1700s, $3000-4000.
e. Silver, 1.25L, Russian, repoussé, gilded, by Pavel Ovchinnikov, Moscow, late 1800s, $3500-4500.
f. Silver-plated, 17" ht., relief, hunting scene, late 1800s, $600-900.

a. Silver, 15" ht., English, repoussé, late 1800s, $2200-2800.
b. Silver, 15" ht., German, repoussé, gilded lid and interior, late 1800s, $3000-4000.
c. Silver, 15.5" ht., German, repoussé, battle scene, late 1800s, $2400-3000.

d. Silver-`plated, 18.5" ht., relief, marked Elkington, late 1800s, $1200-1600.
e. Bronze, 1.0L, relief, marked Elkington, Department of Science & Art, late 1800s, $1400-1600.
f. Meerschaum, 14" ht., marked Elkington & Co., brass-plated lid, base & handle, late 1800s, $3500-5000.

a. Metal, 1.5L, brass-plated, relief, c.1900, $80-120.
b. Metal, .75L, brass-plated, relief, c.1900, $80-120.
c. Metal, 1.0L, brass-plated, relief, c.1900, $80-120.
d. Metal, 1.5L, brass-plated, relief, c.1900, $80-120.
e. Copper, 1.5L, relief, two portraits, c.1900, $100-200.

f. Metal, 1.0L, enameled, inlaid lid, c.1900, $300-450.
g. Metal, 1.0L, enameled, inlaid lid, c.1900, $300-450.
h. Metal, 1.5L, enameled, pewter lid, c.1900, $150-250.

8. Porcelain

In Subsection 1.2 of the Stein History chapter, and in Subsection 4.1, History of Faience, there are some important discussions about the origins of European porcelain steins. Additional information on porcelain steins is provided here, in Section 8.

There were three basic reasons why Oriental porcelain steins were not imported after the Europeans discovered how to make porcelain, but price was not a factor since the cost of products from both geographic areas was originally about equal. The preference for the European variety was due, first of all, to the fact that the kaolin, or white clay, available in Europe produced a harder porcelain than the so-called softer Oriental varieties. Secondly, the cobalt oxide available in Europe was naturally purer, and resulted in sharper, less diffused, blue decorations. And, most importantly, the European artists and decorators knew best how to appeal to European tastes. Thus, the Oriental chapter in the history of steins virtually closed soon after the successful experiments of Johann Böttger and Walter von Tschirnhaus in Meissen in 1708 and 1709.

8.1 History of Porcelain Steins

Walzenkrug, which is the shape of most porcelain steins, probably having originated with the silver steins of the 1600s, was popularized by the faience and stoneware steins of the 1700s. Unlike those faience and stoneware steins, however, pewter mountings are rarely found on early porcelain steins. The expense of the porcelain made silver (often of the gilded variety), the material of choice for lids, thumblifts, and footrings. Porcelain lids, or inlays, became increasingly common until they were used exclusively in the 1800s. In turn, these lids were finally replaced altogether by steepled pewter lids in the late 1800s.

At first, Böttger was unable to make a white porcelain, and a few steins were produced in the early brown color. These were mostly very plain steins, although occasionally engraved and gold decorated pieces are found. In the earliest days after white porcelain had been developed, a few relief steins were

Porcelain, 1.0L, by Johann Böttger, chocolate brown color, first European porcelain, c.1710, silver rim, mount and thumblift, porcelain lid with strawberry silver finial, $40,000-60,000.

produced, but these could not be made to match the intricate details of glazed decorations.

Artists who decorated porcelain in the early 1700s were often quite famous in their time. Until about 1730, though, they seem to have imitated the customary Oriental motifs, as if they were making reproductions. Soon after 1730, however, these Oriental designs quickly lost favor and gave way to the more fashionable Renaissance and Baroque scenes and decorative devices, including exotic floral motifs.

Toward the end of the 1700s, the German flowers, painted in a very naturalistic style, became popular. Copies of famous paintings were common around 1800, and these were often executed by Hausmalers (independent, individual decorators).

Around the same time, transfer-printing techniques, also known as print-under-glaze, were brought to Germany from England. Decorations could thus be cheaply mass-produced, and these were often used on porcelain mugs of this period. Apparently, the expensive silver mountings of the true porcelain steins were rarely mixed with the cheap, new, transfer-decoration techniques, at least not until the late 1800s.

By the late 1800s, transfer printing and pewter lids were commonplace on porcelain steins. Numerous examples are pictured in this section and in the Occupational and Regimental sections.

8.2 Production Techniques

Porcelain recipe ingredients include kaolin, feldspar, some quartz, and traces of various other materials, such as whiting. Once prepared, the materials could either be worked on a potter's wheel or, for relief sections or unusual shapes, thinned to a slip and poured into a gypsum or plaster mold. Section 2 describes these processes in more detail. Handles, relief areas, or separately constructed portions of the stein were then glued together with additional slip.

Once air-dried to a leather-hard consistency, the stein bodies received a bisque firing to about 900°C (or about 1600°F). The glazes used to decorate porcelain steins are merely coloring agents or dyes mixed into the porcelain slips. These glazes soaked into the porous surfaces, and good decorations required a sure hand. This decoration was completed before the second firing to about 1400°C (about 2500°F). In a process similar to that described in Subsection 4.2, porcelain bodies could receive a third, lower-temperature firing, which allowed for the use of myriad low-temperature glaze colors, as well as gold. This process is called muffle-painting or muffle-firing.

8.3 Collecting Porcelain

Porcelain collectors are advised to become familiar with the porcelain marks shown at the end of Section 2. Comparing the consistency of the ages of the mark, the design, and the lid will provide good protection against the mistaken purchase of reproductions. Signed pieces, especially those by famous artists, should be suspect, and subject to extra scrutiny. Reproductions are also often crudely executed, and a visit to a museum or a fine collection will show the quality that should be expected of various eras. The most common reproductions of porcelain steins have been the character steins produced after World War II. Examinations of the marks and the decorations, often in full color, should remove any doubts about authenticity. More information about post-World War II character steins can be found in Sections 16 and 19.

8.4 Evaluation Information

Price trends in the past ten years have been mostly upward for porcelain steins. Most handpainted steins have increased in value significantly. The more common transfer-decorated steins have been steady or are increasing only slightly.

Porcelain, 4.0L, unmarked, probably Dresden, handpainted, relief flowers, late 1800s, porcelain lid, $3000-4000.

a. Porcelain, 1.0L, Meissen mark, handpainted, c.1750, porcelain inlaid lid, $12,000-18,000.

b. Porcelain, 1.0L, Nymphenburg mark, Hausmaler tankard by Johann Huber, dated 1778, silver gilt lid & footring, $14,000-20,000.

c. Porcelain, .5L, Chinese Export, handpainted, c.1675, silver gilt lid and footring (Austrian), $5000-8000.

d. Porcelain, .5L, Nymphenburg mark, relief & handpainted, displayed at The Crystal Palace Exhibition, London, 1851, inlaid lid, $2500-3500.

e. Porcelain, 1.0L, Meissen mark, handpainted, dated 1738 on lid, made in late 1800s, porcelain lid, $2400-3000.

f. Porcelain, 1.0L, Meissen mark, handpainted, late 1800s, porcelain lid, $2800-3400.

g. Porcelain, 1.0L, Meissen mark, handpainted, late 1800s, porcelain lid, $2400-3000.

h. Porcelain, 1.0L, Meissen mark, handpainted, late 1800s, porcelain lid, $2400-3000.

a. Porcelain, 1.0L, Meissen mark, handpainted, late 1800s, porcelain lid, $2400-3000.
b. Porcelain, 1.0L, Meissen mark, handpainted, late 1800s, porcelain lid, $2000-2600.
c. Porcelain, 1.0L, Augustus Rex mark, handpainted, late 1800s, porcelain lid, $2400-3000.
d. Porcelain, 1.0L, Augustus Rex mark, handpainted, late 1800s, porcelain lid, $2400-3000.

e. Porcelain, .5L, Meissen mark, handpainted, late 1800s, porcelain lid, $2400-3000.
f. Porcelain, 1.0L, Meissen mark, handpainted, late 1800s, porcelain lid, $3000-4000.
g. Porcelain, .75L, Meissen mark, handpainted, late 1800s, porcelain lid, $3000-4000.
h. Porcelain, .75L, Meissen mark, handpainted, late 1800s, porcelain lid, $2200-2800.

a. Porcelain, .5L, Meissen mark, handpainted, late 1800s, porcelain inlaid lid, $2000-3000.
b. Porcelain, .5L, Meissen mark, handpainted, late 1800s, porcelain inlaid lid, $2500-3500.
c. Porcelain, .5L, beehive mark, handpainted, c.1900, porcelain inlaid lid, $1800-2400.
d. Porcelain, .5L, beehive mark, handpainted, c.1900, porcelain inlaid lid, $1800-2400.
e. Porcelain, .5L, beehive mark, handpainted, *Schmükung der Venus,* c.1900, porcelain inlaid lid, $1800-2400.

NOTE: Steins with the beehive mark are often referred to as Royal Vienna (type) steins.

f. Porcelain, .5L, beehive mark, handpainted, c.1900, porcelain inlaid lid, $1800-2400.
g. Porcelain, .5L, beehive mark, handpainted, *Meine et Amor,* c.1900, porcelain inlaid lid, $1800-2400.
h. Porcelain, .5L, beehive mark, handpainted, c.1900, porcelain inlaid lid, $1800-2400.
i. Porcelain, .5L, beehive mark, handpainted, *Piadra,* c.1900, porcelain lid, $1600-2200.
j. Porcelain, .5L, beehive mark, handpainted, (Admiral) *Dewey,* c.1900, porcelain inlaid lid, $3000-4000.

a. Porcelain, .5L, marked Germany & beehive mark, handpainted, c.1900, porcelain inlaid lid, $2400-3000.

b. Porcelain, .5L, beehive mark, handpainted, c.1900, porcelain inlaid lid, $2400-3000.

c. Porcelain, .5L, beehive mark, handpainted, c.1900, porcelain inlaid lid, $2600-3400.

d. Porcelain, .5L, beehive mark, handpainted, c.1900, porcelain inlaid lid with silver mounts, $2600-3400.

e. Porcelain, .5L, beehive mark, handpainted, c.1900, porcelain lid, $2800-3600.

f. Porcelain, 1.0L, beehive mark, handpainted, *Alexander und Appelles*, c.1900, porcelain lid, $3500-5500.

g. Porcelain, 1.0L, beehive mark, handpainted, c.1900, porcelain lid, $3500-5500.

h. Porcelain, .05L, marked Dresden, handpainted, c.1900, porcelain inlaid lid, $1800-2400.

i. Porcelain, .05L, beehive mark, handpainted, c.1900, porcelain inlaid lid, $1800-2400.

a. Porcelain, .25L, marked Dresden & with beehive, handpainted, c.1900, porcelain inlaid lid, $1000-1400.
b. Porcelain, .25L, beehive mark, handpainted, *Amor,* c.1900, porcelain inlaid lid, $1800-2400.
c. Porcelain, .25L, beehive mark, handpainted, *Reflexion,* c.1900, porcelain inlaid lid, $1800-2400.
d. Porcelain, .25L, beehive mark, handpainted, *Erbluth,* c.1900, porcelain inlaid lid, $1800-2400.
e. Porcelain, .25L, beehive mark, handpainted, c.1900, porcelain lid, $1200-1600.

f. Porcelain, .75L, beehive mark, handpainted, c.1900, brass mountings, $1400-2000.
g. Porcelain, .75L, beehive mark, handpainted, c.1900, brass mountings, $1400-2000.
h. Porcelain, 1.0L, beehive mark, handpainted, c.1900, brass mountings, $2000-3000.
i. Porcelain, 1.0L, beehive mark, handpainted, *Venus und Adonis,* c.1900, brass mountings, $1800-2600.

a. Porcelain, .5L, marked Royal Worcester, handpainted, c.1880, porcelain lid, $1200-1600.
b. Porcelain, .5L, marked Musterschutz, by Schierholz, relief and handpainted, c.1900, porcelain lid, $300-500.
c. Porcelain, .3L, unmarked, relief, Gambrinus, c.1800, inlaid lid, $250-350.
d. Porcelain, .5L, marked Wächtersbacher, relief, handpainted, c.1900, inlaid lid, $200-300.
e. Porcelain, 1.0L, K.P.M., Berlin mark, late 1800s, pewter lid, $400-600.

f. Porcelain, .5L, Berlin mark, relief & handpainted, *3. Deutsches Turnfest, Leipzig, 1863*, pewter lid, $300-400.
g. Porcelain, .5L, unmarked, relief, white on gray marbleized background, late 1800s, set-on porcelain lid, $300-400.
h. Porcelain, .5L, unmarked, probably by Schierholz, relief, white on brown background, deer & hunter, late 1800s, porcelain inlaid lid, $400-600.
i. Porcelain, .5L, unmarked, late 1800s, figural inlaid lid, $300-400.

a. Porcelain, .5L, unmarked, bisque glaze, Wagner, c.1900, porcelain inlaid lid, $400-600.
b. Porcelain, .5L, unmarked, bisque glaze, Beethoven, c.1900, porcelain inlaid lid, $400-600.
c. Porcelain, .5L, unmarked, bisque glaze, Mozart, c.1900, porcelain inlaid lid, $300-500.

d. Porcelain, 1.0L, Wedgewood, late 1800s, silver-plated lid, $500-700.
e. Porcelain, 1.0L, marked 379, relief, blue & white, c.1900, porcelain lid, $600-800.
f. Porcelain, 1.5L, crown over N mark, relief, c.1900, set-on lid, $600-900.
g. Porcelain, .5L, crown over N mark, Capo di Monte style, relief, late 1800s, porcelain inlaid lid, $800-1200.

a. Porcelain, 1.0L, crown over N mark, Capo di Monte style, relief, late 1800s, porcelain inlaid lid, $400-600.
b. Porcelain, 1.0L, crown over N mark, Capo di Monte style, relief, late 1800s, porcelain inlaid lid, $400-600.
c. Porcelain, .5L, crown over N mark, Capo di Monte style, relief, late 1800s, porcelain inlaid lid, $500-800.
d. Porcelain, 1.0L, crown over N mark, Capo di Monte style, relief, late 1800s, porcelain inlaid lid, $500-800.

e. Porcelain, .5L, crown over N mark, Capo di Monte style, relief, late 1800s, porcelain lid, $300-500.
f. Porcelain, .5L, crown over N mark, Capo di Monte style, relief, middle 1800s, gold on copper lid with porcelain finial, $700-1000.
g. Porcelain, .5L, crown over N mark, Capo di Monte style, relief, late 1800s, porcelain inlaid lid, $500-800.
h. Porcelain, .25L, crown over N mark, Capo di Monte style, relief, middle 1800s, silver lid & base, $1000-1500.

a. Porcelain, 1.0L, crown over N mark, Capo di Monte style, relief, late 1800s, porcelain inlaid lid, $600-900.
b. Porcelain, 1.0L, crown over N mark, Capo di Monte style, relief, late 1800s, porcelain inlaid lid, $700-1000.
c. Porcelain, .5L, crown over N mark, Capo di Monte style, relief, late 1800s, porcelain inlaid lid, $700-1000.
d. Porcelain, 1.25L, crown over N mark, Capo di Monte style, relief, late 1800s, porcelain inlaid lid, $400-600.

e. Porcelain, .75L, crown over N mark, Capo di Monte style, relief, late 1800s, porcelain lid, $700-1000.
f. Porcelain, .75L, crown over N mark, Capo di Monte style, relief, late 1800s, porcelain lid, $800-1200.
g. Porcelain, 1.0L, crown over N mark, Capo di Monte style, relief, late 1800s, porcelain inlaid lid, $900-1200.
h. Porcelain, 1.0L, crown over N mark, Capo di Monte style, relief, late 1800s, porcelain inlaid lid, $1000-1500.

a.   Porcelain, 1.25L, crown over N mark, Capo di Monte style, relief, late 1800s, porcelain inlaid lid, $1000-1500.

b.   Porcelain 5.0L, marked Austria & beehive mark, transfer decoration, c.1910, set-on porcelain lid, $1200-1600.

c.   Porcelain, 1.5L, K.P.M., Berlin mark, handpainted, hunter, late 1800s, pewter lid, $600-900.

d.   Porcelain, 2.0L, K.P.M., Berlin mark, handpainted, late 1800s, pewter lid, $1000-1500.

e.   Porcelain, 2.5L, K.P.M., Berlin mark, handpainted, eagle, late 1800s, pewter lid, $1000-1500.

f.   Porcelain, 2.0L, K.P.M., Berlin mark, handpainted, late 1800s, pewter lid, $300-400.

a. Porcelain, 1.0L, unmarked, made by Royal Copenhagen, blue on white, c.1830, silver lid, $600-900.
b. Porcelain, 1.0L, marked Royal Copenhagen, blue on white, late 1800s, silver lid, $700-1000.
c. Porcelain, .5L, Meissen mark, late 1800s, porcelain lid, $700-1000.
d. Porcelain, 1.0L, Meissen mark, c.1910, set-on porcelain lid, $300-500.

e. Porcelain, 1.0L, Meissen mark, c.1900, porcelain lid, $600-800.
f. Porcelain, .75L, Meissen mark, *1710-1910,* pewter lid, $700-1000.
g. Porcelain, .5L, unmarked, probably Rauenstein, handpainted, blue, red & white, late 1800s, inlaid lid, $500-700.
h. Porcelain, .5L, marked Rauenstein, handpainted, blue & white, late 1800s, inlaid lid, $400-600.

a. Porcelain, .5L, unmarked, windmill, lithophane, c.1900, inlaid lid, $200-300.

b. Porcelain, 1.0L, unmarked, handpainted, blue & white, lithophane, c.1900, inlaid lid, $300-400.

c. Porcelain, .5L, unmarked, handpainted, blue & white, lithophane, c.1900, inlaid lid, $150-250.

d. Porcelain, .5L, unmarked, handpainted, blue & white, *Property of Cherokee Gardens,* lithophane, c.1900, inlaid lid, $250-350.

e. Porcelain, .5L, unmarked, handpainted, blue & white, straw flowers, lithophane, c.1900, inlaid lid, $200-300.

f. Porcelain, .5L, Swaine & Co. mark, blue & white, windmill, lithophane, early 1900s, inlaid lid, $200-300.

g. Porcelain, .5L, Swaine & Co. mark, blue & white, windmill, lithophane, early 1900s, inlaid lid, $200-300.

h. Porcelain, .5L, Swaine & Co. mark, blue & white, boats, lithophane, early 1900s, inlaid lid, $200-300.

a. Porcelain, 1.5L, Rauenstein mark, handpainted, blue & white, late 1800s, porcelain inlaid lid, $500-700.
b. Porcelain, 1.5L, unmarked, made by Rauenstein, handpainted, blue, red and gold, late 1800s, porcelain inlaid lid, $600-800.
c. Porcelain, 2.0L, unmarked, made by Rauenstein, handpainted, blue, red and gold, birds and flowers, late 1800s, porcelain inlaid lid, $500-800.

d. Porcelain, .5L, unmarked, relief & handpainted, targets on side, c.1890, pewter lid, $150-250.
e. Porcelain, .5L, unmarked, relief & transfer, c.1890, pewter lid, $200-300.
f. Porcelain, .5L, marked Musterschutz, by Schierholz, wild turkey, c.1900, pewter lid, $400-500.
g. Porcelain, .5L, marked Musterschutz, by Schierholz, dog, c.1900, pewter lid, $400-500.

a.   Porcelain, .5L, unmarked, *Lindau im Bodensee,* lithophane, c.1900, pewter lid, $75-125.

b.   Porcelain, .5L, unmarked, *Gruss aus Landshut,* lithophane, c.1900, pewter lid, $75-125.

c.   Porcelain, .5L, unmarked, *Cuxhaven v.d. Hafenseite,* lithophane, c.1900, pewter lid, $75-125.

d.   Porcelain, .5L, unmarked, flowers, lithophane, c.1900, pewter lid, $75-125.

e.   Porcelain, .5L, unmarked, *Gruss aus Pfullingen,* lithophane, c.1900, pewter lid, $75-125.

f.   Porcelain, .5L, unmarked, deer, lithophane, c.1900, pewter lid, $100-200.

g.   Porcelain, .5L, unmarked, deer, lithophane, c.1900, pewter lid, $100-200.

h.   Porcelain, .5L, unmarked, deer, lithophane, c.1900, pewter lid, $100-200.

i.   Porcelain, .5L, unmarked, hunters & game warden, lithophane, c.1900, pewter lid, $200-300.

j.   Porcelain, .5L, unmarked, hunters, lithophane, c.1900, relief pewter lid, $100-200.

a. Porcelain, .5L, unmarked, *Sangerrunde, d. B.B. München,* lithophane, c.1900, pewter lid, $150-250.
b. Porcelain, .5L, unmarked, folk dancing club, 1896, lithophane, pewter lid, $150-250.
c. Porcelain, .5L, unmarked, handpainted, musical theme, c.1900, pewter lid with relief music book, $350-500.
d. Porcelain, .5L, unmarked, firefighting tools, lithophane, c.1900 pewter lid, $250-350.
e. Porcelain, .5L, unmarked, dwarfs, lithophane, c.1900, pewter lid, $200-300.

f. Porcelain, .3L, unmarked, man & woman, lithophane, c.1900, pewter lid, $75-125.
g. Porcelain, .5L, unmarked, two women, lithophane, c.1910, pewter lid, $300-400.
h. Porcelain, .5L, unmarked, lithophane, c.1900, pewter lid, $75-125.
i. Porcelain, 1.0L, unmarked, *Gruss aus München,* side scenes of *Der Linderhof & Neu Schwanstein,* lithophane, c.1900, pewter lid, $200-300.
j. Porcelain, .5L, unmarked, *Gruss aus München,* lithophane, c.1900, pewter lid, $150-250.

a. Porcelain, .5L, unmarked, *Sangerrunde,* bicycle rider, lithophane, c.1900, pewter lid, $300-400.

b. Porcelain, .5L, unmarked, bicycle rider, lithophane, c.1900, pewter lid, $250-350.

c. Porcelain, .5L, unmarked, handpainted, high-wheel bicycle rider, lithophane, c.1900, pewter lid, $300-400.

d. Porcelain, .5L, unmarked, *Radfaherer Club, Huglfing* (bicycle club), two side scenes with bicycles, lithophane, dated 1920, pewter lid, $100-200.

e. Porcelain, .5L, unmarked, *All Heil!, Deutscher Radfahren Bund,* bicycle rider, lithophane, c.1900, pewter lid, $300-400.

f. Porcelain, .5L, Swaine & Co. mark, blue & white, bicycle riders, lithophane, early 1900s, inlaid lid, $600-800.

g. Porcelain, .5L, unmarked, handpainted, high-wheel bicycle rider, lithophane, c.1900, pewter lid, $300-400.

h. Porcelain, .5L, Swaine & Co. mark, blue & white, baseball lithophane, early 1900s, inlaid lid, $1000-1500.

i. Reverse side of h.

a. Porcelain, .5L, unmarked, handpainted, student association, lithophane, c.1900, pewter lid, $200-300.
b. Porcelain, .5L, unmarked, handpainted, student association, lithophane, c.1900, pewter lid, $300-400.
c. Porcelain, .5L, unmarked, handpainted, student association, lithophane, c.1900, pewter lid, $300-400.
d. Porcelain, 1.0L, unmarked, *Seminarzeit Königsberg 1897-1900,* lithophane, pewter lid, $300-400.
e. Porcelain, .5L, unmarked, handpainted, the baby Jesus, lithophane, c.1900, pewter lid, $200-300.

f. Porcelain, .5L, unmarked, man bowling, lithophane, c.1900, pewter lid, $100-200.
g. Porcelain, .5L, marked R.P.M., handpainted, c.1890, pewter lid, $250-350.
h. Porcelain, .5L, unmarked, handpainted, Gambrinus, c.1890, inlaid lid, $200-300.
i. Porcelain, .5L, unmarked, lithophane, c.1900, pewter lid, $100-200.
j. Porcelain, .3L, unmarked, handpainted, c.1890, silver lid & base, $300-500.

a. Porcelain, 1.0L, unmarked, military recruits, *1879-89, Rothenburg,* lithophane, pewter lid, $250-350.
b. Porcelain, 1.0L, unmarked, zither, lithophane, c.1900, pewter lid, $200-300.
c. Porcelain, 1.0L, unmarked, *Neues Ratzhaus in München,* lithophane, c.1900, pewter lid, $250-350.
d. Porcelain, .5L, unmarked, Romans at the *Münchener Hofbräu vor 1900,* pewter lid, $500-800.
e. Porcelain, .5L, unmarked, Nürnberg advertising stein, c.1900, pewter lid, $250-350.

f. Porcelain, .5L, unmarked, *Nürnberg 1896, Landes Ausstellung,* lithophane, pewter lid, $300-400.
g. Porcelain, 1.0L, unmarked, *XIV Deutscher Feuerwehrtag München 1893,* lithophane, pewter lid, $500-750.
h. Porcelain, .5L, unmarked, *Proletarier aller Länder vereinigt Euchl,* lithophane, late 1800s, pewter lid, $300-400.
i. Porcelain, 1.0L, marked Beleek, handpainted, c.1900, pewter lid, $200-300.
j. Porcelain, .5L, unmarked, U.S. Military, lithophane, c.1910, inlaid lid, $150-250.

a. Porcelain, .5L, unmarked, photo, lithophane, c.1900, pewter lid, $100-200.
b. Porcelain, 1.0L, unmarked, photo, lithophane, c.1900, pewter lid, $100-200.
c. Porcelain, 1.0L, unmarked, photo, lithophane, c.1900, pewter lid, $100-200.
d. Porcelain, .5L, unmarked, handpainted, Ludwig II, lithophane, c.1900, pewter lid, $150-250.
e. Porcelain, .5L, unmarked, verse, lithophane, c.1900, pewter lid, $75-125.

f. Porcelain, .5L, marked HR 188/20, by Hauber & Reuther, handpainted, c.1900, pewter lid, $150-250.
g. Porcelain, .5L, marked HR 187/54, by Hauber & Reuther, handpainted, c.1900, pewter lid, $150-250.
h. Porcelain, .5L, marked HR 18/42, by Hauber & Reuther, handpainted, c.1900, pewter lid, $150-250.
i. Porcelain, .5L, marked HR 131/34, by Hauber & Reuther, handpainted, c.1900, pewter lid, $150-250.
j. Porcelain, .5L, marked HR 2/103, by Hauber & Reuther, handpainted, c.1900, pewter lid, $200-300.

a.   Porcelain, .5L, marked C.A.C. (Lenox), handpainted, c.1900, silver & copper lid, $300-400.

b.   Porcelain, .5L, marked C.A.C. (Lenox), handpainted, c.1900, silver & copper lid, $300-400.

c.   Porcelain, .5L, marked C.A.C. (Lenox), handpainted, c.1900, silver lid, $300-400.

d.   Porcelain, .5L, marked C.A.C. (Lenox), handpainted, c.1900, silver lid, $300-400.

e.   Porcelain, .5L, marked C.A.C. (Lenox), handpainted, c.1900, silver & copper lid, $400-600.

f.   Porcelain, .5L, marked C.A.C. (Lenox), handpainted, c.1900, silver lid, $2000-2500.

g.   Porcelain, .5L, marked with beehive, transfer decoration, c.1910, inlaid lid, $500-700.

h.   Porcelain, .5L, marked with beehive, transfer decoration, c.1910, inlaid lid, $500-700.

9. Pottery and Stoneware

This section covers the post-1850 ceramic steins that are not etched (see Section 12) or made by Mettlach (see Section 11). Most of the steins in this section are relief types, but there are also some with smooth bodies that have been transfer decorated or handpainted. There is not as much information available on these steins as one might suspect. The production techniques are known, but the identity of the manufacturer is frequently unknown. When good records and other information are available about one of these manufacturers, it is generally because original stein catalogs from that company have been discovered. Many of these catalogs have been reproduced, and Section 20 lists these excellent resources for collectors particularly interested in such steins.

9.1 History

The earliest steins appropriate to this section are those that were created as a direct consequence of the tastes of the Historicism, or neo-Renaissance, period. They are a revival of the 1500s Siegburg style: gray stoneware with relief scenes and a clear glaze. However, unlike the Siegburgs, the relief scenes are usually genre (realistic everyday themes), the steins themselves are squat and .5 liter in size, and the lids have brightly decorated porcelain inlays. The clay is the white-to-grayish, or so-called Rhenish clay, found from Höhr-Grenzhausen to Köln, but the manufacturer of these steins has not been positively identified.

It is worth noting that personal steins were (and in some areas still are) kept at the neighborhood tavern, which allowed regular customers to have a fresh draught of beer served to them almost as soon as they arrived. Oil paintings from the period show customers' steins stored along a high shelf, upside-down and with the open lid resting over the edge of the shelf. This practice makes it clear why so much attention was paid to the decoration of the porcelain inlays, and why they often are portraits, depict occupations, or commemorate some important event or situation with which the stein's owner wished to be associated.

In the early 1860s, Reinhold Hanke turned his attention to resurrecting the lost art of producing fine, cobalt-glazed, stoneware steins. Hanke worked hard to copy the Renaissance styles as closely as possible using the mass-production methods of his day. Although molds had to be used, Hanke insisted that these be finely crafted. The stein shapes ranged from small cylinders to large jugs, as were common in the 1500s and 1600s. Decorations were also in the Renaissance style, but toward the 1890s, they changed to the genre scenes that Hanke continued to produce into the 1900s.

In 1869, Peter Dümler began working for Hanke; his specialty was making copies of Renaissance stoneware designs. In 1883, he left that firm and joined with an in-law to begin a new stoneware company: Dümler & Breiden.

Unfortunately, it is not possible to relate here the histories of all of the stein factories. Records indicate that at one time, in the Höhr-Grenzhausen region alone, there were more than 600 factories. During the short time between the opening of Hanke's factory and that of Dümler, most of the pre-World War I stein makers began their businesses, including Simon Peter Gerz in 1862, Merkelbach & Wick in 1872, and Marzi & Remy in 1879. Two of these firms, J.W. Remy

(1830) and Reinhold Merkelbach (1849), were started earlier but did not produce steins until after Hanke. Other firms were relative latecomers, such as A.J. Thewalt in 1893, Eckhardt & Engler in 1898, and Hauber & Reuther in 1876. All of these companies, with the exception of Hauber & Reuther, were located either in Höhr-Grenzhausen or nearby.

The 1880s were apparently tough times for stein makers, at least those manufacturing the relief-decorated type. Dümler wrote in his notebooks that "after running like a dog" through the streets of Köln trying to sell steins, he "didn't want to see another piece of stoneware." But great numbers of steins were being made, and it was not until about 1909 that economic conditions slowed the stein industry to a near stop.

After World War I, business in relief, handpainted, and transfer-decorated steins rebounded, perhaps more so than for any of the other stein types. And, the same situation occurred after World War II. In fact, beginning in the 1950s, the rebound was so strong that handpainted relief steins began achieving the dominance in the stein market that they still hold today.

9.2 Production

Pottery (Steingut) has a porous structure; stoneware (Steinzeug) is solid. Sometimes, since the same variety of clay colors and glazes can be found on both, weight is the easiest way to tell them apart: pottery is substantially lighter than stoneware. As a result of common usage, all gray ceramics are called *stoneware* and all tan ceramics - including tan steinzeug (stoneware) - are called *pottery*.

The recipe for pottery can vary from a rather ordinary plain clay to a complex and expensive mixture of clay, quartz, feldspar, kaolin (fine white clay), and whiting (chalk). Pottery is usually fired at a lower temperature than stoneware but, occasionally, will be fired at about the same temperature: 1200°C (2100°F).

Because of the porous structure of pottery, it is important that it be glazed to make it waterproof. It is possible to find some lead-glazed pottery steins that were being made as late as the 1870s. Thereafter, however, to protect against the health hazards caused by lead, only the glass-based glazes were used.

The procedures used to make stoneware are described in Section 3, and the common ways of using pottery and stoneware to make steins is explained in Section 2. Therefore, these will not be repeated here, leaving only the subject of decorations.

The relief steins were almost always decorated by hand, while the steins with smooth surfaces could have been decorated in several ways. Handpainted designs are quite common, especially on steins from around 1900 and before. Occasionally, especially on these older steins or on Regimentals, metal-plate engraving was used to print a decal, which was then transferred to the stein, after which it was touched up or colored in, by hand. A few of the decals were silk-screened, but the detail on these was not as precise as that achieved with engraved plates, especially those that were prepared using photographic reductions. Most modern steins are decorated solely with decals and exhibit no handwork. It is not very difficult to determine which decorating technique has been used: handpainted areas do not feel as smooth as decal, or transfer-decorated, areas.

9.3 Collecting

The relief, handpainted, and transfer-decorated steins are the styles most frequently seen for sale. Their tremendous variety opens up many avenues for collecting strategies. Topical specialties include steins decorated with a Munich Child, scenes from Defregger paintings, card playing, frogs, dwarfs, eagles, military themes, designs by Franz Ringer, occupationals (covered in Section 13), hunting scenes, and sports-related designs. Besides specializing in certain types of decorations, collectors can focus on steins with music boxes, ornate pewter lids, inlaid lids, very deep relief or pottery figural lids, or early steins made from gray relief stoneware or those from specific factories.

When displayed together, these fine steins greatly enhance each other's attractiveness. Recently, the demand for these old pottery and stoneware steins has increased significantly.

9.4 Evaluation Information

Price trends in the past ten years have been mostly upward or level for pottery and stoneware steins. Most handpainted steins have increased in value. The more commonly decorated (subjects) steins have been steady or are increasing only slightly. The more unusual steins and those with popular subject matter have increased significantly.

a. Pottery, .5L, relief, Thewalt & HR marks, #131, c.1900, pewter lid, $80-120.
b. Pottery, .5L, relief, c.1900, pewter lid, $60-100.
c. Pottery, .5L, relief, #300, c.1900, pewter lid, $50-80.
d. Pottery, .5L, relief, #34, c.1900, pewter lid, $60-100.
e. Pottery, .5L, relief, Merkelbach & Wick mark, c.1900, pewter lid, $60-100.

f. Pottery, .5L, relief, c.1900, pewter lid, $50-80.
g. Pottery, .5L, relief, c.1900, pewter lid, $60-100.
h. Pottery, .5L, relief, c.1900, pewter lid, $60-100.
i. Pottery, 1.0L, relief, c.1900, pewter lid, $60-100.
j. Pottery, .5L, relief, #233, c.1900, pewter lid, $60-100.

a. Pottery, 1.0L, relief, #119/500, c.1900, pewter lid, $50-80.
b. Pottery, 1.0L, relief, #325, c.1900, pewter lid, $60-100.
c. Pottery, 1.0L, relief, #57, c.1900, pewter lid, $60-100.
d. Pottery, .5L, relief, #449, c.1900, pewter lid, $60-100.
e. Pottery, .5L, relief, #179, c.1900, pewter lid, $60-100.

f. Pottery, 1.0L, relief, #67, c.1900, pewter lid, $60-100.
g. Pottery, .5L, relief, #11045, c.1900, pewter lid, $50-80.
h. Pottery, .5L, relief, #240, c.1900, pewter lid, $60-100.
i. Pottery, .5L, relief, #68, c.1900, pewter lid, $80-120.
j. Pottery, .5L, relief, #67, c.1900, pewter lid, $80-120.

a. Pottery, .5L, relief, Dümler & Breiden, c.1900, pewter lid, $80-120.
b. Pottery, .5L, relief, #6062, *Souvenir of St. Augustine, Fla.,* early 1900s, inlaid lid, $150-250.
c. Pottery, .5L, relief, Yale University, early 1900s, pewter lid, $150-250.
d. Pottery, .5L, relief, Thewalt, #315, Heidelberg, c.1900, pewter lid, $100-150.
e. Pottery, .5L, relief, Diesinger, *St. Louis Exposition, 1904,* pewter lid, $150-250.

f. Pottery, .5L, relief, *Washington Monument, Washington, D.C.,* early 1900s, pewter lid, $60-100.
g. Pottery, .5L, relief, *Atlantic City, N.J.,* early 1900s, pewter lid, $60-100.
h. Pottery, .5L, relief, *Lee Monument, New Orleans,* early 1900s, inlaid lid, $60-100.
i. Pottery, .5L, relief, *Capitol, Washington, D.C.,* early 1900s, inlaid lid, $60-100.
j. Pottery, .5L, relief, *State Capitol, Denver, Colo.,* early 1900s, pewter lid, $60-100.

a.   Pottery, .5L, relief, Gerz, #1109, c.1900, pewter lid, $100-200.

b.   Pottery, .5L, relief, #1542, horses jumping fences, c.1900, pewter lid, $100-200.

c.   Pottery, .5L, relief, #1742, c.1900, pewter lid, $100-200.

d.   Pottery, .5L, relief, #1825, *B.P.O.E., Portland, Oregon*, c.1900, pewter lid, $100-200.

e.   Pottery, .5L, relief, #1402, monkey reading Darwin, c.1900, inlaid lid, $350-450.

f.   Pottery, .5L, relief, Steinzeugwerke, #1272, early 1900s, inlaid lid, $150-250.

g.   Pottery, .5L, relief, Steinzeugwerke, #1272, early 1900s, pewter lid, $100-200.

h.   Pottery, .5L, relief, #368, c.1900, inlaid lid, $150-250.

i.   Pottery, .5L, relief, Steinzeugwerke, #1401, card game, early 1900s, pewter lid, $200-300.

j.   Pottery, 1.0L, etched & relief, #37, three panels, singing, drinking, lovers, c.1900, pewter lid, $200-300.

a. Pottery, .5L, relief, #1411, c.1900, inlaid lid, $250-350.

b. Pottery, .5L, relief, #715, G. Verdi, early 1900s, pewter lid, $80-120.

c. Pottery, .5L, relief, Steinzeugwerke, #1279, composers, early 1900s, inlaid lid, $150-250.

d. Pottery, .5L, relief, Steinzeugwerke, #1278, composers, early 1900s, inlaid lid, $150-250.

e. Pottery, .5L, relief, #1707, early 1900s, pewter lid, $100-150.

f. Pottery, .5L, relief, Saarguemines, c.1900, pottery lid, $200-300.

g. Pottery, .5L, relief, c.1900, inlaid lid, $100-200.

h. Pottery, .5L, relief, #776, *Jungfrau vom Drachenfels*, c.1900, inlaid lid, $350-450.

i. Pottery, .5L, relief, #1730, soccer game, c.1900, pottery lid, $300-400.

j. Pottery, .5L, relief, #1735, frogs, c.1900, pottery lid, $100-200.

a.   Pottery, .5L, relief, #874, Diesinger, early 1900s, pewter lid, $150-250.

b.   Pottery, .5L, relief, #873, Diesinger, early 1900s, pewter lid, $150-250.

c.   Pottery, .5L, relief, #799, Diesinger, early 1900s, pewter lid, $150-250.

d.   Pottery, 1.0L, relief, Dümler & Breiden, #682, c.1900, pewter lid, $150-250.

e.   Pottery, 1.0L, relief, Dümler & Breiden, #547, c.1900, pewter lid, $150-250.

f.   Pottery, .5L, relief, railroad scenes, c.1900, pewter lid, $100-200.

g.   Pottery, .5L, relief, #1547, early 1900s, pewter lid, $200-300.

h.   Pottery, .5L, relief, #1408, Wilhelm II, early 1900s, pewter lid, $300-400.

i.   Pottery, .5L, relief, #1415, Frederich III, early 1900s, pewter lid, $350-500.

j.   Pottery, .5L, relief, #1415, Wilhelm II, early 1900s, pewter lid, $350-500.

a. Pottery, .5L, relief, #1232, c.1900, pewter lid, $150-250.
b. Pottery, 1.0L, threading, #1306, c.1900, pewter lid, $250-350.
c. Pottery, 1.0L, relief, #577, c.1900, pewter lid, $300-400.
d. Pottery, 1.0L, threading & relief, c.1900, inlaid lid, $150-250.
e. Pottery, 1.0L, relief, #702, c.1900, pottery lid, $250-350.

f. Pottery, .5L, relief & etched, Steinzeugwerke, #1714, Lawyer Book stein, early 1900s, inlaid lid, $300-450.
g. Pottery, .5L, relief & etched, Steinzeugwerke, #1714, Doctor Book stein, early 1900s, inlaid lid, $300-450.
h. Pottery, 1.0L, relief & etched, #1787, Doctor Book stein, early 1900s, inlaid lid, $700-1000.
i. Pottery, .5L, relief, Dümler & Breiden, anti-Semitic scenes, early 1900s, inlaid lid, $1000-1400.
j. Pottery, .5L, relief, Dümler & Breiden, anti-Semitic scenes, early 1900s, inlaid lid, $1000-1400.

a.   Pottery, 1.0L, relief, #157, signed G.K., c.1900, pottery lid, $150-250.

b.   Pottery, 1.5L, relief, #1066, c.1900, pottery lid, $250-350.

c.   Pottery, 2.5L, relief, #1008, c.1900, pottery lid, $250-350.

d.   Pottery, 2.5L, relief, #156, c.1900, pottery lid, $250-350.

e.   Pottery, 1.0L, relief, c.1900, pottery lid, $100-200.

a. Pottery, 3.0L, relief, c.1900, pottery lid, $300-400.
b. Pottery, 2.5L, relief, #1636, c.1900, pottery lid, $350-500.
c. Pottery, 3.0L, relief, Diesinger, #902, early 1900s, pewter lid, $400-500.
d. Pottery, 3.0L, relief, #1615, early 1900s, pewter lid, $150-250.
e. Pottery, 3.0L, relief, #359, early 1900s, pewter lid, $150-250.
f. Pottery, 2.0L, relief, #415, early 1900s, pewter lid, $100-200.
g. Pottery, 2.0L, relief, Gerz, #992B, early 1900s, pewter lid, $100-200.

Opposite Bottom:
f. Pottery, 2.0L, relief, #87, early 1900s, pewter lid, $250-350.
g. Pottery, 3.0L, relief, #82/460, early 1900s, pewter lid, $150-250.
h. Pottery, 1.5L, relief, #457, early 1900s, pewter lid, $100-200.
i. Pottery, 2.0L, relief, Diesinger, #810, early 1900s, pewter lid, $400-500.
j. Pottery, 2.5L, relief, #653, c.1900, pewter lid, $200-300.

a. Pottery, .5L, relief, Hauber & Reuther, HR, #459, c.1900, pewter lid, $300-400.
b. Pottery, .5L, relief, Hauber & Reuther, HR, #458, c.1900, pewter lid, $100-150.
c. Pottery, 1.0L, relief, Hauber & Reuther, HR, #454, c.1900, pewter lid, $150-250.
d. Pottery, 1.0L, relief, Hauber & Reuther, HR, #452, c.1900, pewter lid, $150-250.
e. Pottery, .5L, relief, Hauber & Reuther, HR, #453, c.1900, pewter lid, $125-200.

f. Pottery, .5L, relief, Hauber & Reuther, HR, #451, c.1900, pewter lid, $100-150.
g. Pottery, .5L, relief, Hauber & Reuther, HR, #455, c.1900, pewter lid, $100-150.
h. Pottery, .5L, relief, Hauber & Reuther, HR, #457, c.1900, pewter lid, $150-250.
i. Pottery, .5L, transfer, *Bayern und die Pfalz Gotterhalt's*, early 1900s, pewter lid, $100-150.
j. Pottery, .5L, transfer, Dorfner Brothers, c.1900, pewter lid, $50-100.

a. Pottery, .5L, transfer, music box, early 1900s, pewter lid, $100-150.
b. Pottery, .5L, transfer, Merkelbach & Wick, c.1900, pewter lid, $50-100.
c. Pottery, .5L, transfer, c.1900, pewter lid, $50-100.
d. Pottery, .5L, transfer, c.1900, pewter lid, $100-150.
e. Pottery, .5L, handpainted, c.1900, pewter lid with relief scene of *Munich*, $100-200.

f. Pottery, .5L, relief & handpainted, #6049, alligator handle, early 1900s, inlaid lid, $150-250.
g. Pottery, .5L, relief & transfer, Rosskopf & Gerz, #570, early 1900s, pewter lid, $50-100.
h. Pottery, .5L, relief & transfer, Rosskopf & Gerz, #384, early 1900s, pewter lid, $50-100.
i. Pottery, .5L, relief & transfer, Rosskopf & Gerz, early 1900s, pewter lid, $50-100.
j. Pottery, .5L, relief & transfer, #662, *Reichenhall*, c.1900, pewter lid, $50-100.

a.   Pottery, .5L, transfer, c.1900, pewter lid, $50-100.
b.   Pottery, .5L, transfer, *Berlin,* c.1900, pewter lid, $80-120.
c.   Pottery, .5L, transfer, c.1900, pewter lid, $50-100.
d.   Pottery, .5L, transfer, Reinhold Hanke, #653, mold 1090, c.1900, pewter lid, $80-120.
e.   Pottery, .5L, transfer, Reinhold Hanke, #565, mold 1090, c.1900, pewter lid, $80-120.

f.   Pottery, .5L, transfer, Reinhold Merkelbach, bicycle rider, early 1900s, pewter lid with relief scene of bicycle rider, $250-400.
g.   Pottery, .5L, handpainted, bicycle rider, early 1900s, pewter lid, $250-400.
h.   Pottery, .5L, transfer, bicycle rider, late 1800s, pewter lid with relief scene of bicycle rider, $300-500.
i.   Pottery, .5L, handpainted, Royal Bonn, early 1900s, pewter lid, $500-750.
j.   Pottery, .5L, transfer, Munich fireman, early 1900s, pewter lid, $150-250.

a. Pottery, 4.0L, handpainted, Merkelbach & Wick, early 1900s, pewter lid, $400-600.
b. Pottery, 2.0L, transfer, #1183, c.1900, pewter lid, $150-250.
c. Pottery, 2.0L, handpainted, Merkelbach & Wick, early 1900s, pewter lid, $200-300.
d. Pottery, 4.0L, transfer, Munich Child, c.1900, pewter lid, $150-250.

e. Pottery, .5L, transfer, Merkelbach & Wick, *4F*, early 1900s, pewter lid, $60-100.
f. Pottery, .5L, transfer, 1920s, pewter lid, $50-80.
g. Pottery, .5L, transfer, 1920s, pewter lid, $50-80.
h. Pottery, .5L, transfer, early 1900s, pewter lid, $60-100.
i. Pottery, .5L, handpainted, HR, 143a, early 1900s, pewter lid, $125-200.

a. Pottery, 1.0L, transfer, Dorfner Brothers, c.1900, pewter lid, $50-100.

b. Pottery, 1.0L, transfer, Dorfner Brothers, early 1900s, pewter lid, $100-200.

c. Pottery, .5L, transfer, Thomsberger & Herman, bowling, early 1900s, inlaid lid, $250-350.

d. Pottery, .5L, handpainted, carrier pigeon, 1933, pewter lid, $200-300.

e. Pottery, .5L, transfer, *IX Deutsches Turnfest, Hamburg, 1898,* pewter lid, $200-300.

f. Pottery, .5L, transfer, early 1900s, metal lid, $50-80.

g. Pottery, .5L, transfer, early 1900s, pewter lid, $60-100.

h. Pottery, .5L, transfer, early 1900s, pewter lid with relief scene of *Munich,* $80-120.

i. Pottery, .25L, transfer, early 1900s, pewter lid with relief scene of *Munich,* $60-100.

j. Stoneware, .5L, relief, Eckhart & Engler, #1436, Munich Olympics, 1936, metal lid, $600-800.

a. Stoneware, .5L, relief, #957, gnomes and frogs, c.1900, inlaid lid, $250-350.
b. Stoneware, .5L, relief, #939, cats, figural cat handle, c.1900, inlaid lid, $200-300.
c. Stoneware, .5L, relief, #83/221, monkeys, c.1900, inlaid lid, $150-250.
d. Stoneware, .5L, relief, c.1900, inlaid lid, $200-300.
e. Stoneware, .5L, relief, Reinhold Hanke, #1150, *Christoph Columbus,* c.1900, inlaid lid, $350-500.

f. Stoneware, 1.0L, relief, Reinhold Hanke, #3200, c.1900, pewter lid, $100-200.
g. Stoneware, 1.0L, relief, c.1900, pewter lid, $60-100.
h. Stoneware, 1.0L, relief, Reinhold Merkelbach, #33, c.1900, pewter lid, $60-100.
i. Stoneware, 1.0L, relief, Marzi & Remy, dwarfs & verse, c.1900, porcelain inlaid lid, $100-150.
j. Stoneware, 1.0L, relief, c.1900, pewter lid, $60-100.

a. Stoneware, .5L, relief, #207, Wilhelm I, Wilhelm II, Bismarck, Von Moltke, Frederich III, early 1900s, pewter lid, $200-300.
b. Stoneware, .5L, relief, Gerz, #27, c.1900, pewter lid, $150-250.
c. Stoneware, .5L, relief, #1492, Munich Child, c.1900, pewter lid, $100-200.
d. Stoneware, .5L, relief, design by Franz Ringer, early 1900s, pewter lid, $300-400.
e. Stoneware, .5L, relief, chickens, early 1900s, inlaid lid, $200-300.

f. Stoneware, .5L, relief, Gerz, with music box, c.1900, pewter lid, $80-120.
g. Stoneware, .4L, relief, Gerz, #968, c.1900, inlaid lid, $50-80.
h. Stoneware, .5L, relief, Merkelbach & Wick, c.1900, pewter lid with small inlaid glass, $50-80.
i. Stoneware, .5L, relief & threading, Hauber & Reuther, #152, c.1900, pewter lid, $80-120.
j. Stoneware, .5L, relief, #67, anti-Semitic scenes, c.1900, pewter lid, $500-800.

a. Stoneware, .5L, relief, Marzi & Remy, #2323, c.1900, pewter lid, $125-200.
b. Stoneware, .5L, relief, Marzi & Remy, #1802, c.1900, pewter lid, $125-200.
c. Stoneware, .5L, relief, Marzi & Remy, #1800, c.1900, pewter lid, $125-200.
d. Stoneware, .4L, relief, Marzi & Remy, #1848, c.1900, pewter lid, $125-200.
e. Stoneware, .5L, relief, Marzi & Remy, #1702, c.1900, pewter lid, $125-200.

Stoneware, 1.0L, relief, Rosskopf & Gerz, #647, early 1900s, pewter lid, $150-250.
Stoneware, 1.0L, relief, Rosskopf & Gerz, #780, early 1900s, pewter lid, $150-250.
Stoneware, 1.0L, relief, *Bundesschießen, Donauwörth, 1888,* pewter lid, $300-400.
Stoneware, 1.0L, threading, Reinhold Merkelbach, Art Nouveau, early 1900s, pewter lid, $100-200.
Stoneware, .5L, relief, #1507, early 1900s, inlaid lid, $300-500.

a.   Stoneware, 1.0L, relief, Whites Utica, #42, late 1800s, pewter lid, $200-300.

b.   Stoneware, .5L, relief, Whites Utica, #43, late 1800s, pewter lid, $250-350.

c.   Stoneware, 1.0L, relief, Whites Utica, #46, late 1800s, pewter lid, $150-250.

d.   Stoneware, .3L, relief, Whites Utica, *Pan American Exposition, Buffalo N.Y., 1901,* pewter lid, $200-300.

e.   Stoneware, 2.0L, relief, Whites Utica, #5, two glaze colors, late 1800s, pewter lid, $500-700.

f.   Stoneware, 3.0L, relief, Whites Utica, #000, three glaze colors, late 1800s, pewter lid, $500-700.

g.   Stoneware, 2.0L, relief, Whites Utica, late 1800s, pewter lid, $300-400.

a.   Stoneware, 2.0L, relief, Whites Utica, #7, two glaze colors, late 1800s, pewter lid, $400-600.
b.   Stoneware, 2.0L, incised, Whites Utica, #5 and #1032, late 1800s, pewter lid, $1200-1600.
c.   Stoneware, 1.5L, handpainted, Sältzer decorated, late 1800s, pewter lid, $600-1000.

d.   Stoneware, .5L, handpainted, Sältzer decorated, late 1800s, pewter lid, $100-200.
e.   Stoneware, .5L, handpainted, Sältzer decorated, late 1800s, pewter lid, $300-500.
f.   Stoneware, 1.5L, handpainted, Sältzer decorated, late 1800s, pewter lid, $600-900.
g.   Stoneware, 1.5L, relief & handpainted, Sältzer decorated, late 1800s, pewter lid, $400-600.

a. Stoneware, 1.0L, relief, Saargemund, #2888, c.1900, pewter lid, $800-1000.
b. Stoneware, 1.0L, relief, Saargemund, #2717, monkey handle, c.1900, pewter lid, $800-1000.
c. Stoneware, 1.0L, relief, Saargemund, dog handle, c.1900, pewter lid, $900-1200.
d. Stoneware, 1.0L, relief, Saargemund, #2668, cat handle, c.1900, pewter lid, $800-1000.

e. Stoneware, 1.0L, relief, Saargemund, Darmstadt crest, c.1900, pewter lid, $800-1000.
f. Stoneware, 1.0L, relief, Saargemund, Imperial Eagle, c.1900, pewter lid, $1000-1400.
g. Stoneware, 1.0L, relief, Saargemund, #2784, Munich Child, c.1900, pewter lid, $900-1200.
h. Stoneware, 1.0L, relief, Saargemund, #2783, fox handle, c.1900, pewter lid, $900-1200.
i. Stoneware, 1.0L, relief, Saargemund, c.1900, pewter lid, $600-800.

a. Stoneware, 1.0L, relief, Regensburg, late 1800s, pewter lid, $80-120.
b. Stoneware, 1.0L, relief, Regensburg, late 1800s, pewter lid, $80-120.
c. Stoneware, .5L, relief, Regensburg, late 1800s, inlaid lid, $80-120.
d. Stoneware, 2.0L, incised, Westerwald, late 1800s, pewter lid, $150-250.
e. Stoneware, 1.0L, incised, Westerwald, late 1800s, pewter lid, $200-300.

f. Stoneware, .5L, transfer, design by Franz Ringer, early 1900s, pewter lid, $200-300.
g. Stoneware, .5L, transfer, design by Franz Ringer, early 1900s, pewter lid, $200-300.
h. Stoneware, .5L, transfer, design by Franz Ringer, early 1900s, pewter lid, $150-250.
i. Stoneware, .5L, transfer, design by Franz Ringer, early 1900s, pewter lid, $200-300.
j. Stoneware, .5L, transfer, design by Franz Ringer, early 1900s, pewter lid, $150-250.

a.   Stoneware, .5L, transfer, design by Franz Ringer, early 1900s, pewter lid with embossed heart, $300-400.
b.   Stoneware, .5L, transfer, design by Franz Ringer, early 1900s, pewter lid with embossed heart, $300-400.
c.   Stoneware, .5L, transfer, design by Franz Ringer, early 1900s, pewter lid with embossed heart, $300-400.
d.   Stoneware, .5L, transfer, design by Franz Ringer, early 1900s, pewter lid, $250-350.
e.   Stoneware, .5L, transfer, design by Franz Ringer, early 1900s, pewter lid, $250-350.

f.   Stoneware, 1.0L, transfer, design by Franz Ringer, early 1900s, pewter lid with embossed heart, $350-500.
g.   Stoneware, 1.0L, transfer, design by Franz Ringer, early 1900s, pewter lid, $300-400.
h.   Stoneware, 1.0L, transfer, Munich Child on horse, design by F. Ringer, early 1900s, pewter lid, $250-350.
i.   Stoneware, 1.0L, transfer, design by Franz Ringer, early 1900s, pewter lid, $300-400.
j.   Stoneware, 1.0L, transfer, design by Franz Ringer, early 1900s, pewter lid, $300-400.

a.   Stoneware, .5L, transfer, design by Franz Ringer, early 1900s, pewter lid, $250-350.
b.   Stoneware, .5L, transfer, design by Franz Ringer, early 1900s, metal lid, $200-300.
c.   Stoneware, .5L, transfer, design by Franz Ringer, early 1900s, pewter lid, $350-450.
d.   Stoneware, .5L, transfer, design by Franz Ringer, early 1900s, pewter lid, $200-300.
e.   Stoneware, .5L, transfer, design by Franz Ringer, early 1900s, pewter lid, $250-350.

f.   Stoneware, 1.0L, transfer, design by Franz Ringer, early 1900s, pewter lid, $250-350.
g.   Stoneware, 1.0L, transfer, design by Franz Ringer, early 1900s, pewter lid, $300-400.
h.   Stoneware, 1.0L, transfer, design by Franz Ringer, early 1900s, pewter lid, $350-450.
i.   Stoneware, 1.0L, transfer, design by Franz Ringer, early 1900s, pewter lid, $500-800.
j.   Stoneware, .5L, transfer, design by Franz Ringer, early 1900s, pewter lid, $250-350.

a. Stoneware, .5L, transfer, design by Franz Ringer, student association, early 1900s, pewter lid, $300-400.
b. Stoneware, .5L, transfer, design by Franz Ringer, *4F* decoration, early 1900s, pewter lid, $250-350.
c. Stoneware, .5L, transfer, design by Franz Ringer, early 1900s, pewter lid, $250-350.
d. Stoneware, .5L, transfer, design by Franz Ringer, early 1900s, pewter lid, $250-350.
e. Stoneware, .5L, transfer, design by Franz Ringer, early 1900s, pewter lid, $250-350.

f. Stoneware, .125L, transfer, design by Franz Ringer, early 1900s, pewter lid, $150-250.
g. Stoneware, .05L, transfer, design by Franz Ringer, early 1900s, pewter lid, $200-300.
h. Stoneware, .5L, transfer, design by Franz Ringer, early 1900s, pewter lid, $300-450.
i. Stoneware, .5L, transfer, design by Franz Ringer, early 1900s, pewter lid, $300-450.
j. Stoneware, .5L, transfer, design by Franz Ringer, early 1900s, pewter lid, $300-400.

a. Stoneware, .5L, transfer, design by Franz Ringer, early 1900s, pewter lid, $350-450.
b. Stoneware, .5L, transfer, design by Franz Ringer, early 1900s, pewter lid, $250-350.
c. Stoneware, .5L, transfer, design by Franz Ringer, early 1900s, pewter lid, $250-350.
d. Stoneware, .5L, transfer, design by Franz Ringer, early 1900s, pewter lid, $250-350.
e. Stoneware, .5L, transfer, design by Franz Ringer, early 1900s, pewter lid, $200-300.

f. Stoneware, .5L, transfer, *Prinz Rupprecht, 20. Inft. Regt. Lindau,* c.1910, pewter lid, $200-300.
g. Stoneware, .5L, transfer, *Wilhelm II, Hort des Friedens, 1888-1913,* signed F. Ringer, pewter lid, $300-400.
h. Stoneware, .5L, transfer, *Graf Zeppelin, Volkerkrieg 1914-1915,* pewter lid dated 1915, $250-350.
i. Stoneware, 1.0L, transfer, *Prinz-Regent Luitpold von Bayern, c.1912,* pewter lid with city crests, $300-400.
j. Stoneware, .5L, transfer, Thurm & Taxis, early 1900s, pewter lid with scene of *Regensburg,* $200-300.

a. Stoneware, 1.0L, transfer, Marzi & Remy, 1920s, pewter lid, $100-150.

b. Stoneware, .5L, transfer, Eckhardt & Engler, *Hofbräuhaus*, early 1900s, pewter lid with scene of *Munich,* $125-200.

c. Stoneware, .5L, transfer, early 1900s, pewter lid with scene of *Munich,* $125-200.

d. Stoneware, .5L, transfer, Merkelbach & Wick, early 1900s, pewter lid with mountain climbing tools, $125-200.

e. Stoneware, 1.0L, transfer, *Bayrische Gewerbe Schau München, 1912,* signed Franz Ringer, pewter lid, $400-500.

f. Stoneware, 1.0L, transfer, *15. Deutsch Bundesschießen, München, 1906,* signed Franz Ringer, pewter lid with Munich Child, $500-700.

g. Stoneware, 1.0L, transfer, *18. Deutsch Bundesschießen, München, 1927,* signed Franz Ringer, pewter lid with Munich breweries, $450-650.

h. Stoneware, 1.0L, incised, *XVI Bundestag, München, 1899,* pewter lid with bronze inlay: *Deutsche Radfahrer Bund,* $400-600.

i. Stoneware, 1.0L, transfer, *Jubilaums des Oktoberfest München, 1810-1935,* signed P. Neu, pewter lid, $400-600.

j. Stoneware, 1.0L, transfer, *125 Jahre Münchener Oktoberfest, 1810-1935,* pewter lid, $700-1000.

a. Stoneware, 1.0L, transfer, *München 1927,* Chimney Sweepers Convention, pewter lid with scene of a fire being extinguished, $400-600.

b. Stoneware, 1.0L, transfer, *Münchener Kunstausstelhung,* early 1900s, pewter lid with Munich Child, $400-600.

c. Stoneware, 1.0L, transfer, *American Society of Mechanical Engineers, München, 7 Juli, 1913,* pewter lid, $350-500.

d. Stoneware, 1.0L, impressed, Keramisch Werkstätten, München-Herrsching, *Deutsches Museum München, 1925,* pewter lid with Munich breweries, $250-350.

e. Stoneware, 1.0L, transfer, *Frei Heil!* (Freie Turner Schaft, Solidarität München), 1920s, pewter lid $250-350.

f. Stoneware, .5L, transfer, *100 jährige Jubiläum des Münchener Oktoberfestes, 1810-1910,* signed Franz Ringer, pewter lid, $400-550.

g. Stoneware, .5L, transfer, *Jubilaums des Oktoberfest München, 1810-1935,* signed P. Neu, pewter lid, $400-550.

h. Stoneware, .5L, transfer, *15. Deutsches Bundesschießen, München, 1906,* signed Franz Ringer, pewter lid with Munich Child, $450-600.

i. Stoneware, .5L, transfer, *German Engineers Society, Munich, 1903,* signed Franz Ringer, pewter lid, $250-350.

j. Stoneware, .5L, transfer, *Deutschen Brau v. Malz Meisterbund, 1909,* signed Franz Ringer, pewter lid with Munich Child, $300-450.

a. Stoneware, 1.0L, transfer, *12. Deutsches Turnfest, Liepzig, 1913,* signed Franz Ringer, pewter lid with *4F,* $300-400.

b. Stoneware, .5L, transfer, *VIII Deutsches Sängerbundes Fest Nürnberg, 1912,* signed F. Ringer, relief pewter lid with scene of *Nürnberg,* $150-250.

c. Stoneware, .5L, transfer, *14.Oberbayrisches Berzirksturnfest, 1914,* pewter lid, $125-200.

d. Stoneware,1.0L, transfer, *Deutschen Handwerks u. Gewerbekammertag Würzburg, 1912,* pewter lid, $250-400.

e. Stoneware,1.0L, transfer, *Kreis-Ausstellung Regensburg, 1910,* pewter lid, $400-550.

f. Stoneware, .5L, transfer, *11. Deutsches Turnfest, Frankfurt, 1908,* pewter lid, $200-300.

g. Stoneware, .5L, transfer, *12. Deutsches Turnfest, Liepzig, 1913,* signed Franz Ringer, pewter lid with *4F,* $250-350.

h. Stoneware, .5L, transfer, *11. Deutsches Turnfest, Frankfurt, 1908,* signed Franz Ringer, pewter lid with scene of *Frankfurt,* $300-400.

i. Stoneware, .5L, transfer, *16. Deutsches Bundesschießen, Hamburg, 1909,* signed Franz Ringer, pewter lid with scene of *Hamburg,* $250-350.

j. Stoneware, .5L, transfer, *17. Deutsches Bundes-und Goldenes Jubiläums Schiessen, Frankfurt, 1912,* signed Franz Ringer, pewter lid with scene of *Frankfurt,* $300-400.

a. Stoneware, 1.0L, transfer, *Keramisch Werkstätten, München-Herrsching, 600 Jahrfeier des Marktes Diessena 1326-1926,* pewter lid with St. George, $300-400.

b. Stoneware, .5L, transfer, *4F,* early 1900s, pewter lid, $80-120.

c. Stoneware, .5L, transfer, *4F, Gut Heil,* early 1900s, pewter lid, $80-120.

d. Stoneware, .5L, transfer, *4F, Gut Heil, München, 1911,* pewter lid with Munich Child, $125-200.

e. Stoneware, .5L, transfer, *Arbeiter Athleten Bund Deutschlands, Frei-Heil, 1932,* pewter lid with mountain climbing tools, $300-400.

f. Stoneware, 1.0L, handpainted, dated 1893, pewter lid with boar, $300-400.

g. Stoneware, .5L, transfer, early 1900s, relief pewter lid with target, $100-150.

h. Stoneware, .5L, transfer, target scene, early 1900s, pewter lid, $100-200.

i. Stoneware, .5L, incised and enameled, Dümler & Breiden, #1202, early 1900s, pewter lid, $200-300.

j. Stoneware, .5L, transfer, early 1900s, pewter lid with carved horn, $300-400.

a. Stoneware, .5L, handpainted, student association, early 1900s, pewter lid, $200-300.

b. Stoneware, .5L, handpainted, student association, dated 1931, pewter lid, $150-250.

c. Stoneware, .5L, handpainted, student association, dated 1913, pewter lid, $150-250.

d. Stoneware, .5L, transfer, student at a trade school, 1909-1910, pewter lid, $200-300.

e. Stoneware, 1.0L, transfer, student, early 1900s, pewter lid, $200-300.

f. Stoneware, .5L, handpainted, student association, early 1900s, pewter lid, $150-250.

g. Stoneware, .5L, handpainted, student association, dated 1909, pewter lid, $200-300.

h. Stoneware, .5L, R. Merkelbach, handpainted, student association, dated 1914, pewter lid, $300-500.

i. Stoneware, .5L, transfer, Merkelbach & Wick, *Gut Heil!*, early 1900s, pewter lid, $80-120.

j. Stoneware, .5L, transfer, high-hurdle race, pewter lid dated 1936, $350-500.

a.   Stoneware, .5L, transfer, 1920s, pewter lid, $50-80.
b.   Stoneware, .5L, transfer, early 1900s, pewter lid, $50-80.
c.   Stoneware, .5L, transfer, 1920s, metal lid, $50-80.
d.   Stoneware, .5L, transfer, Gerz, early 1900s, pewter lid, $60-100.
e.   Stoneware, .5L, transfer, *D' Hax'n Schlager,* early 1900s, pewter lid with climbing tools, $100-200.

f.   Stoneware, 1.0L, Wick-Werk, transfer, 1920s, pewter lid, $60-100.
g.   Stoneware, 1.0L, Marzi & Remy, handpainted, c.1900, pewter lid with tavern scene, $200-300.
h.   Stoneware, 1.0L, transfer, baby in carriage, early 1900s, pewter lid, $250-350.
i.   Stoneware, .5L, transfer, 1920s, metal lid, $125-200.
j.   Stoneware, .5L, #1741, transfer, early 1900s, pewter lid, $125-200.

a. Stoneware, 1.0L, transfer, Marzi & Remy, #5, early 1900s, pewter lid, $100-150.
b. Stoneware, 1.0L, transfer, Merkelbach & Wick, early 1900s, pewter lid, $100-150.
c. Stoneware, 1.0L, transfer, early 1900s, pewter lid, $100-150.
d. Stoneware, 1.0L, transfer, early 1900s, pewter lid, $100-150.
e. Stoneware, .5L, transfer, early 1900s, pewter lid, $125-200.

f. Stoneware, .5L, transfer, Rosskopf & Gerz, *Nürnberg*, early 1900s, pewter lid with *Denkmal Nürnberg,* $60-100.
g. Stoneware, .5L, transfer, early 1900s, pewter lid with crest, $60-100.
h. Stoneware, .5L, transfer, early 1900s, pewter lid, $100-150.
i. Stoneware, .5L, transfer, early 1900s, pewter lid, $100-150.
j. Stoneware, .5L, transfer, Wick-Werke, 1920s, pewter lid, $50-80.

a. Stoneware, .5L, transfer, early 1900s, pewter lid, $125-200.
b. Stoneware, .5L, transfer, soldier, early 1900s, pewter lid, $200-300.
c. Stoneware, .5L, transfer, design by Ludwig Hohlwein, early 1900s, pewter lid, $400-600.
d. Stoneware, .5L, transfer, design by Ludwig Hohlwein, early 1900s, pewter lid, $400-600.
e. Stoneware, .5L, transfer, design by Ludwig Hohlwein, early 1900s, pewter lid, $600-800.

f. Stoneware, 1.0L, handpainted, Wick-Werke, pewter lid with carved horn: dachshund, dated 1928, $300-400.
g. Stoneware, 1.0L, transfer, street scene, early 1900s, pewter lid, $200-300.
h. Stoneware, .5L, transfer, street scene, early 1900s, pewter lid, $80-120.
i. Stoneware, 1.0L, enameled, coach driver, early 1900s, pewter lid, $200-300.
j. Stoneware, 1.0L, transfer, coach driver, early 1900s, pewter lid, $150-250.

a. Stoneware, 1.0L, handpainted, early 1900s, pewter lid and footring, $500-700.

b. Stoneware, 1.0L, handpainted, early 1900s, pewter lid and footring, $500-700.

c. Stoneware, 1.0L, transfer, handwork occupations, early 1900s, pewter lid, $400-500.

d. Stoneware, 1.0L, transfer, *For Home Consumption*, c.1930, pewter lid, $400-500.

e. Stoneware, 1.0L, impressed design, early 1900s, pewter lid, $150-250.

f. Stoneware, .5L, transfer, early 1900s, pewter lid, $125-200.

g. Stoneware, 3.0L, transfer, signed T.O.H., double handle, early 1900s, double pewter lid with *Munich* scene, $900-1200.

h. Stoneware, 3.0L, incised, double handle, late 1800s, double pewter lid, $700-1000.

i. Stoneware, .05L, transfer, early 1900s, pewter lid, $150-250.

a. Earthenware, 1.0L, handpainted, faience style, design by Franz Ringer, early 1900s, pewter lid, $500-700.
b. Stoneware, 1.0L, handpainted, faience style, design by Franz Ringer, early 1900s, pewter lid & footring, $500-700.
c. Stoneware, 1.0L, handpainted, faience style, c.1900, pewter lid, $350-500.
d. Stoneware, 1.0L, handpainted, signed Anton Lang (Oberammergau), c.1930, pewter lid & footring, $800-1100.
e. Pottery, .5L, Zsolnay, handpainted, c.1900, pewter lid, $700-900.

f. Pottery, .5L, swirled, brown, blue, green, white & tan, early 1900s, inlaid lid, $300-500.
g. Pottery, .5L, relief, high glaze, early 1900s, inlaid lid, $300-500.
h. Stoneware, 1.0L, relief, handpainted, Creussen style, c.1900, pewter lid, $450-650.
i. Stoneware, 1.0L, relief, handpainted, Creussen style, c.1900, pewter lid, $450-650.

a. Pottery, .5L, handpainted & relief, Rookwood Pottery (Cincinnati, Ohio), made for *Commercial Club of Cincinnati,* dated 1895, pewter lid, $2000-2500.

b. Pottery, .5L, handpainted, Rookwood Pottery, signed M.A. Daly, dated 1895, Rembrandt, pewter lid, $6000-8000.

c. Pottery, 1.0L, handpainted, Rookwood Pottery, signed A. Van Briggle, dated 1896, James Hamilton, inlaid lid, $6000-8000.

d. Pottery, 1.0L, handpainted, by Rookwood Pottery, signed Sallie Toohey, dated 1896, inlaid lid, $3000-4000.

e. Pottery, .5L, handpainted, Deldare Ware, Buffalo Pottery, 1908, inlaid lid: *Seattle Hotel,* $600-900.

f. Earthenware, 3.0L, handpainted, glazed, late 1800s, pewter lid, $800-1000.

10. Art Nouveau

This chapter is devoted to stoneware and pottery steins primarily made by manufacturers in the Höhr-Grenzhausen area. Only those steins that are Art Nouveau by form or shape are included. Refer to Section 9 for examples of Art Nouveau decorations on plainly formed steins, and to Section 6 for Art Nouveau glass steins. See the Color Section for other examples of Art Nouveau steins.

10.1 History

The Art Nouveau or modern style offered a strong contrast to the popular Historicism style of the late 1800s. Bold and flat sinuous motifs were used, frequently based upon seaweed and other plant forms. Many artists devoted their work entirely to this new style, working in the different mediums, which included glass, porcelain, stoneware, wood, silver, gold, pewter, and paper.

While hundreds of different designs of Art Nouveau steins were produced by the Höhr-Grenzhausen area manufacturers, actual production was relatively small; consequently, these steins are generally not found too easily.

10.2 Production

We will not go into the details of production of stoneware and pottery steins since they are covered in Sections 2 and 9. The artists who designed the Art Nouveau steins for the factories played a very important role. Most designs can be attributed to a specific artist. In many cases the artist already enjoyed a significant reputation aside from designing beer steins. This was especially true for Ludwig Hohlwein, Henry Van de Velde, and Richard Riemerschmid.

10.3 Collecting

Stein collectors usually view Art Nouveau steins from the approach of a generalist, not focusing on one artist, designer, or factory. However, some collectors will focus on one or more of the more prolific artists, such as Richard Riemerschmid, Paul Wynand, or Ludwig Hohlwein.

10.4 Evaluation Information

Price trends in the past ten years have been very mixed for Art Nouveau steins. The more common steins have been steady or are increasing only slightly. The more unusual and rarer steins increased significantly in the early 1990s, decreased during the late 1990s, then started moving up once again. These steins are relatively popular in Germany, so price trends are affected by the changes in German collectors' interests, as well as fluctuating exchange rates.

a. Stoneware, .5L, Reinhold Merkelbach, #508, gray & red glaze, design by
    L. Capeller, early 1900s, pewter lid, $700-1000.
b. Pottery, 1.0L, Johann von Schwarz, Nürnberg, light brown saltglaze, early
    1900s, pewter lid, $200-300.
c. Pottery, .3L, Fulper Pottery, brown saltglaze, early 1900s, pewter lid,
    $300-500.
d. Stoneware, .5L, #672, blue glaze, early 1900s, inlaid lid, $250-350.
e. Stoneware, .5L, Reinhold Merkelbach, #2112, brown saltglaze, ealry 1900s,
    pewter lid, $200-300.

Opposite page top:

a. Stoneware, .5L, Reinhold Merkelbach, #1741, blue saltglaze, design by
    Richard Riemerschmid, early 1900s, pewter lid, $400-500.
b. Stoneware, .5L, Reinhold Merkelbach, #1770, brown saltglaze, design by Richard Riemerschmid, early 1900s,
    pewter lid, $500-750.
c. Stoneware, .5L, Reinhold Hanke, blue saltglaze, design by Henry Van de Velde, early 1900s, inlaid lid, $700-1000.

Opposite page middle:

d. Stoneware, .5L, Reinhold Merkelbach, #2026, brown saltglaze, design by Richard Riemerschmid, early 1900s,
    pewter lid, $450-650.
e. Stoneware, .5L, Reinhold Merkelbach, #5173, brown saltglaze, design by Richard Riemerschmid, early 1900s,
    pewter lid, $350-500.
f. Stoneware, .5L, #2204, blue & red glazes, early 1900s, inlaid lid, $300-400.

Opposite page bottom:

g. Stoneware, .5L, J. Thewalt, brown & blue saltglazes, early 1900s, pewter lid, $300-400.
h. Stoneware, .5L, #1637, blue glaze, early 1900s, metal lid, $120-180.
i. Stoneware, .5L, Reinhold Merkelbach, #2121, brown saltglaze, design by Paul Wynand, early 1900s, $150-250.

a. Stoneware, .5L, Eckhardt & Engler, #1417, blue glaze, 1920s, pewter lid, $60-100.
b. Stoneware, .5L, Reinhold Merkelbach, #3226, blue & green glazes, early 1900s, pewter lid, $80-120.
c. Stoneware, .5L, Reinhold Merkelbach, #2215, blue glaze, design by Paul Neu, early 1900s, pewter lid, $100-150.
d. Stoneware, .5L, Eckhardt & Engler, blue glaze, 1920s, pewter lid, $60-100.

e. Stoneware, .5L, Reinhold Merkelbach, #2311, blue & green glazes, design by Bruno Mauder, early 1900s, metal lid, $80-120.
f. Stoneware, .5L, Reinhold Merkelbach, #2196, blue glaze, design by Paul Neu, early 1900s, pewter lid, $100-150.
g. Stoneware, .5L, Marzi & Remy, #2167, blue saltglaze, early 1900s, pewter lid, $100-150.
h. Stoneware, .5L, Reinhold Merkelbach, #3267, blue & green glazes, design by Karl Mehlem, 1920s, pewter lid, $100-150.

a. Stoneware, .5L, Otto Blum, #154, blue & green saltglazes, early 1900s, pewter lid, $80-120.
b. Stoneware, .5L, Otto Blum, blue saltglaze, early 1900s, pewter lid, $80-120.
c. Stoneware, .5L, Wick-Werke, #2119, blue glaze, early 1900s, pewter lid, $80-120.
d. Stoneware, .5L, Wick-Werke, blue glaze, early 1900s, pewter lid, $80-120.

e. Stoneware, 1.0L, Marzi & Remy, #2012, blue saltglaze, early 1900s, pewter lid, $100-150.
f. Stoneware, 1.0L, Marzi & Remy, #2201, blue saltglaze, early 1900s, pewter lid, $120-180.
g. Stoneware, 1.0L, Marzi & Remy, #2106, brown saltglaze, early 1900s, pewter lid, $100-150.
h. Stoneware, 1.0L, Marzi & Remy, #1919, blue saltglaze, early 1900s, pewter lid, $100-150.

a. Stoneware, .5L, #1702, blue glaze, 1920s, pewter lid, $80-120.
b. Stoneware, .5L, #2235, incised, blue glaze, early 1900s, pewter lid, $120-180.
c. Stoneware, .5L, Marzi & Remy, #1779, blue, brown & black glazes, early 1900s, inlaid lid, $120-180.
d. Stoneware, .5L, #1650, blue glaze, 1920s, pewter lid, $80-120.

e. Stoneware, .5L, Reinhold Merkelbach, #2060, brown saltglaze, design by Herta Kasten, early 1900s, pewter lid, $250-350.
f. Stoneware, .5L, #600, brown saltglaze, early 1900s, pewter lid, $150-250.
g. Stoneware, .5L, Reinhold Merkelbach, #2134, early 1900s, pewter lid, $200-300.
h. Stoneware, .5L, Reinhold Merkelbach, #2085, brown saltglaze, design by Herta Kasten, early 1900s, pewter lid, $250-350.

a. Stoneware, .5L, Reinhold Merkelbach, #2390, brown saltglaze, early 1900s, pewter lid, $200-300.
b. Stoneware, .5L, Reinhold Merkelbach, #2118, brown saltglaze, design by Paul Wynand, for Frohsinn Glarius, early 1900s, pewter lid, $150-250.
c. Stoneware, .5L, #3202, blue saltglaze, early 1900s, pewter lid, $100-150.
d. Pottery, .5L, Reinhold Merkelbach, #1736, blue glaze, early 1900s, pewter lid, $80-120.

e. Pottery, 1.0L, Reinhold Merkelbach, #1737, blue glaze, early 1900s, pewter lid, $100-150.
f. Terra Sigillata, 1.0L, Dümler & Breiden, #981, black & white glazes, early 1900s, pewter lid, $150-250.
g. Terra Sigillata, 1.0L, Dümler & Breiden, #980, black & white glazes, early 1900s, pewter lid, $150-250.
h. Stoneware, 1.0L, unmarked, blue glaze, early 1900s, pewter lid, $80-120.

a.   Pottery, .5L, #302, brown & blue glazes, early 1900s, pewter lid, $80-120.
b.   Pottery, .5L, #3, brown & blue glazes, early 1900s, pewter lid, $100-150.
c.   Stoneware, .5L, Reinhold Merkelbach, #6046, early 1900s, pewter lid, $100-150.
d.   Stoneware, .5L, Marzi & Remy, #2010, blue saltglaze, early 1900s, pewter lid, $100-150.

e.   Stoneware, .5L, Merkelbach & Wick, #320, blue & purple saltglazes, early 1900s, pewter lid, $150-250.
f.   Pottery, 1.0L, relief, Gambrinus, early 1900s, pewter lid, $150-250.
g.   Pottery, .5L, relief, red, green & blue glazes, early 1900s, pewter lid, $100-150.
h.   Pottery, .5L, relief, pink & blue glazes, early 1900s, inlaid lid, $250-350.

a. Clear glass, .5L, blue stained, wheel engraved, late 1800s, glass inlaid lid, $2500-3500.
b. Overlay glass, .5L, clear on blue & white, middle 1800s, gilded mounts, glass inlaid lid, $3000-4000.
c. Clear glass, .5L, blue stained, wheel engraved, late 1800s, glass inlaid lid, $2500-3500.

d. Overlaid glass, .5L, Bohemian, wheel engraved, blue & white on clear, middle 1800s, glass inlaid lid, $6000-8000.
e. Overlaid glass, .5L, cut, blue & white on clear, late 1800s, porcelain inlaid lid, $3500-4500.
f. White & blue glass, .5L, probably southern Germany, late 1600s, pewter lid & footring by Johann Kirstein, $10,000-15,000.

a. Overlaid glass, .75L, Bohemian, wheel engraved, pink & white on clear, middle 1800s, glass inlaid lid, $5000-6500.
b. Clear glass, .5L, ruby stained, wheel engraved, late 1800s, figural porcelain inlaid lid, $600-800.
c. Clear glass, .75L, ruby stained, wheel engraved, late 1800s, glass inlaid lid, $2500-3500.

d. Clear glass, .5L, amber stained, wheel engraved, late 1800s, glass inlaid lid, $1500-2000.
e. Overlaid glass, 1.0L, cut, blue & white on clear, middle 1800s, porcelain inlaid lid, $4000-5000.
f. Clear glass, .5L, amber stained, wheel engraved, late 1800s, glass inlaid lid, $4000-5000.

a. Overlaid glass, .75L, cut, pink & white on clear, middle 1800s, gilded lid, $3000-4000.
b. Opaline glass, .5L, blue, enameled, late 1800s, silver lid, $2400-3000.
c. Uranium glass, .5L, faceted, middle 1800s, gilded lid, $1600-2200.

d. Opaline glass, .5L, pink, enameled, late 1800s, inlaid glass lid, $1200-1600.
e. Clear glass, .3L, ruby stained, faceted, middle 1800s, gilded lid, $1200-1600.
f. Opaline glass, .5L, pink, late 1800s, inlaid glass lid, $350-500.

a. Clear glass, .5L, ruby stained, wheel engraved, late 1800s, glass inlaid lid, $1000-1300.
b. Clear glass, .5L, ruby stained, wheel engraved, late 1800s, glass inlaid lid, $1000-1300.
c. Clear glass, .5L, ruby stained, wheel engraved, mercury layer, late 1800s, silver mounts, glass inlaid lid, $1800-2400.
d. Clear glass, .5L, blue stained, wheel engraved, late 1800s, glass inlaid lid, $2500-3500.

a. Milk glass, .5L, enameled, early 1800s, pewter lid & footring, $700-1000.
b. Milk glass, 1.0L, enameled, late 1700s, pewter lid & footring, $1000-1300.
c. Milk glass, .5L, enameled, late 1700s, pewter lid & footring, $1400-1800.

Opposite page bottom:
e. Clear glass, 1.0L, wheel engraved, middle 1700s, pewter lid & footring, $3000-4000.

f. Clear glass, 1.0L, enameled, late 1700s, pewter lid & footring, $5000-7500.

g. Milk glass, 1.0L, enameled, late 1700s, pewter lid & footring, $2500-3500.

Right:
d. Milk glass, .5L, enameled, late 1700s, pewter lid & footring, $4000-5000.

a.   Stoneware, 1.0L, Creussen, relief, enameled, Apostles, late 1600s, $10,000-14,000.
b.   Stoneware, 1.0L, Creussen, relief, enameled, Apostles, dated 1699, $10,000-14,000.
c.   Stoneware, 1.0L, Creussen, relief, enameled, crest, dated 1655, $18,000-24,000.

d.   Stoneware, 1.25L, Creussen, relief, enameled, Apostles, late 1600s, $14,000-18,000.
e.   Stoneware, 1.5L, Creussen, relief, enameled, Electors, late 1600s, $16,000-22,000.
f.   Stoneware, 1.0L, Creussen, relief, enameled, Electors, dated 1682, $16,000-22,000.

a. Stoneware, 1.0L, Creussen, relief, enameled, planetary symbols, dated 1667, $20,000-30,000.
b. Stoneware, 1.0L, Freiberg, applied relief & cut design, enameled, middle 1600s, $5000-7000.
c. Stoneware, .5L, Freiberg, applied relief & cut design, enameled, middle 1600s, $12,000-18,000.
d. Stoneware, 1.75L, Muskau, relief & cut design, saltglaze, middle 1600s, $5000-7000.

e. Earthenware, 1.25L, Annaberg, applied relief, enameled, late 1600s, $3000-4000.
f. Earthenware, 1.25L, Annaberg, applied relief & cut design, enameled, late 1600s, $3000-4000.
g. Earthenware, .75L, Annaberg, applied relief, enameled, late 1600s, $5000-7000.

a. Stoneware, 1.5L, Altenburg, enameled, saltglazed, c.1700, $5000-7000.

b. Stoneware, 1.5L, Altenburg, beading, saltglazed, Occupational Weaver, dated 1711, $6000-8000.

c. Stoneware, 1.5L, Altenburg, enameled, coats of arms, Poland & Saxony, middle 1700s, $6000-8000.

d. Stoneware, 1.5L, Altenburg, beading, saltglazed, c.1700, $4500-6000.

e. Earthenware, 1.8L, Saxony, glazed redware, pewter & brass mounts, c.1700, $3000-4000.

f. Stoneware, 1.0L, Waltenburg (Saxony), saltglaze, late 1600s, $3000-4000.

g. Stoneware, 1.5L, Muskau, cut & stamped, saltglaze, middle 1700s, $1500-2000.

h. Stoneware, 1.0L, Westerwald, applied relief, saltglaze, crest of the King of Netherlands, c.1700, $1800-2400.

a. Stoneware, 1.0L, Siegburg, applied relief, saltglaze, dated 1576, $5000-7500.
b. Stoneware, .5L, Siegburg, applied relief, saltglaze, signed H.H. (Hans Hilgers), late 1500s, $3000-4000.
c. Stoneware, 1.75L, Muskau, cut & stamped, saltglaze, late 1600s, $2500-3500.
d. Stoneware, 1.25L, Frechen, tigerware glaze, English silver mounts, dated 1608, $3000-4000.

e. Earthenware, .75L, Probstei, north German Folk Pottery, late 1700s, $1500-2000.
f. Faience, 1.0L, Austrian, middle 1700s, $1500-2000.
g. Faience, 1.0L, Ottingen-Schrattenhofen, middle 1700s, $1800-2400.
h. Faience, 1.25L, Austrian, Salzburg, *St. Simonn. AP*, middle 1700s, $1500-2000.

a. Faience, 1.25L, Nürnberg, signed Kordenbusch, middle 1700s, $5000-7000.
b. Faience, 1.0L, Crailsheim, middle 1700s, $4500-6000.
c. Faience, 1.25L, Nürnberg, St. Marten, signed Kordenbusch, middle 1700s, $4000-6000.
d. Faience, 1.0L, Crailsheim, *S. Afra*, middle 1700s, $4500-6000.

Left:

e. Faience, 1.5L, Nürnberg, middle 1700s, $6000-8000.

f. Faience, 1.25L, Nürnberg, signed A. Kordenbusch, dated 1728, $7000-10,000.

Opposite page bottom:

d. Faience, 1.25L, Schrezheim, muffle fired, signed I.B. (Johann Bechdolff), late 1700s, $10,000-14,000.

e. Faience, 1.5L, Proskau, late 1700s, $4000-5000.

f. Faience, 1.0L, Bayreuth, Hausmaler, by Johann Georg Fliegel, middle 1700s, $40,000-60,000.

a. Faience, 1.25L, Ansbach, green family, middle 1700s, $25,000-35,000.
b. Faience, 1.0L, Hanau, Hausmaler, signed Abraham Helmback, c.1700, $40,000-60,000.
c. Faience, 1.25L, Ansbach, green family, middle 1700s, $25,000-35,000.

a. Silver, 2.0L, repoussé, marked 800, late 1800s, $3000-4000.
b. Silver, .5L, repoussé, 1800s, $1800-2400.
c. Silver, 1.5L, repoussé, middle 1800s, $2000-2500.

d. Silver, 2.0L, Norwegian, dated 1906, $2000-2500.
e. Silver, 1.0L, covered with sharkskin, late 1800s, $3000-4000.
f. Silver, 1.0L, Woman character, late 1800s, $1500-2000.

a. Silver, .1L, coins, engraved, 1800s, $600-1000.
b. Silver, .3L, repoussé, 1800s, $1200-1600.
c. Silver, .25L, repoussé, gilded, 1800s, $1200-1600.

d. Silver, 1.8L, German, marked 800, E. Timmermann, coins from 1858-1912, $4000-5000.
e. Horn, .4L, silver-plated mounts, late 1800s, $1000-1400.
f. Mother-of-Pearl, 2.0L, 1700s, $10,000-15,000.

a. Enamel on copper, .5L, Austrian, late 1800s, $2500-3500.
b. Silver, .5L, Russian, by P. Ovchinnikov, gilded, enamel, transparent enamel base, 1893, $35,000-45,000.
c. Leather, .75L, handpainted, silver mounts and liner, middle 1800s, $5000-6500.

d. Jade, .4L, Russian, silver mounts, late 1800s, $8000-10,000.
e. Serpentine, .5L, German, pewter mounts, early 1700s, $2500-3500.
f. Silver, .3L, gilded, filigree, set with stones, probably late 1700s, $3500-4500.

a. Enamel on silver, 3.5" ht., Austrian, late 1800s, $700-1000.
b. Ivory, .1L, stained green, silver mounts, late 1800s, $1000-1300.
c. Wood & pewter, .75L, Daubenkrug, Thuringia, middle 1700s, $3000-4000.
d. Wood & pewter, 1.0L, Daubenkrug, Grimma (Saxony), by Christian Vettermann d.A., middle 1600s, $4000-5000.

e. Wood, 1.0L, handcarved, signed Johann Rent, middle 1800s, $15,000-20,000.
f. Bronze & Horn, 3.0L, enameled, late 1800s, $10,000-15,000.

a. Ivory, .75L, carved, silver mounts, late 1800s, $5000-6500.

b. Ivory, .5L, carved, 1800s, $9000-12,000.

c. Ivory, .25L, carved, late 1800s, $2500-3000.

Left:

d. Meerschaum, 1.0L, carved, Elkington Mason & Co., gilded, late 1800s, $2500-3500.

Opposite page top:

a. Ivory, 19.5" ht., carved, 1800s, $18,000-24,000.

b. Ivory, 17.5" ht., carved, silver mounts, 1800s, $10,000-14,000.

Opposite page bottom:

c. Woven reed, 1.75L, Saxony, lined with pitch, early 1700s, $5000-7500.

d. Wood, .75L, Norwegian, carved, late 1700s, $1200-1500.

e. Wood, 1.0L, Norwegian, burl, middle 1700s, $1800-2400.

a.   Porcelain, .5L, relief & transfer, late 1800s, inlaid lid, $800-1200.

b.   Porcelain, .3L, Capo di Monte style, late 1800s, inlaid lid, $800-1100.

c.   Porcelain, .3L, handpainted, Meissen mark, late 1800s, inlaid lid, $1800-2400.

d.   Porcelain, 1.0L, crown with N mark, Capo di Monte style, late 1800s, inlaid lid, $1000-1500.

e.   Porcelain, 1.0L, handpainted, Meissen mark, late 1800s, gilded lid, $2200-2800.

f.   Porcelain, 1.0L, handpainted, Meissen mark, late 1800s, silver lid, $3500-4500.

g.   Porcelain, 1.0L, handpainted, Meissen, middle 1700s, silver lid, $8000-12,000.

a. Porcelain, .5L, beehive mark, handpainted, c.1900, inlaid lid, $1800-2400.
b. Porcelain, .5L, beehive mark, handpainted, c.1900, inlaid lid, $1800-2400.
c. Porcelain, .5L, beehive mark, handpainted, c.1900, inlaid lid, $2400-3000.
d. Porcelain, .5L, beehive mark, handpainted, c.1900, inlaid lid, $2400-3000.

e. Porcelain, .25L, beehive mark, handpainted, c.1900, inlaid lid, $1800-2400.
f. Porcelain, .25L, beehive mark, handpainted, c.1900, inlaid lid, $1800-2400.
g. Porcelain, .25L, beehive mark, handpainted, c.1900, inlaid lid, $1800-2400.
h. Porcelain, .25L, beehive mark, handpainted, c.1900, inlaid lid, $1800-2400.
i. Porcelain, .1L, beehive mark, handpainted, c.1900, inlaid lid, $1500-2000.

a.   Porcelain, .5L, handpainted, Belleek/Willets mark, signed J.V. Fries, 1900, inlaid lid, $800-1100.

b.   Stoneware, .4L, Mettlach, transfer, 3342/546, early 1900s, inlaid lid, $1500-2000.

c.   Porcelain, .5L, O'Hara Dial, golfer, early 1900s, inlaid lid, $1200-1400.

d.   Porcelain, .5L, Occupational Chauffeur, early 1900s, pewter lid, $1300-1700.

e.   Porcelain, .5L, Occupational Pharmacist, dated 1901, pewter lid, $1500-2000.

f.   Pottery, .5L, handpainted, Fischer, Budapest, early 1900s, glass inlaid lid, $500-750.

g.   Porcelain, 1.0L, handpainted, *Vivat crescat, florecat, A.E.V.! Berlin, 1890-1891,* pewter lid, $1600-2200.

a. Pottery, .5L, relief #1276, The Baby Stein, early 1900s, pewter lid, $400-600.
b. Stoneware, .5L, Gerz, #314, balloon scenes, c.1900, inlaid lid, $1000-1500.
c. Pottery, .5L, etched, Hauber & Reuther, #1000, golfer, early 1900s, pewter lid, $2500-3000.
d. Pottery, .5L, etched, #5044, golfer, early 1900s, pewter lid, $2500-3000.

e. Stoneware, 1.0L, transfer, crest, Munich, late 1800s, pewter lid & footring, $350-500.
f. Stoneware, 1.0L, transfer, *Tief Grotte Eltmann,* c.1900, pewter lid & footring, $800-1100.
g. Stoneware, 1.0L, transfer, Munich Shooting Club, early 1900s, pewter lid, $600-800.
h. Stoneware, 1.0L, transfer, (Munich) *Jubiläum Oktoberfestes, 1810-1910,* pewter lid, $600-800.

a. Stoneware, .5L, Mettlach, #2683, design by Richard Riemerschmid, early 1900s, pewter lid, $600-900.

b. Stoneware, .5L, Mettlach, #2685, design by Richard Riemerschmid, early 1900s, pewter lid, $600-900.

c. Stoneware, .5L, Reinhold Merkelbach, #1729, design by Richard Riemerschmid, early 1900s, pewter lid, $750-1000.

d. Stoneware, 1.5L, Reinhold Merkelbach, #1769, design by Richard Riemerschmid, early 1900s, pewter lid, $1200-1600.

e. Stoneware, .5L, Reinhold Merkelbach, #1757, design by Richard Riemerschmid, early 1900s, pewter lid, $800-1000.

f. Stoneware, .5L, Reinhold Merkelbach, #1757, design by Richard Riemerschmid, early 1900s, pewter lid, $900-1200.

g. Stoneware, .5L, Reinhold Merkelbach, #1728, design by Richard Riemerschmid, early 1900s, pewter lid, $550-750.

a.   Stoneware, .5L, Reinhold Merkelbach, #2176, design by Ludwig Hohlwein, early 1900s, pewter lid, $1000-1500.
b.   Stoneware, .5L, Reinhold Merkelbach, #2176, design by Ludwig Hohlwein, early 1900s, pewter lid, $1000-1500.
c.   Stoneware, .5L, Reinhold Merkelbach, #2176, design by Ludwig Hohlwein, early 1900s, pewter lid, $1000-1500.
d.   Stoneware, .5L, Reinhold Merkelbach, #2176, design by Ludwig Hohlwein, early 1900s, pewter lid, $1000-1500.

e.   Stoneware, 1.0L, Jacob Scharvogel, early 1900s, pewter lid, $1000-1400.
f.   Stoneware, 2.0L, Alphons Lötschert, #243, early 1900s, pewter lid, $1200-1600.
g.   Pottery, 1.0L, Maximilian von Heider & Söhne, early 1900s, inlaid lid, $750-1000.

a. Character, .5L, porcelain, Norwegian Fisherman, E. Bohne Söhne, c.1900, $1800-2400.
b. Character, .3L, porcelain, Owl, E. Bohne Söhne, c.1900, $2500-3500.
c. Character, .5L, porcelain, Student Dueler, c.1900, $2000-2500.
d. Character, .5L, porcelain, Uncle Sam, Schierholz, c.1900, $5000-6000.

e. Character, .5L, porcelain, Nürnberg Gooseman, c.1900, $1600-2200.
f. Character, .5L, stoneware, Bustle Lady, R. Hanke, #895, c.1900, $2000-2500.
g. Character, .5L, porcelain, Cat with Hangover, music box base, Schierholz, c.1900, $1000-1300.
h. Character, .5L, stoneware, Pug Dog, Mettlach, c.1900, $700-900.

a. Character, .25L, stoneware, The King, J. Reinemann, early 1900s, $500-700.
b. Character, .5L, stoneware, Wendelstein Mountain, Martin Pauson, c.1900, $500-750.
c. Character, .5L, pottery, Falstaff, Merkelbach & Wick, c.1900, $250-350.
d. Character, .5L, pottery, Fox, #8672, Marzi & Remy, c.1900, $300-400.

e. Character, .5L, porcelain, East Berlin Town Hall, c.1900, $2000-3000.
f. Character, .5L, porcelain, Acorn, E. Bohne Söhne, c.1900, $500-700.
g. Character, .5L, porcelain, Coffee Bag, Schierholz, c.1900, $2400-3000.
h. Character, .5L, pottery, Cat, #1197, early 1900s, $700-1000.

a. Mettlach, .5L, 3329, etched, gamblers, inlaid lid, $1800-2400.

b. Mettlach, .5L, 1856, etched, Postman stein, inlaid lid, $1600-2000.

c. Mettlach, .5L, 2730, etched, Butcher Occupational stein, inlaid lid, $2500-3500.

d. Mettlach, .5L, 2717, etched, Venus Target stein, inlaid lid, $3500-4500.

e. Mettlach, .5L, 2049, etched, Chess stein, inlaid lid, $2500-3000.

f. Mettlach, .5L, 2074, etched, Bird in Cage stein, inlaid lid, $2000-2500.

g. Mettlach, .4L, 2106, etched & relief, Monkeys in Cage stein, inlaid lid, $4000-5000.

h. Mettlach, .5L, 3279, etched, Prosit, inlaid lid, $1000-1500.

a. Regimental, .5L, porcelain, *Matrosen Artillerie Abthl., Wilhelmshaven, 1906-1909,* $1600-2200.

b. Regimental, .5L, porcelain, *Bayerisches Infanterie Nr. 12, Neu Ulm, 1900-1902,* medic, $2500-3200.

c. Regimental, .5L, pottery, *Eisenbahn, Regt. Nr. 3, Berlin-Hanau, 1909-1911,* $1200-1500.

d. Regimental, .5L, porcelain, *4. Ostasiatisches Inft. Regt., 1900-1901,* served in Asia, $6000-8000.

e. Regimental, 1.0L, pottery, screwoff lid, *S.M.S. Breslau, Wilhelmshaven, 1911-1914,* $1200-1600.

f. Regimental, 1.0L, pottery, *Pionier Bataillon Nr. 9, Harburg, 1911-1913,* $900-1200.

The steins on the following four pages are currently being produced in Germany. The values listed are the approximate retail prices at stores in the United States.

a. Porcelain, .75L, American Police Dog Stein, Limited Edition of 3000, $200-225.
b. Porcelain, .75L, German Police Dog Stein, Limited Edition of 2000, $200-225.
c. Porcelain, .75L, Bulldog Stein II, Limited Edition of 5000, $200-225.
d. Porcelain, .75L, Max the Bavarian Boar Stein, Limited Edition of 5000, $200-220.
e. Porcelain, .75L, Rosie the Bavarian Boaress Stein, Limited Edition of 5000, $200-220.

f. Porcelain, .6L, Biker Eagle Stein, Limited Edition of 5000, $200-225.
g. Porcelain, .6L, Biker Bob Stein, Limited Edition of 5000, $225-250.
h. Porcelain, .6L, Corona© Sea Turtle Stein, Limited Edition of 5000, $200-225.
i. Porcelain, 1.0L, Maximilian the Knight Stein, Medieval Series, Limited Edition of 5000, pewter lid, $200-220.

a. Stoneware, 1.0L, Batman Stein, Limited Edition of 5000, $250-275.
b. Stoneware, 1.0L, Superman Stein, Limited Edition of 5000, $250-275.
c. Porcelain, .75L, Millennium Stein, Limited Edition of 2000, $280-300.
d. Reverse of previous stein.
e. Stoneware, .5L, Millennium Stein, pewter lid, Limited Edition of 2000, $200-225.

f. Porcelain, .75L, Coca-Cola® Collector Stein, Santa Hospitality, Gold Edition, Limited Edition of 2500, $250-275.
g. Stoneware, .6L, Coca-Cola® Collector Stein, The Seal, Limited Edition of 5000, $200-225.
h. Porcelain, .6L, Corona© Toucan Stein, by Albert Stahl & Co., Limited Edition of 5000, $180-200.
i. Porcelain, .6L, Corona© Iguana Stein, by Albert Stahl & Co., Limited Edition of 5000, $180-200.
j. Porcelain, .6L, Corona© Parrot Stein, by Albert Stahl & Co., Limited Edition of 5000, $180-200.

a. Porcelain, .5L, The Looney Tunes Yosemite Sam Collectible Stein, Limited Edition of 10,000, $200-225.

b. Porcelain, .6L, The Looney Tunes Road Runner & Wile E. Coyote Collectible Stein, Limited Edition of 10,000, $225-250.

c. Porcelain, .6L, The Looney Tunes Tweety & Sylvester Collectible Stein, Limited Edition of 10,000, $225-250.

d. Porcelain, .5L, The Looney Tunes Tasmanian Devil Collectible Stein, Limited Edition of 10,000, $200-225.

e. Porcelain, .5L, The Looney Tunes Bugs Bunny Collectible Stein, Limited Edition of 10,000, $200-225.

f. Stoneware, .5L, Euro Dollar Stein, European Coin Stein Collectors Series, Limited Edition of 9000, pewter lid, $180-200.

g. Stoneware, 1.0L, Rome City Commemorative Stein, Famous Cities of the World Series, Limited Edition of 9000, pewter lid, $230-250.

h. Stoneware, .75L, Moscow Commemorative Stein, Famous Cities of the World Series, Limited Edition of 2500, gold-plated lid, $240-270.

i. Stoneware, .5L, Titanic Stein, Limited Edition of 4000, inlaid lid, $160-180.

j. Stoneware, 1.0L, Paris Commemorative Stein, Famous Cities of the World Series, Limited Edition of 9000, inlaid lid, $230-250.

a. Porcelain, .6L, Corona© Jaguar Stein, Limited Edition of 5000, $200-225.

b. Porcelain, .75L, Corona© Bulldog Stein, Limited Edition of 5000, $200-225.

c. Porcelain, .75L, Chocolate Labrador Stein, (also black and yellow versions), Limited Edition of 5000, $200-225.

d. Stoneware, .5L, Kaissereich Stein, European Coin Stein Collectors Series, Limited Edition of 9000, pewter lid, $200-220.

e. Stoneware, .5L, Imperial German Crest Stein, Royal Series, Limited Edition of 999, gold-plated lid & footring, $400-450.

f. Stoneware, .5L, Vintage U.S. Coins Stein, Morgan Silver Dollar, Limited Edition of 5000, pewter lid, $240-260.

g. Pewter, .5L, Pewter Gothic Campaign Stein, handpainted gold & copper, Limited Edition of 500, $350-375.

h. Stoneware, .5L, Austrian-Hungarian Empire Stein, Masterworks Series, Limited Edition of 500, gold-plated lid & footring, $500-550.

i. Stoneware, 1.0L, Magnificent Bavaria Stein, Limited Edition of 999, gold-plated lid, $300-325.

j. Stoneware, 1.5L, Peter Dümler Jousting Tankard, pewter relief, Limited Edition of 2000, pewter lid, $375-400.

k. Stoneware, .5L, The Looney Tunes Coat of Arms Stein, body made in China, pewter lid made in Germany, $50-70.

a. Anheuser-Busch, 1.0L, Budweiser Centennial, 1976, $300-400.
b. Anheuser-Busch, 1.0L, U.S. Bicentennial, 1976, $300-400.
c. Anheuser-Busch, .5L, A & Eagle, 1976, $80-120.
d. Anheuser-Busch, .5L, Bud Man, 1975, $300-450.
e. Anheuser-Busch, .5L, German Tavern Scene, 1975, $150-250.
f. Anheuser-Busch, .5L, Katakombe, 1976, $200-300.
g. Anheuser-Busch, .5L, Grant's Farm, 1976, $100-200.

h. Anheuser-Busch, .5L, Das Festhaus, Busch Gardens, 1970s, $100-200.
i. Anheuser-Busch, .5L, Busch, 1980, $200-300.
j. Anheuser-Busch, .5L, Budweiser Centennial, 1976, $200-300.
k. Anheuser-Busch, .5L, Clydesdales, 1976, $100-200.
l. Anheuser-Busch, .5L, Clydesdales, 1976, $100-200.
m. Anheuser-Busch, .5L, Grant's Farm, short version, 1976, $300-400.

n. Anheuser-Busch, .5L, Collectors Club, 1995-1998, $100-400 each.

11. Mettlach

Ever since they were first produced in about 1850, Mettlach steins have been cherished as very high-quality art objects. *The Mettlach Book*, with information, pictures, and prices similar to those of this book, is devoted entirely to Mettlach wares. Most of the book is relevant to stein collecting, and some of the information is repeated here. Those interested in more details should consult that reference.

11.1 Mettlach History

Mettlach, from the Latin word for mid-lakes, is a small village on the Saar River in what is now the far western part of Germany, near both Luxembourg and France. Although the ceramic products made there were produced by the Villeroy & Boch Company, they have commonly been called Mettlach wares. Apparently, this has been done partly to avoid confusion with the very different products made at the eight Villeroy & Boch factories in other cities, and partly because the name Mettlach dominates the important incised old tower, or castle, trademark used by the Mettlach factory.

Pierre-Joseph Boch, the founder of the family pottery business, had a son, Jean Francis Boch, who studied chemistry and mineralogy at the École des Sciences in Paris. After Jean Francis completed his studies, he began searching for a place to begin a pottery so that he could make use of his education. In 1809, utilizing the fortunes of his family and of his wife, Rosalie Buschmann, he purchased the old Benedictine Abbey of Mettlach, including its expansive central buildings and its famous old tower, as the site for their firm, Boch-Buschmann.

The government had imposed as a condition on the sale of the buildings that the abundant hard coal, and not the scarce wood, be used to fire the kilns. This presented a tremendous obstacle because it required the invention of a coal-burning kiln, which was only accomplished in 1816 but resulted in a far superior and more uniform firing.

Mettlach innovations did not come solely through necessity. Water power was harnessed for turning the potters' wheels and for the clay-preparation machinery. These novel labor-saving advances helped the company cope with the skyrocketing wage demands of the new middle class following the French Revolution. Other advances came when the copperplate engraving and transfer-printing techniques from Staffordshire, England, were brought to Mettlach in 1820, and excellent commonplace wares were produced that appealed to the newly monied middle class. Art studios, archives, museums, art schools, and famous artists were all brought to Mettlach in an effort to further promote the artistic accomplishments of the factory.

In 1836, with the business in the hands of Jean Francis's son Eugene, a merger with Nicholas Villeroy's factory was undertaken in order to eliminate the only significant competition in the region. This created the Villeroy & Boch Company. Soon afterward, the influence of the Empire and Biedermeier styles, which demanded only mundane wares, diminished. Mettlach found a market for the decorative relief Historicism beakers and steins, which they then produced in great numbers.

The golden age of Mettlach lasted from approximately 1880 to 1910, during which time their etched, glazed, and cameo wares were at their pinnacles. Using secret techniques, Mettlach produced new designs in an explosion of color. An extensive display at the 1885 Antwerp World's Fair propelled the firm into the forefront of the ceramics field, with reviewers using descriptions such as *Vollkommenes* (perfection) and *geradezu unerreicht* (frankly unrivalled). Production continued to increase until, at its height, the Mettlach plant employed about 1250 people.

About 1909, and certainly by the start of the First World War, business seems to have slacked off considerably. Researchers tend to blame unfavorable economic conditions and a lack of skilled labor. In 1921, a fire destroyed molds, production records, and formulas for the manufacturing processes and materials, including the 30 colored clay slips, 150 under-glaze colors, and 176 hard-colored glazes. From 1925 until the early 1930s, a few etched and PUG articles were again produced at the Mettlach plant. Although tiles, dishes, plumbing fixtures, and other wares continued to be manufactured, there was almost a fifty-year lapse before Mettlach revived stein and plaque production. Although some of the most desirable steins and plaques have been reproduced, the processes and materials are mostly different. The quality of these reproduced pieces is very admirable but not as fine as the original chromolithographed items. More information about currently produced Mettlach steins can be found in Section 19.

11.2 Production Techniques

The Villeroy & Boch Company produced steins and other wares that were, almost without exception, both original in design and in production technique. The majority of V&B steins have certain common characteristics. They were made from a very hard, impervious stoneware material that was homogeneous and vitrified. A pure white, porcelain-like glaze was applied inside all items, except those marked BAVARIA, which are a gray color inside and out. The same general type of stoneware that formed the bodies of the wares was also used to decorate the etched, relief, and mosaic items. Mold marks are generally not visible, indicating either that the seams were very carefully cleaned after the body was formed or a potters' wheel was used to form and clean the bodies.

The earliest steins produced at Mettlach were bas-relief, commonly called relief. The earliest decorations usually consisted of green or brown leaves and vines, eventually evolving into figures and other more decorative relief scenes. These relief steins were produced from the 1840s through the early 1880s, when production methods became more diversified.

The designs on the relief wares seem to have been produced in two ways. In rare instances, it appears that the relief was applied by hand; apparently, the common method was to form the design in a full-bodied mold. After an opaque tan relief material was set into the mold, stoneware slip was painted into the mold to produce a colored background, usually a light blue, green, brown, gray, or coral red.

Cameo and relief wares, which are often confused with each other, are produced in similar ways, except that: (1) a cameo does not protrude as far from the body as a relief decoration, thus calling for closer tolerances; and (2) the material used in cameo is a more translucent, porcelain-like material that allows the shading of background colors to show through the thinnest portions. The results are products similar to the gemstone and shell cameos from which they get their name.

The simplest steins to produce were the print under-glaze, or PUG, steins. After the blank body was formed, fired, and glazed, a decal or transfer-printed scene was applied and the body was then covered with an additional coat of transparent glaze and refired. Actually, the process could best be described as print between glazes. After the final firing, the transfer scene had become an integral part of the product.

The decorations on the Mettlach faience, Delft and Rookwood steins were primarily handpainted.

When the name Mettlach is recognized, it is most commonly associated with the etched, or chromolithographed, steins. With no tangible evidence other than autopsies of broken pieces, there have been a number of theories advanced to explain the process for making chromolithographed products.

There are some elements that are common to many of the chromolithograph theories. The design is generally recognized to be a separate section that was applied and fused to the body with pressure and great heat. The hard white glaze on the interior was applied separately and vitrified during one of the firings. While it would appear that the design materials were wrapped around the body, there are some knowledgeable researchers who feel that the body could have been poured into the design.

A reverse-painting theory that seems to be picking up more support lately is best explained in several steps. A flat or curved tray was developed on which the lines were etched in reverse, that is protruding from its surface. Colored clay slips were handpainted onto this perhaps plaster or metal tray. Colors for which atomizer-sprayed shadings were required were sprayed after all other colors had been painted and then painted over with the solid background color. An eighth-inch-or-so layer of slip (moist stoneware) was then placed on the tray and the decoration was lifted from the design tray and set into the appropriate portion of a body or a body mold. The rest of the body had already been, or was then, poured or hand-worked into its mold, which was then cleaned on a potter's wheel.

Virtually all theories suggest that the handle was applied separately on most of the steins. Bases were sometimes also applied, but the frieze bands are generally considered integral to the body of a stein. It is generally accepted that the black lines that form the distinctive outlining in the decoration were produced by rubbing a black glaze into the incised lines after the decoration had been fired.

The so-called Art Nouveau wares were etched with the bold sinuous designs that became popular at the beginning of the twentieth century. Blue and tan or rust and green color schemes often dominated the designs. The mosaic wares generally followed the relief era and preceded the etched era. Although some mosaic pieces contain etched sections, they were usually totally decorated with colored glazes on surfaces that are actually quite complex compared to the usual etched pieces. The glazed wares are similar to mosaics but have no protrusions.

It is difficult to estimate the number of steins originally produced. A tremendous number of steins were destroyed over the years, particularly during the wars. There are any number of soldiers who have recalled machine-gunning hundreds of shelves full of steins throughout Germany—apparently this was a pervasive form of cultural vandalism perpetrated by the invading forces. Because of this destruction, the U.S. inventory constitutes a significant portion of the current world supply. Based partly on extrapolating recent observations and partly by using cost and wage figures, it seems improbable that the average production of a particular Mettlach item could have exceeded 2000 pieces. The most common items, however, were produced in larger quantities, perhaps as high as 10,000 or more. In the case of the extremely rare steins, it seems unlikely that more than 100 were ever produced.

11.3 Marks

Many of the trademarks used by Villeroy & Boch, Mettlach, are shown below and at the end of Section 2. Fortunately, throughout the important Mettlach period from about 1880 to 1910, the factory marked their products consistently and profusely. Of course, some of these marks are of little importance to collectors because they were intended to identify individual craftsmen and to serve quality-control purposes. However, the marks of interest to collectors are described here.

A most important mark is the one that shows the form number, sometimes called the mold or stock number; it is the large Arabic number impressed into the base or back of Mettlach wares. This is generally a three- or four-digit number and is usually located below the trademark. Even when the trademark is not present, the distinctive crisp style of the form number, together with an examination of quality, identify Mettlach items.

A decoration number was used to identify the design of PUG, Rookwood, and some faience products. This number was stamped on PUGs and Rookwoods and painted on faiences, usually in black or blue, and was generally accompanied by the word Geschützt (patented) or DEC.

The exact year of production can often be discerned from the marks on an item. All of the known dating systems are described in *The Mettlach Book*. The most important date code is the two-digit incised number that is often located to the right of and below the trademark, as illustrated in the figure below. Items made between 1882 and 1887 have a number ranging from 82 to 87 incised inside a small rectangle. The rectangle was not used after 1887 so, for example, 88 means 1888; 95 indicates 1895; 00, 1900; 05, 1905; and so on.

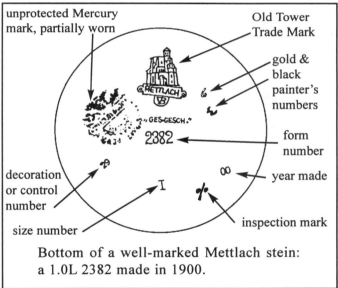

Bottom of a well-marked Mettlach stein: a 1.0L 2382 made in 1900.

11.4 Evaluation Information

Price trends in the past ten years have been mostly level or upward for Mettlach steins. Many mosaic, and Art Nouveau steins have increased in value significantly. The PUG and relief steins have been fairly steady. Etched steins have been steady or increasing only slightly, except for some of the rarer steins which have increased significantly.

a. Mettlach, .5L, 1132, etched, man fiddling and dancing crocodile in front of pyramids, inlaid lid, $500-700.
b. Mettlach, .5L, 1146, etched, student drinking in tavern, inlaid lid, $450-600.
c. Mettlach, 1.0L, 1154, etched, hunting scenes, inlaid lid, $750-950.
d. Mettlach, .5L, 1164, etched, musician and girl, inlaid lid, $450-600.
e. Mettlach, .5L, 1395, etched, French card stein, inlaid lid, $450-600.

f. Mettlach, .5L, 1403, etched, man bowling in tavern, inlaid lid, $400-500.
g. Mettlach, .5L, 1527, etched, four men drinking, inlaid lid, $450-550.
h. Mettlach, .5L, 1675, etched, scene of Heidelberg, inlaid lid, $500-650.
i. Mettlach, .5L, 1725, etched, lovers, inlaid lid, $500-650.
j. Mettlach, .5L, 1742, etched, scene of Göttingen, inlaid lid, $550-700.

a.   Mettlach, .5L, 1786, etched and glazed, St. Florian stein, pewter lid, $600-800.
b.   Mettlach, .5L, 1795, etched, scene of Freiburg, inlaid lid, $550-700.
c.   Mettlach, .5L, 1796, etched, cavalier drinking, inlaid lid, $450-600.
d.   Mettlach, .5L, 1863, etched, scene of Stuttgart, inlaid lid, $550-700.
e.   Mettlach, 1.0L, 1932, etched, cavaliers drinking, inlaid lid, $550-750.

f.   Mettlach, .5L, 1934, etched, four panels of soldiers, inlaid lid, $800-1000.
g.   Mettlach, .25L, 1968, etched, two lovers, inlaid lid, $250-350.
h.   Mettlach, .25L, 1972, etched, four seasons in four panels, inlaid lid, $250-350.
i.   Mettlach, .5L, 1986, etched, two ladies, inlaid lid, $550-700.
j.   Mettlach, .5L, 1995, etched, fat man drinking, inlaid lid, $400-550.

a.   Mettlach, .5L, 1997, etched & PUG, George Ehret brewer, inlaid lid, $250-350.

b.   Mettlach, .5L, 1998, etched, Trumpeter from Sachingen, inlaid lid, $450-600.

c.   Mettlach, .5L, 2001A, glazed & handpainted, Book stein for law, inlaid lid, $550-750.

d.   Mettlach, .5L, 2001K, glazed & handpainted, Book stein for banking or commerce, inlaid lid, $450-600.

e.   Mettlach, .5L, 2002, etched, Munich stein, inlaid lid, $400-500.

f.   Mettlach, .5L, 2024, etched & glazed, Berlin stein, inlaid lid, $500-700.

g.   Mettlach, .5L, 2027, etched, Gambrinus, inlaid lid, $800-1100.

h.   Mettlach, .3L, 2035, etched, Bacchus carousing, inlaid lid, $200-300.

i.   Mettlach, .5L, 2044, etched, drinking scene, inlaid lid, $500-700.

j.   Mettlach, .5L, 2051, etched, seven students drinking, inlaid lid, $500-700.

a. Mettlach, .3L, 2057, etched, peasants dancing, inlaid lid, $200-300.
b. Mettlach, .5L, 2075, etched & glazed, Telegrapher stein, inlaid lid, $1500-2000.
c. Mettlach, .5L, 2082, etched, William Tell stein, inlaid lid, $1100-1300.
d. Mettlach, .5L, 2083, etched, Boar Hunt stein, inlaid lid, $1100-1300.
e. Mettlach, .5L, 2089, etched, angel serving dinner and beer to gentlemen, inlaid lid, $750-950.

f. Mettlach, .5L, 2091, etched, St. Florian pouring water on a man's head, inlaid lid, $750-950.
g. Mettlach, .5L, 2092, etched, keeper of clock tower, gnome on ladder setting clock, inlaid lid, $750-950.
h. Mettlach, .5L, 2093, etched, Card stein, inlaid lid, $600-750.
i. Mettlach, .5L, 2097, etched, musical notes, inlaid lid, $500-600.
j. Mettlach, .3L, 2100, etched, Prosit stein, knight with stein and man, inlaid lid, $500-650.

a. Mettlach, .5L, 2134, etched, gnome in nest, holding two steins, inlaid lid, $2200-2800.

b. Mettlach, .5L, 2136, etched & PUG, *Anheuser Busch Brewery,* inlaid lid, $2500-3500.

c. Mettlach, 1.0L, 2204, decorated relief, Prussian eagle on tan body, inlaid lid, $800-1100.

d. Mettlach, .5L, 2231, etched, tavern scene, inlaid lid, $500-650.

e. Mettlach, .5L, 2235, etched, barmaid holding steins, target in background, inlaid lid, $500-650.

f. Mettlach, 1.0L, 2255, etched, wedding scene, inlaid lid, $800-1000.

g. Mettlach, .5L, 2373, etched, *St. Augustine, Florida,* alligator handle, inlaid lid, $600-750.

h. Mettlach, 1.0L, 2382, etched, Thirsty Rider stein, conical inlaid lid, $700-850.

i. Mettlach, 1.0L, 2391, etched, Lohengrin stein, inlaid lid, $1800-2400.

j. Mettlach, .5L, 2394, etched, scenes from Siegfried's youth, inlaid lid, $650-850.

a. Mettlach, .5L, 2401, etched, Tannhauser in the Venusberg, inlaid lid, $700-900.
b. Mettlach, .5L, 2402, etched, courting of Siegfried, inlaid lid, $700-900.
c. Mettlach, .5L, 2520, etched, student and barmaid, inlaid lid, $550-750.
d. Mettlach, .5L, 2531, etched, monk with jug of beer, inlaid lid, $550-750.
e. Mettlach, .5L, 2580, etched, die Kannenburg stein, knight in castle, conical inlaid lid, $650-850.

f. Mettlach, 1.0L, 2582, etched, Jester stein, performing on table, in front of tavern, inlaid lid, $700-900.
g. Mettlach, .5L, 2583, etched, Egyptian stein, inlaid lid, $700-1000.
h. Mettlach, .5L, 2765, etched, Knight on White Horse stein, turret inlaid lid, $2000-2500.
. Mettlach, .5L, 2776, etched, Keeper of Wine Cellar stein, inlaid lid, $600-800.
. Mettlach, .5L, 2778, etched, Carnival stein, carnival player and drinkers, inlaid lid, $1100-1400.

a. Mettlach, .5L, 2798, etched, Richard Wagner, inlaid lid, $600-800.

b. Mettlach, .5L, 2808, etched, bowling, inlaid lid, $500-650.

c. Mettlach, .5L, 2811, etched, Art Nouveau, inlaid lid, $400-500.

d. Mettlach, .3L, 2833E, etched, soldiers in forest in winter, inlaid lid, $300-400.

e. Mettlach, .3L, 2833F, etched, students drinking, inlaid lid, $300-400.

f. Mettlach, .5L, 2886, etched, five politicians seated at table, inlaid lid, $500-650.

g. Mettlach, .5L, 2935, etched, Art Nouveau, inlaid lid, $500-700.

h. Mettlach, .5L, 2938, etched, hunter with his dog, inlaid lid, $550-750.

i. Mettlach, .5L, 2959, etched, boy bowling, inlaid lid, $400-500.

j. Mettlach, .5L, 2994, etched, Art Nouveau, inlaid lid, $600-800.

a. Mettlach, .5L, 3043, etched & glazed, Munich stein, inlaid lid, $1200-1600.
b. Mettlach, .5L, 3089, etched, Diogenes stein, Diogenes sitting in barrel, inlaid lid, $700-900.
c. Mettlach, .5L, 3092, etched, Whiskey Man stein, inlaid lid, $700-900.
d. Mettlach, .5L, 3237, etched, Art Nouveau, blue and white, inlaid lid, $400-550.

e. Mettlach, .5L, 2530, cameo, Boar Hunt stein, inlaid lid, $600-800.
f. Mettlach, .3L, 2628, cameo, three panels, bowling and tavern scenes, inlaid lid, $400-500.
g. Mettlach, .5L, 2628, cameo, three panels, bowling and tavern scenes, inlaid lid, $600-800.
h. Mettlach, .5L, 2652, cameo, Rodenstein stein, three panels, conical inlaid lid, $650-850.
i. Mettlach, 1.0L, 2949, cameo, Munich Child and coat of arms, pewter lid, $700-1000.

a. Mettlach, .5L, 626(280), PUG, tavern scene, pewter lid, $200-300.

b. Mettlach, .5L, 702(1909), PUG, high-spirited parade, pewter lid, $250-350.

c. Mettlach, .5L, 726(1909), PUG, steins with legs, filling up at tap, pewter lid, $275-375.

d. Mettlach, .5L, 732(1909), PUG, owl shining lantern on drunken man, pewter lid, $250-350.

e. Mettlach, .5L, 1008(1909), PUG, singer with harp, pewter lid, $275-375.

f. Mettlach, .25L, 957(2181), PUG, barmaid, pewter lid, $150-250.

g. Mettlach, .25L, 959(2177), PUG, knight resting, pewter lid, $150-250.

h. Mettlach, .25L, 961(2179), PUG, gnomes under bottle, pewter lid, $150-250.

i. Mettlach, .25L, 962(2179), PUG, gnomes drinking, pewter lid, $150-250.

j. Mettlach, .5L, 1038(1909), PUG, frogs drinking, pewter lid, $450-600.

a. Mettlach, .5L, 1074(1909), PUG, peasant smoking pipe, pewter lid, $275-375.
b. Mettlach, .5L, 1110(1909), PUG, soldiers drinking, pewter lid, $300-400.
c. Mettlach, .5L, 1143(1909), PUG, men drinking, pewter lid, $300-400.
d. Mettlach, .5L, 1212(1909), PUG, man bowling, pewter lid, $250-350.
e. Mettlach, .5L, 1218(1526), PUG, scene of Heidelberg, pewter lid, $250-350.

f. Mettlach, 1.0L, 24, relief, figures in four separate panels, inlaid lid, $300-400.
g. Mettlach, .25L, 171, relief, figures representing activity during twelve months, blue or terra cotta background, inlaid lid, $100-150.
h. Mettlach, .5L, 228, relief, four panels, musical scenes, blue or brown background, inlaid lid, $250-350.
i. Mettlach, .5L, 675, relief, barrel shape, inlaid lid, $100-150.
j. Mettlach, 1.0L, 1005, relief, brown background, inlaid lid, $300-400.

a.   Mettlach, .5L, 1028, relief, background like tree trunk, man carrying hay, with woman, inlaid lid, $100-150.
b.   Mettlach, .25L, 1266, relief, drinking scenes, blue, terra cotta or gray background, inlaid lid, $100-150.
c.   Mettlach, .25L, 1745, relief, leaves and scroll design, inlaid lid, $100-150.
d.   Mettlach, .5L, 2182, relief, bowling scene, blue or terra cotta background, inlaid lid, $150-250.
e.   Mettlach, .3L, 2211, relief, bowling scene, blue or terra cotta background, inlaid lid, $100-150.

f.   Mettlach, .5L, 2263, relief, terra cotta background, inlaid lid, $300-400.
g.   Mettlach, .5L, 2556, relief, drinking scenes, three panels, inlaid lid, $250-350.
h.   Mettlach, 1.0L, 1643, tapestry, student drinking, pewter lid, $400-500.
i.   Mettlach, 1.0L, 1644, tapestry, man smoking, pewter lid, $300-400.
j.   Mettlach, .5L, 1645, tapestry, man with guitar and stein, pewter lid, $300-400.

a. Mettlach, .5L, 1068, mosaic, geometric design, inlaid lid, $500-700.
b. Mettlach, .5L, 1130, mosaic, geometric design, inlaid lid, $400-600.
c. Mettlach, .5L, 1191, mosaic, geometric design, inlaid lid, $400-600.
d. Mettlach, .25L, 1828, mosaic, geometric design, inlaid lid, $300-450.
e. Mettlach, .5L, 2789/6145, Rookwood type, man smoking pipe and drinking, pewter lid, $350-475.

f. Mettlach, .5L, 5013, faience type, München, pewter lid, $550-750.
g. Mettlach, 1.0L, 5019, faience type, pewter lid, $800-1100.
h. Mettlach, 1.0L, 5023, faience type, pewter lid, $2000-2500.
i. Mettlach, .5L, 5190, Delft type, pewter lid, $450-600.
j. Mettlach, .3L, 5191, Delft type, pewter lid, $400-500.

a. Mettlach, 2.3L, 1028, relief, background like tree trunk, man carrying hay, inlaid lid, $250-350.

b. Mettlach, 2.0L, 1737, relief, wheat design, inlaid lid, $200-300.

c. Mettlach 1.4L, 1734, etched, lovers, inlaid lid, $1100-1400.

d. Mettlach, 1.5L, 2065, etched, man and barmaid, inlaid lid, $1100-1400.

e. Mettlach, 3.2L, 2076, relief, coat of arms, master to 2077, inlaid lid, $250-375.

f. Mettlach, 4.4L, 2098, mosaic, floral design, master to 2099, inlaid lid, $450-650.

g. Mettlach, 2.75L, 2428, etched, tavern scenes, inlaid lid, $1000-1300.

h. Mettlach, 2.25L, 1012(2261), PUG, drinking scene, pewter lid, $500-650.

12. Other Etched Ceramics

The success of the Villeroy & Boch, Mettlach, etched steins attracted the interest of many other stein factories. The first Mettlach steins to use the inlaid-clay-etched technique were made around 1879. They immediately captured the Grand Prizes at the world trade fairs. This Mettlach technique was often advertised as secret, which added to the steins' public appeal, and thus stimulated the interest of other manufacturers.

12.1 History of Etched Ceramics

It is not known which competitor was first to follow Mettlach's lead, but by about 1890, etched steins from other companies were available. In fact, by 1900, Simon Peter Gerz, Marzi & Remy, J.W. Remy, A.J. Thewalt, Merkelbach & Wick, Matthias Girmscheid, and Hauber & Reuther all made etched steins.

12.2 Production and Collecting

The factories mentioned above had one thing in common: they produced etched steins in the same way, and it was not the Mettlach method. Rather than painting the colored slips into molds, as was done at Villeroy & Boch, decorators at the other factories painted the colored slips directly onto the outside of molded steins. The resulting products lack the uniformity, clarity, and soft finish of the Mettlach examples.

It was obviously easier to decorate these steins from the outside, but not all manufacturers were looking to capture the low end of the etched stein market.

In fact, Hauber & Reuther's original price lists show etched steins at higher prices than those sold by Mettlach. Apparently, some manufacturers were trying to appeal to the special order market.

The Steinzeugwerke, literally Stoneware Works, was a consortium of several factories that banded together from around 1900 until about 1910. The major factories that joined the Steinzeugwerke were Reinhold Merkelbach, Simon Peter Gerz, and Marzi & Remy, all from the Höhr-Grenzhausen area. Collective marketing seems to have been the primary purpose of the consortium.

The Steinzeugwerke had no separate trademark, and the only way its members have been identified has been by examining a catalog illustrating their steins. This catalog shows that it was possible to purchase these steins plain, blue or brown saltglazed, sparsely painted, or fully painted.

Many steins (including both etched and character) that are illustrated in catalogs have not as yet been found, making the search for steins an exciting pastime, as well as attesting to the large number of steins that were damaged during the two World Wars.

The marks and dates of factories producing etched steins are shown at the end of Section 2. Books and articles about individual factories are listed in the Bibliography, Section 20.

12.3 Evaluation Information

Values of these steins have fluctuated over the last ten years, experiencing both ups and downs in some categories. The net trends show only moderate changes for most manufacturers.

a.   Stoneware, .5L, Marzi & Remy, #1765, c.1900, inlaid lid, $250-400.

b.   Stoneware, .5L, Marzi & Remy, #1764, c.1900, inlaid lid, $250-400.

c.   Stoneware, .5L, Marzi & Remy, #1615, c.1900, inlaid lid, $200-300.

d.   Stoneware, .5L, Marzi & Remy, #1768, c.1900, inlaid lid, $250-400.

e.   Stoneware, .5L, Marzi & Remy, #1653, c.1900, inlaid lid, $250-400.

f.   Stoneware, .5L, Marzi & Remy, #1620, c.1900, inlaid lid, $250-400.

g.   Stoneware, .5L, Marzi & Remy, #1614, c.1900, inlaid lid, $250-400.

h.   Stoneware, .5L, Marzi & Remy, #1622, c.1900, inlaid lid, $250-400.

i.   Stoneware, .5L, Marzi & Remy, #1767, c.1900, inlaid lid, $250-400.

j.   Stoneware, .5L, Marzi & Remy, #1613, c.1900, inlaid lid, $250-400.

a.   Stoneware, 1.0L, Marzi & Remy, #1619, c.1900, inlaid lid, $300-500.
b.   Stoneware, 1.0L, Marzi & Remy, #1620, c.1900, inlaid lid, $300-500.
c.   Stoneware, 1.0L, Marzi & Remy, #1629, c.1900, inlaid lid, $250-400.
d.   Stoneware, 1.0L, Marzi & Remy, #1618, c.1900, inlaid lid, $250-400.
e.   Stoneware, .5L, Marzi & Remy, #1644, handpainted scene of Heidelberg, c.1900, pewter lid, $250-350.

f.   Stoneware, .5L, Marzi & Remy, #1637, c.1900, inlaid lid, $300-450.
g.   Stoneware, .5L, Marzi & Remy, #1688, c.1900, inlaid lid, $300-450.
h.   Stoneware, .5L, Marzi & Remy, #6044, *Souvenir of Florida* (St. Augustine), c.1900, inlaid lid, $200-300.
i.   Stoneware, .5L, Marzi & Remy, #972, c.1900, inlaid lid, $250-400.
j.   Stoneware, .5L, Marzi & Remy, #1898, c.1900, inlaid lid, $300-450.

a. Stoneware, .5L, Marzi & Remy, #1644, handpainted scene, c.1900, pewter lid, $200-350.
b. Stoneware, .5L, Marzi & Remy, #1635, c.1900, inlaid lid, $150-250.
c. Stoneware, .5L, Marzi & Remy, #1636, c.1900, inlaid lid, $100-200.
d. Stoneware, .5L, Marzi & Remy, #1637, c.1900, inlaid lid, $100-200.
e. Pottery, .5L, Gerz, #1314, card game, c.1900, inlaid lid, $300-400.

f. Pottery, .4L, Gerz, #1345BI, sleigh ride, c.1900, inlaid lid, $200-300.
g. Pottery, .4L, Gerz, #1209, c.1900, inlaid lid, $100-200.
h. Pottery, .5L, Gerz, #1219, c.1900, pewter lid, $100-200.
i. Pottery, .3L, Gerz, #1214B, c.1900, inlaid lid, $100-200.
j. Pottery, .5L, Gerz, #1220, c.1900, inlaid lid, $150-250.

a. Pottery, .5L, Gerz, #1423, *Parsival Acts 1, 2, and 3,* c.1900, inlaid lid, $250-400.
b. Pottery, .5L, Gerz, #1428, *Siegfried,* c.1900, inlaid lid, $250-400.
c. Pottery, .5L, Gerz, #1421, *Siegfried,* c.1900, inlaid lid, $250-400.
d. Pottery, .5L, Gerz, #1422, *Lohengrin,* c.1900, inlaid lid, $250-400.
e. Pottery, .5L, Gerz, #1420, *Brünehilde,* c.1900, inlaid lid, $250-400.

f. Pottery, .5L, Gerz, #1216, c.1900, pewter lid, $200-300.
g. Pottery, .5L, Gerz, #1265, hunter and dogs, c.1900, pewter lid, $200-300.
h. Pottery, .5L, Gerz, #1254, c.1900, inlaid lid, $250-400.
. Pottery, .5L, Gerz, #1210, c.1900, inlaid lid, $250-400.
. Pottery, .5L, Gerz, #265, c.1900, inlaid lid, $250-400.

a.   Pottery, 1.0L, Gerz, #1215, c.1900, inlaid lid, $250-400.
b.   Pottery, 1.0L, Gerz, #1318, c.1900, inlaid lid, $250-400.
c.   Pottery, 1.0L, Gerz, #1388, c.1900, inlaid lid, $250-400.
d.   Pottery, 1.0L, Gerz, #1389, c.1900, inlaid lid, $250-400.
e.   Pottery, 1.0L, Gerz, #1326, c.1900, inlaid lid, $250-400.

f.   Pottery, 1.0L, Gerz, #1334, c.1900, pewter lid, $200-300.
g.   Pottery, 1.0L, Gerz, #1210, c.1900, inlaid lid, $250-400.
h.   Pottery, 1.0L, Gerz, #1709, c.1900, pewter lid, $250-400.
i.   Pottery, .5L, J.W. Remy, #1221, c.1900, inlaid lid, $125-225.
j.   Pottery, .5L, J.W. Remy, #1493, c.1900, inlaid lid, $200-300.

a. Pottery, .4L, J.W. Remy, #907, c.1900, inlaid lid, $100-200.
b. Pottery, .5L, J.W. Remy, #1291, c.1900, inlaid lid, $100-200.
c. Pottery, .5L, J.W. Remy, #1294, c.1900, inlaid lid, $100-200.
d. Pottery, .4L, J.W. Remy, #1334, c.1900, inlaid lid, $100-200.
e. Pottery, .5L, J.W. Remy, #883, c.1900, inlaid lid, $100-200.

f. Pottery, 1.0L, J.W. Remy, #1333, c.1900, inlaid lid, $150-250.
g. Pottery, 1.0L, J.W. Remy, #1222, c.1900, inlaid lid, $150-250.
h. Pottery, .5L, J.W. Remy, #829, c.1900, inlaid lid, $125-225.
i. Pottery, .5L, J.W. Remy, #828, c.1900, inlaid lid, $125-225.
j. Pottery, .5L, J.W. Remy, #1496, c.1900, inlaid lid, $200-300.

a.   Pottery, .5L, J.W. Remy, #1227, c.1900, inlaid lid, $125-225.
b.   Pottery, .5L, TP mark (Paulus & Thewalt), #1227, same mold as preceding stein, c.1900, inlaid lid, $125-225.
c.   Pottery, .5L, J.W. Remy, #884, c.1900, inlaid lid, $125-225.
d.   Pottery, .5L, J.W. Remy, #1409, c.1900, inlaid lid, $200-300.
e.   Pottery, .5L, J.W. Remy, #11041, c.1900, inlaid lid, $400-500.

f.   Pottery, .5L, J.W. Remy, #1394, Freshy, c.1900, inlaid lid, $250-400.
g.   Pottery, .5L, J.W. Remy, #1395, Soph, c.1900, inlaid lid, $300-450.
h.   Pottery, .5L, J.W. Remy, #1393, Junior, c.1900, inlaid lid, $250-400.
i.   Pottery, .5L, J.W. Remy, #1396, Senior, c.1900, inlaid lid, $300-450.
j.   Pottery, .3L, Paulus & Thewalt, #1434, c.1900, inlaid lid, $100-200.

a. Pottery, .5L, Paulus & Thewalt, #1227, c.1900, inlaid lid, $150-250.
b. Pottery, .5L, Paulus & Thewalt, #1218, c.1900, inlaid lid, $150-250.
c. Pottery, .5L, Paulus & Thewalt, #1410, c.1900, inlaid lid, $200-350.
d. Pottery, .5L, Paulus & Thewalt, #954, c.1900, inlaid lid, $300-450.
e. Pottery, 1.0L, Paulus & Thewalt, #1411, c.1900, inlaid lid, $250-400.

f. Pottery, .5L, Hauber & Reuther, #421, c.1900, pewter lid, $250-350.
g. Pottery, .5L, Hauber & Reuther, #436, c.1900, pewter lid, $250-350.
h. Pottery, .5L, Hauber & Reuther, #426, c.1900, pewter lid, $300-400.
i. Pottery, .5L, Hauber & Reuther, #420, c.1900, pewter lid, $300-400.
j. Pottery, .5L, Hauber & Reuther, #528, c.1900, pewter lid, $300-400.

a.   Pottery, .5L, Hauber & Reuther, #405, c.1900, inlaid lid, $300-400.

b.   Pottery, .5L, Hauber & Reuther, #444, c.1900, inlaid lid, $300-400.

c.   Pottery, .5L, Hauber & Reuther, #528, c.1900, inlaid lid, $300-400.

d.   Pottery, .5L, Hauber & Reuther, #476, c.1900, inlaid lid, $300-400.

e.   Pottery, .5L, Hauber & Reuther, #443, c.1900, pewter lid, $250-350.

f.   Pottery, .5L, Hauber & Reuther, #429, c.1900, pewter lid, $300-400.

g.   Pottery, .5L, Hauber & Reuther, #439, c.1900, pewter lid, $300-400.

h.   Pottery, .5L, Hauber & Reuther, #417, Lohengrin, c.1900, pewter lid, $300-400.

i.   Pottery, .5L, Hauber & Reuther, #418, Lohengrin, c.1900, pewter lid, $300-400.

j.   Pottery, .5L, Hauber & Reuther, #441, c.1900, pewter lid, $250-350.

a. Pottery, .5L, Hauber & Reuther, #427, c.1900, pewter lid, $250-350.
b. Pottery, .5L, Hauber & Reuther, #411, c.1900, pewter lid, $250-350.
c. Pottery, .5L, Hauber & Reuther, #437, c.1900, pewter lid, $250-350.
d. Pottery, .5L, Hauber & Reuther, #494, c.1900, pewter lid, $250-350.
e. Pottery, .5L, Hauber & Reuther, #164, c.1900, pewter lid, $250-350.

f. Pottery, .5L, Hauber & Reuther, #175, c.1900, pewter lid, $200-300.
g. Pottery, .5L, Hauber & Reuther, #489, c.1900, pewter lid, $250-350.
h. Pottery, .5L, Hauber & Reuther, #428, c.1900, pewter lid, $250-350.
i. Pottery, .5L, Hauber & Reuther, #413, c.1900, pewter lid, $250-350.
j. Pottery, .5L, Hauber & Reuther, #161, c.1900, pewter lid, $250-350.

a.   Pottery, .5L, Hauber & Reuther, #407, c.1900, pewter lid, $300-400.
b.   Pottery, .5L, Hauber & Reuther, #425, c.1900, pewter lid, $250-350.
c.   Pottery, .5L, Hauber & Reuther, #425, c.1900, pewter lid, $250-350.
d.   Pottery, .5L, Hauber & Reuther, #482, c.1900, pewter lid, $150-250.

e.   Pottery, .5L, Hauber & Reuther, #424, *Heidelberg,* c.1900, pewter lid, $250-350.
f.   Pottery, .5L, Hauber & Reuther, #531, *Nürnberg,* c.1900, pewter lid, $250-350.
g.   Pottery, .5L, Hauber & Reuther, #423, *München,* c.1900, pewter lid, $250-350.
h.   Pottery, .5L, Hauber & Reuther, #408, c.1900, pewter lid, $250-350.
i.   Pottery, .5L, Hauber & Reuther, #203, c.1900, pewter lid with relief scene of *Fraü Helvetia,* $250-350.

a. Pottery, .5L, Hauber & Reuther, #1001, golf, c.1900, pewter lid, $2000-2500.
b. Pottery, .5L, Hauber & Reuther, #1002, tennis, c.1900, pewter lid, $600-900.
c. Pottery, .5L, Hauber & Reuther, #1003, rowing, c.1900, pewter lid, $350-500.
d. Pottery, .5L, Hauber & Reuther, #1004, football, c.1900, pewter lid, $400-600.
e. Pottery, .5L, Hauber & Reuther, #1005, jockey, c.1900, pewter lid, $400-600.

f. Pottery, .5L, Hauber & Reuther, #520, c.1900, pewter lid, $300-400.
g. Pottery, .5L, Hauber & Reuther, #166, c.1900, pewter lid, $600-900.
h. Pottery, .5L, Hauber & Reuther, #438, c.1900, pewter lid, $500-750.
i. Pottery, .5L, Hauber & Reuther, #466, c.1900, pewter lid, $250-350.
j. Pottery, .5L, Hauber & Reuther, #522, c.1900, pewter lid, $250-350.

a. Pottery, .5L, Hauber & Reuther, #510, c.1900, pewter lid, $250-350.
b. Pottery, .5L, Hauber & Reuther, #156, c.1900, pewter lid, $200-300.
c. Pottery, .5L, Hauber & Reuther, #159, c.1900, pewter lid, $100-200.
d. Pottery, .25L, Hauber & Reuther, #502, c.1900, pewter lid, $150-250.
e. Pottery, .25L, Hauber & Reuther, #500, c.1900, pewter lid, $150-250.

f. Stoneware, .5L, Hauber & Reuther, #157, c.1900, pewter lid, $100-200.
g. Stoneware, .5L, Hauber & Reuther, #158, c.1900, pewter lid, $100-200.
h. Stoneware, .5L, Hauber & Reuther, #163, c.1900, pewter lid, $100-200.
i. Stoneware, .5L, Hauber & Reuther, #167, c.1900, pewter lid, $100-200.
j. Stoneware, .5L, Hauber & Reuther, #162, c.1900, pewter lid, $100-200.

a. Porcelain, .5L, Hauber & Reuther, #214, c.1900, pewter lid, $200-300.
b. Porcelain, .5L, Hauber & Reuther, #216, c.1900, pewter lid, $100-200.
c. Porcelain, .5L, Hauber & Reuther, #160, c.1900, pewter lid, $200-300.
d. Porcelain, .5L, Hauber & Reuther, #168, c.1900, pewter lid, $100-200.
e. Porcelain, .5L, Hauber & Reuther, #414, c.1900, pewter lid, $150-250.

f. Pottery, 1.0L, Hauber & Reuther, #431, c.1900, pewter lid, $300-400.
g. Pottery, 1.0L, Hauber & Reuther, #514, c.1900, pewter lid, $300-400.
h. Pottery, 1.0L, Hauber & Reuther, #526, c.1900, pewter lid, $500-700.
i. Pottery, .5L, Merkelbach & Wick, #3002B, c.1900, pewter lid, $150-250.
j. Pottery, 1.0L, Merkelbach & Wick, c.1900, pewter lid, $200-300.

a.   Pottery, .5L, Merkelbach & Wick, #1175A, c.1900, pewter lid, $150-250.
b.   Pottery, .5L, Merkelbach & Wick, #1175B, c.1900, pewter lid, $150-250.
c.   Pottery, .5L, Merkelbach & Wick, #1171, c.1900, pewter lid, $150-250.
d.   Pottery, .5L, Merkelbach & Wick, #3002E, c.1900, pewter lid, $150-250.
e.   Pottery, .5L, Merkelbach & Wick, #3002F, c.1900, pewter lid, $150-250.

f.   Pottery, .5L, unmarked, #1693, c.1900, pewter lid, $100-200.
g.   Pottery, .5L, unmarked, #820, signed KB, *Heidelberg* scene, c.1900, inlaid lid, $250-400.
h.   Pottery, 1.0L, unmarked, #335, c.1900, inlaid lid, $200-300.
i.   Pottery, .5L, unmarked, Universities: Pennsylvania, Harvard, Princeton, Cornell, Yale & Columbia, c.1900, pewter lid, $500-700.
j.   Pottery, 1.0L, unmarked, #1138, *In Treue fest, 3. Pol. Rev. Berlin,* c. 1900, metal lid, $250-400.

a. Pottery, .5L, A.J. Thewalt, #474, c.1900, inlaid lid, $100-200.
b. Pottery, 1.0L, A.J. Thewalt, #407, c.1900, inlaid lid, $125-225.
c. Pottery, .5L, Reinhold Hanke, #1263, c.1900, inlaid lid, $100-200.
d. Pottery, .5L, Reinhold Merkelbach, #1272, c.1900, pewter lid, $150-250.
e. Stoneware, 1.0L, Matthias Girmscheid, #1087A, c.1900, stoneware lid, $150-250.

f. Stoneware, 1.0L, Matthias Girmscheid, #1088, c.1900, pewter lid, $100-200.
g. Stoneware, .5L, Matthias Girmscheid, #1085, c.1900, stoneware lid, $150-250.
h. Stoneware, .5L, Matthias Girmscheid, #963, c.1900, pewter lid, $100-200.
i. Stoneware, .5L, Matthias Girmscheid, #843, c.1900, pewter lid, $100-200.
j. Stoneware, .5L, Matthias Girmscheid, #1088, same scene as Mettlach 2599, c.1900, pewter lid, $150-250.

a.   Pottery, .5L, unmarked, #1453, bicycles, c.1900, inlaid lid, $450-600.
b.   Pottery, .5L, unmarked, #1512, duck run over by car, early 1900s, inlaid lid, $200-300.
c.   Pottery, .5L, unmarked, #1513, speeding car, early 1900s, inlaid lid, $200-300.
d.   Pottery, .5L, unmarked, #155, c.1900, pewter lid, $100-200.
e.   Pottery, 1.0L, unmarked, #1284, c.1900, inlaid lid, $125-225.

f.   Pottery, .5L, unmarked, c.1900, inlaid lid, $100-200.
g.   Pottery, .5L, unmarked, c.1900, inlaid lid, $150-250.
h.   Pottery, .5L, unmarked, c.1900, pewter lid, $100-200.
i.   Pottery, .5L, Steinzeugwerke, #1720, signed R.D., early 1900s, inlaid lid, $100-200.
j.   Pottery, 1.0L, Steinzeugwerke, #1851, early 1900s, inlaid lid, $100-200.

a. Pottery, .5L, unmarked, #848, bawdy house scene, c.1900, inlaid lid, $300-500.
b. Pottery, .5L, unmarked, #849, bawdy house scene, c.1900, inlaid lid, $300-500.
c. Pottery, .5L, unmarked, #722, c.1900, inlaid lid, $200-300.
d. Pottery, .5L, unmarked, signed GK, c.1900, inlaid lid, $150-250.
e. Pottery, 1.0L, unmarked, #1666, c.1900, inlaid lid, $200-300.

f. Pottery, .5L, unmarked, c.1900, inlaid lid, $100-200.
g. Pottery, .5L, unmarked, #1013, c.1900, inlaid lid, $100-200.
h. Pottery, .5L, unmarked, #334, c.1900, inlaid lid, $200-300.
i. Pottery, .5L, unmarked, #327, c.1900, inlaid lid, $200-300.
j. Pottery, .3L, unmarked, c.1900, inlaid lid, $150-250.

a.   Pottery, .3L, Coblenz Rheinland, #1360, c.1900, inlaid lid, $100-200.

b.   Pottery, .5L, Coblenz Rheinland, #1757, c.1900, inlaid lid, $125-225.

c.   Pottery, .5L, Coblenz Rheinland, #1507, c.1900, inlaid lid, $300-450.

d.   Pottery, .5L, unmarked, #1583, *An Exciting Moment,* c.1900, inlaid lid, $100-200.

e.   Pottery, .5L, unmarked, #1581, c.1900, pewter lid, $100-200.

f.   Pottery, .5L, unmarked, #1555, c.1900, pewter lid, $100-200.

g.   Pottery, .5L, unmarked, #1553, c.1900, pewter lid, $100-200.

h.   Pottery, .5L, unmarked, #1551, c.1900, pewter lid, $100-200.

i.   Pottery, .5L, unmarked, #1514, c.1900, pewter lid, $150-250.

j.   Pottery, .5L, unmarked, #768, c.1900, pewter lid, $125-225.

a. Stoneware, 3.0L, Marzi & Remy, #1682, c.1900, inlaid lid, $400-600.
b. Stoneware, 1.5L, Marzi & Remy, #1518, c.1900, inlaid lid, $350-550.
c. Stoneware, 3.0L, Marzi & Remy, #1681, c.1900, inlaid lid, $400-600.
d. Pottery, 2.0L, Merkelbach & Wick, #3002, c.1900, pewter lid, $400-600.

e. Pottery, 2.0L, Merkelbach & Wick, #3002, c.1900, inlaid lid, $200-300.
f. Pottery, 1.5L, Merkelbach & Wick, #3002, c.1900, inlaid lid, $150-250.

Opposite page top:

a. Pottery, 3.0L, A.J. Thewalt, #391, c.1900, pewter lid, $250-350.
b. Pottery, 3.0L, A.J. Thewalt, #411, c.1900, pewter lid, $250-350.
c. Pottery, 1.0L, Steinzeugwerke, #1664, early 1900s, inlaid lid, $150-250.
d. Pottery, 1.5L, Steinzeugwerke, #1316, early 1900s, inlaid lid, $200-300.

a. Pottery, 1.5L, unmarked, c.1900, inlaid lid, $250-350.
b   Pottery, 2.0L, unmarked, #1601, c.1900, inlaid lid, $250-400.
c. Stoneware, 2.0L, Matthias Girmscheid, #170, c.1900, stoneware lid, $300-500.
d. Stoneware, 2.0L, Matthias Girmscheid, #1089, c.1900, stoneware lid, $300-450.

Opposite page bottom:

e. Pottery, 2.0L, unmarked, #1612, c.1900, inlaid lid, $300-450.
f. Pottery, 2.0L, unmarked, #1638, c.1900, pewter lid, $300-450.
g. Pottery, 2.0L, unmarked, c.1900, inlaid lid, $300-450.
h. Pottery, 1.5L, unmarked, signed GK, c.1900, inlaid lid, $250-350.

Opposite page top:
a. Pottery, 2.0L, J.W. Remy, #962, c.1900, inlaid lid, $300-450.
b. Pottery, 3.0L, J.W. Remy, #848, c.1900, inlaid lid, $400-600.
c. Pottery, 1.5L, J.W. Remy, #846, c.1900, inlaid lid, $250-400.
d. Pottery, 2.0L, J.W. Remy, #961, c.1900, inlaid lid, $250-400.

a. Pottery, 3.0L, Gerz, # 275A, c.1900, inlaid lid, $250-400.
b. Pottery, 2.0L, Gerz, #1235, c.1900, inlaid lid, $300-450.
c. Pottery, 2.0L, Gerz, #1383, c.1900, inlaid lid, $300-450.
d. Pottery, 2.0L, Gerz, #1222A, c.1900, inlaid lid, $300-450.

Opposite page bottom:
e. Pottery, 1.5L, J.W. Remy, #1339, c.1900, inlaid lid, $250-400.
f. Pottery, 2.0L, J.W. Remy, #961, c.1900, inlaid lid, $250-400.
g. Pottery, 1.5L, J.W. Remy, #1397, card game, c.1900, inlaid lid, $400-600.
h. Pottery, 2.0L, TP mark (Paulus & Thewalt), #1223, c.1900, pewter lid, $250-400.

a.   Pottery, 2.0L, Hauber & Reuther, #433, c.1900, pewter lid, $500-700.

b.   Pottery, 2.0L, Hauber & Reuther, #434, c.1900, pewter lid, $450-600.

c.   Pottery, 2.0L, Hauber & Reuther, #435, c.1900, pewter lid, $450-600.

13. Occupational

It is understandable that in previous centuries many people chose to purchase steins that depicted their particular occupations. In fact, because that subject matter became so popular, there are those who now specialize in collecting these so-called occupational steins.

13.1 History of Occupational Steins

There is a predictable pattern to the frequency with which certain occupations are depicted on steins. The most commonly seen are merchants, tradesmen, public servants, and professionals, including tailors, butchers, bakers, brewers, shoemakers, blacksmiths, locksmiths, teamsters, machinists, dairy workers, farmers, carpenters, firemen, and postmen.

Three factors perhaps best explain why certain occupations were rarely depicted:

1. There may have been too little money to purchase a stein or too little pride in being associated with some occupations, as those of servants, gravediggers, or street crews.

2. Prudence may have played a role, such as for those examples associated with teachers, clergy, or judges.

3. Some occupations would obviously have had very few members: goldsmiths, streetcar operators, or circus performers.

The representation of the occupation is usually obvious, even to the untrained modern observer. The decoration on the body usually shows the worker in action or in uniform, or the products or tools of his occupation are pictured. Some tools that may at first be difficult to recognize are a brewer's bucket, stirrer, and scoop in a barrel, or a tailor's scissors and divider. Oxheads and pretzels are occasionally used rather casually as symbols of butchers and bakers, respectively. Steins in the form of books or sets of books often indicate professional occupations that can be identified by examining the titles of the books.

The fact that a stein belongs to the occupational category may be overlooked when a famous craftsman is depicted. The most common examples are those featuring the poet Hans Sachs—a shoemaker—or the Hapsburg double-headed eagle, which was the symbol of the first printer, Johann Gutenberg.

13.2 Collecting Occupational Steins

Occupational steins can be found from all eras and in all materials (with the possible exception of ivory), from the incised stoneware of the 1600s to glass from the 1800s and porcelain from the 1900s. Occupational stein collectors, however, rarely concentrate on acquiring the scarcer forms unless the collector's own occupation is depicted. The most commonly collected occupationals are those with steepled pewter lids and porcelain or stoneware bodies. These were made around 1900 and are shown on the following pages.

13.3 Evaluation Information

Price trends in the past ten years have been mostly upward for occupational steins. Most rare occupational steins have increased in value significantly. The more common occupational steins have been steady or are increasing only slightly.

a.   Cheesemaker, .5L, porcelain, lithophane, c.1900, pewter lid, $300-450.

b.   Cheesemaker, .5L, porcelain, lithophane, c.1900, pewter lid, $300-450.

c.   Chimney sweeper, .5L, porcelain, lithophane, dated 1929, pewter lid, $400-550.

d.   Butcher, .5L, porcelain, lithophane, c.1900, pewter lid, $250-350.

e.   Butcher, .5L, porcelain, lithophane, c.1900, pewter lid, $300-450.

f.   Newspaper deliverer, 1.0L, porcelain, lithophane, dated 1906, pewter lid, $1200-1600.

g.   Brewmaster, .5L, porcelain, lithophane, c.1900, pewter lid, $300-450.

h.   Brewmaster, .5L, porcelain, lithophane, c.1900, pewter lid, $350-500.

i.   Beer Wagon Driver, .5L, porcelain, lithophane, c.1900, pewter lid, $400-600.

j.   Beer Wagon Driver, .5L, porcelain, lithophane, c.1900, pewter lid, $400-600.

a. Postman, 1.0L, stoneware, dated 1913, pewter lid, $400-600.
b. Railroad worker, 1.0L, stoneware, c.1900, pewter lid, $450-650.
c. Potter, .5L, porcelain, lithophane, c.1900, pewter lid, $800-1200.
d. Miner, .5L, porcelain, lithophane, c.1900, pewter lid, $500-700.
e. Machinist, .5L, pottery, c.1900, pewter lid, $350-500.

f. Farmer, .5L, porcelain, lithophane, c.1900, pewter lid, $300-450.
g. Farmer, .5L, porcelain, lithophane, c.1900, pewter lid, $300-450.
h. Dairy farmer, .5L, porcelain, lithophane, c.1900, pewter lid, $300-450.
i. Farmer, .5L, porcelain, lithophane, c.1900, pewter lid, $300-450.
j. Horse trader, .5L, porcelain, lithophane, c.1900, pewter lid, $700-1000.

a. Miller, .5L, porcelain, lithophane, c.1900, pewter lid, $250-400.
b. Miller, .5L, porcelain, lithophane, c.1900, pewter lid, $250-400.
c. Miller, .5L, porcelain, lithophane, c.1900, pewter lid, $300-450.
d. Miller, .5L, porcelain, lithophane, c.1900, pewter lid, $300-450.
e. Musician, .5L, porcelain, lithophane, c.1900, pewter lid, $500-700.

f. Construction carpenter, .5L, porcelain, lithophane, c.1900, pewter lid, $300-450.
g. Construction carpenter, .5L, porcelain, lithophane, c.1900, pewter lid, $300-450.
h. Carpenter, .5L, stoneware, dated 1914, pewter lid, $300-450.
i. Locksmith, .5L, porcelain, lithophane, c.1900, pewter lid, $400-550.
j. Wheelwright, .5L, porcelain, lithophane, c.1900, pewter lid, $500-750.

a. Mason, .5L, porcelain, lithophane, c.1900, pewter lid, $450-600.
b. Mason, .5L, porcelain, lithophane, c.1900, pewter lid, $450-600.
c. Mason, .5L, porcelain, lithophane, c.1900, pewter lid, $350-500.
d. Glassworker, .5L, porcelain, lithophane, dated 1899, München, pewter lid, $800-1200.
e. Electrician, .5L, porcelain, lithophane, c.1900, pewter lid, $700-1000.

f. Blacksmith, .5L, porcelain, lithophane, dated 1910, pewter lid, $300-450.
g. Roof gutter installer, .5L, porcelain, lithophane, c.1900, pewter lid, $700-1000.
h. Farrier (graduate of veterinary college), .5L, porcelain, lithophane, dated 1903, prism lid, $500-700.
i. Barrel maker, .5L, porcelain, lithophane, dated 1910, pewter lid, $300-450.
j. Coach driver, .5L, porcelain, lithophane, dated 1910, pewter lid, $300-450.

a. Hotel concierge, .5L, porcelain, lithophane, *Hotel Glocke & Krone,* c.1900, pewter lid, $1000-1400.

b. Hotel bellhop, .5L, porcelain, lithophane, *Hotel Bäyer Hof,* c.1900, pewter lid, $1000-1400.

c. Fireman, .5L, porcelain, lithophane, c.1900, pewter lid, $300-450.

d. Sulky race driver, .5L, porcelain, lithophane, c.1900, pewter lid, $1200-1600.

14. Regimental

Steins have served as souvenirs of military service ever since the 1600s. The popularity of Regimental—or perhaps more accurately *Reservist*—steins has undergone somewhat of a revival since 1950. These modern-era souvenirs very often have no lid—and thus are mugs—and have simple decal-transferred decorations that make them less interesting to most collectors. The Regimental steins generating the most interest, outside of a few scattered between the 1860s and the 1940s, have been the large number of steins made as souvenirs of service in the German Imperial Armies in the period from 1890 to 1918. These are the steins briefly described and pictured in this section. Some excellent reference books about this specialty are available, and these are listed in Section 20.

14.1 History

With an upsurge of nationalism, pride in the success of the Franco-Prussian War, and a young, popular Emperor—Kaiser Wilhelm II—Germany began an expansion of its military system in 1888.

Military service was obligatory for men 17 to 45 years old, the primary exceptions being criminals or others without civil rights. The tour of active duty was three years for cavalry and navy and two years for the other services, with the exception of one year for certain professionals or volunteers. Upon completion of their active duty, these men became reservists. It was the reservists, and not the career soldiers, who ordered souvenirs such as steins, pipes, flasks, beakers, cups, and swords.

All reservists reported to their units in October and all graduated with the same class in September. The cost of Regimental steins, deducted automatically from wages, was very high, generally about two or three times the cost of a Mettlach stein. But the men had great pride in their class and unit; some cases have been recorded in which all the reservists in a given company ordered steins.

There were several branches of the Army: infantry, cavalry, artillery, *Pionier* (engineering), *Jäger* (hunter or rifleman), and the military train. There were also technical service units such as railway (*Eisenbahn*), telegraph, aviation, and airship (*Luftschiffer*). Volunteers from all of these units were provided to the colonial troops (*Schutztruppen*). The Navy was separate from the Army but had all the same types of souvenirs.

14.2 Production

Regimental steins were usually made of porcelain or pottery, though occasionally they were stoneware or, in some rare instances, glass or pewter. A few character Regimentals exist, such as skulls, sailors, or soldiers, but most Regimentals have vertical sides, a built-up base, and raised frieze bands above and below the main decorations.

The decorations were handpainted on early Regimentals. The later steins were primarily transfer decorated; that is, the designs were printed or silk screened onto a decal that was put on the body, touched up and augmented, then fired.

These decorations generally depict typical training scenes or portraits or, on occasion, combat scenes. The glazes on these steins include great varieties of color and brilliance that were made with formulas that have mostly been lost and cannot be easily duplicated.

Rosters, which are usually near the handle, are found on most steins, except the early Regimentals. It is possible that steins without rosters were ordered individually following discharge.

The pewterwork on most Regimental steins is both elaborate and meaningful.

Some of the varieties of lids include:

steeples	usually early date
fuses	field or foot artillery
prisms	usually southern Germany
over scenes	
flat relief	usually Bavarian or Saxony
crowns	used on some Bavarian units
helmets	used on infantry, artillery, or mounted
screw-off lids	mostly southern Germany
finial-type lid	all types of units

The finials are also informative:

field guns	artillery
locomotives	Eisenbahn
machine guns	machine gun companies
tschako	Jäger
horse and rider	most often cavalry but could be other types
eagle	mostly Prussian
seated or standing soldiers	almost any type of unit

Different types of thumblifts tend to be more indicative of the region of the unit, but occasionally they represent different types of units. Examples include:

eagle	Prussian
lion	Bavarian or Hessen
griffin	Baden
bird	Ulm
St. Barbara	artillery
St. Hubertus	Jäger
engineering implements	Pionier

Villeroy & Boch of Mettlach produced many Regimental steins for a great number of different units. They all have print under glaze (PUG) decoration, usually of several soldiers in a single scene. The lids are flat domes, as were used on most of the Mettlach PUG steins.

14.3 Collecting Regimentals

The strategy of many Regimental collectors is to seek the beautiful, the unusual, and the rare. Some of the more predictably rare Regimentals include those from units started after 1912, those in sizes other than .5L or 1.0L, and, of course, those for small or specialty units. Unfortunately, there is also a great deal of unpredictable rarity in Regimental steins; for instance, no steins have been found for some larger units. Collections and prices must be studied to understand Regimentals. The following picture section provides a very good start.

Reproductions of Regimentals, which have been manufactured at least since the 1950s, are generally made of porcelain and have finial-type lids. Reproductions can usually be identified by the presence of inaccurate historical information and by an examination of the decoration and lid. Since casual collectors may not be familiar with these factors, some production clues are described below.

Original Regimentals dated after 1900 almost never had tapered bodies; reproductions frequently do. Some reproductions have flimsy, stamped lids rather than carefully cast ones as on the originals. Reproductions often have an uncrowned, rampant lion for a thumblift. And finally, lithophanes of nudes, dancing girls, or girls in suggestive poses are definitely reproductions; originals usually have lithophanes of a soldier and girl, busts of King Ludwig or Kaiser Wilhelm II, or scenes of the home, nature, outdoors, or the military. Examples of new or reproduction Regimental steins can be found in Section 19.

14.4 Evaluation Information

The value range for the steins illustrated in this chapter reflects the normal price that can be expected from a knowledgeable dealer selling to a serious collector in the United States. Prices can vary in other countries. Prices can and will change in the United States to reflect both price changes in Germany and other countries, as well as changes in currency exchange rates.

Price trends in the past ten years have been mostly upward for Regimental steins. Many rare Regimental steins have increased in value significantly. The more common Regimental steins have also been increasing in value. There have been some inconsistencies with certain types of Regimentals advancing and then falling for an overall unchanged result.

Military Glossary

Abteilung, Abtl., Abt.:	detachment	Kürassier:	cuirassier
Armee-Korps:	Army Corps	Lazarett:	hospital
Armierungs:	armament	Lehr-:	instruction, training
Artillerie:	artillery	Lehrschmiede:	blacksmith school
Bäckerie:	bakery unit	Leib:	life or personal
Bataillon, Batl., Bat.:	battalion	Leib-Garde:	bodyguard unit
Batterie, Battr., Batt.:	artillery battery	Leichte:	light (weight)
Bayr.:	Bavarian	Luftschiffer:	airship
Bekleidung:	uniforms	Marine:	Naval
Bespannungs:	draft horse	Maschinengewehr:	machine gun
Betriebs:	railway traffic	Matrose:	seaman, lowest rank in
Bezirkskommando;	district headquarters		naval units
Chevauleger:	Bavarian light cavalry	Miltärbäcker:	military baker
Comp., Komp.:	company	Musketier:	musketeer, infantry soldier
Dragoner:	dragoon	Nr., No.:	number
Einjähr. Freiwilliger:	one-year volunteer	Pferde:	horse
Eisenbahn:	railway	Pferdewärter:	horse groom
Eskadron, Eskr., Esk.:	squadron	Pionier:	engineer or technician
Fahrer:	driver	Radfahrer:	bicyclist
Feld:	field	Regiment, Regt., Rgt.:	regiment
Flieger:	airman, lowest rank in air	Reiter:	rider
	force unit	Reservist:	soldier who served
Freiwilliger:	volunteer		minimum service time
Fusilier:	fusilier	Sanitätsgefreiter:	medical private or
Fuss:	foot		medical corporal
Garde:	guard	Schule:	school
Garnison:	garrison	Schütze:	sharpshooter
Gefreiter:	private first class	Schutztruppen:	colonial troops
Grenadier:	grenadier	Schwadron:	squadron (cavalry)
Handwerker:	tailor or shoemaker	Schwer:	heavy
Hornist:	bugler (foot troops)	See-Bataillon:	sea battalion,
Husar(en):	Hussar		Naval infantry, marines
Infanterie:	infantry	S.M.S.:	ship
Jäger:	rifleman, hunter	Tambour:	drummer
Jäger zu Pferde:	mounted rifleman	Train:	supply
Kanonier:	gunner	Trompeter:	trumpeter (mounted troops)
Kavallerie:	cavalry	Tschako:	head gear for
Kompagnie, Komp.:	company		Jäger regiments
Kraftfahr:	motor vehicle unit	Ulan(en):	lancer
Krankenträger:	stretcher bearer	Versuchs:	experimental or testing
Krankenwärter:	medical assistant, attendant	Verkehrstruppen:	technical troops

The Military Glossary listed above provides the meanings of many of the foreign words and abbreviations used in the picture captions in this section. For the most part, the italic portion of a caption is a copy of the words actually found on the stein; only a few obvious errors or important inconsistencies have been changed. Because many of the military names originated with Napoleon, the unit names on the steins are an ambiguous combination of French, German, and Germanized-French words. Hopefully, the resulting confusion will be outweighed by the convenience of having these unit names listed as they actually appear on the steins.

a.   Porcelain, .5L, *Bayerisches Infanterie Nr. 14, Nürnberg, 1905-1907,* $400-550.
b.   Porcelain, .5L, *Bayerisches Infanterie Nr. 2, München, 1907-1909,* $450-600.
c.   Porcelain, .5L, *Bayerisches Infanterie Nr. 17, Germersheim, 1899-1901,* $400-550.
d.   Stoneware, .5L, *Bayerisches Infanterie Nr. 8, Metz, 1910-1912,* $400-550.
e.   Porcelain, .5L, *Bayerisches Infanterie Leib Regt., München, 1909-1911,* 1909 Kaiser's Prize, $500-700.

a. Porcelain, .5L, *Infanterie Regt. Nr. 109, Karlsruhe, 1897-1899,* $300-400.

b. Porcelain, .5L, *Infanterie Regt. Nr. 113, Freiburg, 1898-1900,* $300-400.

c. Porcelain, .5L, *Infanterie Regt. Nr. 126, Straßburg, 1902-1904,* $300-400.

d. Porcelain, .5L, *Infanterie Regt. Nr. 169, Lahr, 1904-1906,* $350-450.

e. Porcelain, .5L, *Infanterie Regt. Nr. 20, Wittenberg, 1901-1903,* $350-450.

Opposite page bottom:

f. Porcelain, .5L, *Bayerisches Infanterie Nr. 19, Erlangen, 1912-1914,* finial screws off, $500-650.

g. Porcelain, .5L, *Bayerisches 21. u. 23. Infanterie Regts., Eichstatt u. Germersheim, 1912-1914,* finial unscrews to reveal owner's photo, $600-800.

h. Porcelain, .5L, *Bayerisches Infanterie Nr. 1, München, 1910-1912,* $500-700.

i. Porcelain, .5L, *Infanterie Nr. 124, Weingarten, 1909-1911,* $500-700.

j. Porcelain, .5L, *Bayerisches Infanterie Leib Regt., München, 1909-1911,* pewter crown lid covers glass dome, under glass dome are guardhouse, soldier, and officer on horse, $1400-1800.

a. Porcelain, .5L, *Bayerisches Infanterie Nr. 18, Landau, 1904-1906,* $400-500.

b. Porcelain, .5L, *Infanterie Nr. 110, Heidelberg, 1907-1909,* $450-600.

c. Porcelain, .5L, *Infanterie Nr. 122, Heilbron, 1912-1914,* $450-600.

d. Porcelain, .5L, *Infanterie Nr. 115, Darmstadt, 1908-1910,* $400-550.

e. Porcelain, .5L, *Garde Regt. zu Fuss Nr. 4, Berlin, 1904-1906,* $550-750.

Opposite page bottom:

f. Porcelain, .5L, *Infanterie Nr. 100, Dresden, 1909-1911,* $400-550.

g. Porcelain, .5L, *Infanterie Nr. 110, Mannheim, 1912-1914,* $450-600.

h. Porcelain, .5L, *Infanterie Nr. 159, Mülheim, 1904-1906,* $400-550.

i. Porcelain, .5L, *Infanterie Nr. 103, Bautzen, 1905-1907,* $400-550.

j. Porcelain, .5L, *Infanterie Regt. Nr. 88, Mainz, 1897-1899,* thumblift is bust of Wilhelm II, $450-600.

a.   Porcelain, .5L, *Infanterie Nr. 120, Ulm, 1902-1904,* named to a medic, $600-750.
b.   Porcelain, .5L, *Infanterie Regt. Nr. 172, Neubreissach, 1909-1911,* $400-500.
c.   Porcelain, .5L, *Infanterie Regt. Nr. 167, Cassel, 1903-1905,* $400-500.
d.   Porcelain, .5L, *Infanterie Regt. Nr. 80, Bad Homburg, 1902-1904,* $400-500.
e.   Porcelain, .5L, *Infanterie Nr. 32, Meiningen, 1901-1903,* $400-550.

a. Pottery, .5L, *Feld Artillerie Regt. Nr. 10, Hannover, 1902-1905,* $500-650.

b. Pottery, .5L, *Feld Artillerie Regt. Nr. 10, Hannover, 1902-1904,* $500-650.

c. Pottery, 1.0L, *Feld Artillerie Regt. Nr. 34, Metz, 1910-1912,* horse and rider thumblift, $600-800.

d. Porcelain, .5L, *Feld Artillerie Regt. Nr. 15, Mörchingen, 1911-1913,* $450-600.

e. Porcelain, .5L, *Feld Artillerie Regt. Nr. 63, Mainz, 1910-1912,* $500-650.

Opposite page top:

a. Porcelain, .5L, *Infanterie Nr. 118, Worms, 1906-1908,* $400-550.

b. Porcelain, .5L, *Garde Regt. Zu Fuss, Leib Cp., Potsdam, 1901-1903,* miter helmet finial, $2400-3000.

c. Porcelain, .5L, *Infanterie Nr. 143, Mautzig, 1902-1904,* $450-650.

d. Porcelain, .5L, *Infanterie Regt. Nr. 111, Rastatt, 1906-1907, u. Infanterie Schiess Schule* (Marksmanship School), *Spandau-Rühleben, 1907-1908,* $750-1000.

e. Pottery, .5L, *Infanterie Regt. Nr. 28, Ehrenbreitstein, 1904-1906,* $400-500.

Opposite page bottom:

f. Pottery, .5L, *Infanterie Regt. Nr. 79, Hildesheim, 1903-1905,* inscription for Gibraltar campaign, $500-650.

g. Pottery, .5L, *Infanterie Regt. Nr. 149, Schneidemuhl, 1911-1913,* $500-650.

h. Porcelain, .5L, *Infanterie Nr. 114, Constanz, 1911-1913,* $400-550.

i. Porcelain, .5L, *Infanterie Regt. Nr. 112, Mülhausen, 1906-1907, u. Infanterie Schiess Schule* (Marksmanship School), *Spandau, 1907-1908,* $700-900.

a. Pottery, .5L, *Feld Artillerie Regt. Nr. 46, Wolfenbüttel*, $300-450.

b. Porcelain, .5L, *Feld Artillerie Regt. Nr. 48, Dresden, 1902-1904*, $400-550.

c. Porcelain, .5L, *Feld Artillerie Regt. Nr. 49, Ulm 1899-1901*, $350-500.

d. Porcelain, .5L, *Bayerisches 2, Feld Artillerie Regt., Würzburg, 1901-1903*, porcelain inlaid lid, $700-1000.

e. Porcelain, .5L, *Feld Artillerie Regt. Nr. 5, Sagan, 1905-1907*, $600-750.

Opposite page bottom:

f. Porcelain, .5L, *Maschinengewehr Comp., Bayerisches 7 Infanterie Regt., Bayreuth, 1909-1911*, prism lid, $800-1000.

g. Pottery, .5L, *Maschinengewehr Comp., Infanterie Regt. Nr. 118, Worms, 1912-1914*, $1400-1800.

h. Porcelain, .5L, *Maschinengewehr, Abteilung Nr. 11, Metz, 1908-1910*, $1500-2000.

i. Porcelain, .5L, *Maschinengewehr Comp., Infanterie Regt. Nr. 120, Ulm, 1910-1912*, $1200-1600.

j. Porcelain, .5L, *Maschinengewehr Comp., Infanterie Regt. Nr. 120, Ulm, 1912-1914*, $800-1000.

a.   Porcelain, .5L, *Feld Artillerie Regt. Nr. 44, Trier, 1912-1914*, $450-600.
b.   Porcelain, .5L, *Feld Artillerie Regt. Nr. 61, Darmstadt, 1909-1911*, $450-600.
c.   Porcelain, .5L, *Feld Artillerie Regt. Nr. 4, Potsdam, 1908-1910*, $400-550.
d.   Porcelain, .5L, *Fuss Artillerie Regt. Nr. 13, Ulm, 1903-1905*, $400-600.
e.   Porcelain, .5L, *Fuss Artillerie Regt. Nr. 14, Strassburg, 1911-1913*, $550-700.

a. Porcelain, .5L, *Train Bataillon Nr. 13, Ludwigsburg, 1908-1909*, $600-800.

b. Porcelain, .5L, *Train Bataillon Nr. 14, Durlach, 1907-1909*, $500-700.

c. Porcelain, .5L, *Train Bataillon Nr. 14, Durlach, 1897-1899*, $400-550.

d. Pottery, .5L, *Bayerisches 2. Jäger Bataillon, Aschaffenburg, 1908-1910*, King's Prize, tschako finial, $1600-2000.

e. Porcelain, .5L, *Bayerisches 2. Jäger Bataillon, Aschaffenburg, 1902-1904*, $1100-1400.

Opposite page top:

a. Porcelain, .5L, *Jäger Bataillon Nr. 4, Bitsch, 1903-1905*, $1200-1600.

b. Porcelain, .5L, *Bayerisches 1. Jäger Bataillon, Straubing, 1898-1900*, $800-1000.

c. Stoneware, .5L, *Jäger Bataillon Nr. 13, Dresden, 1909-1910*, King's Prize, one-year volunteer, tschako finial, $1000-1300.

d. Porcelain, .5L, *Jäger Bataillon Nr. 4, Bitsch, 1903-1905*, $1300-1700.

e. Porcelain, .5L, *Bayerisches 2. Jäger Bataillon, Aschaffenburg, 1907-1909*, carved horn on lid, tschako finial, $1300-1600.

Opposite page bottom:

f. Porcelain, .5L, *Pionier Bataillon Nr. 14, Kehl, 1904-1906*, $550-700.

g. Porcelain, .5L, *Pionier Bataillon Nr. 16, Metz, 1906-1908*, $550-700.

h. Porcelain, .5L, *Pionier Bataillon Nr. 11, Hannover-Münden, 1910-1912*, $600-750.

i. Pottery, .5L, *Pionier Bataillon Nr. 25, Mainz-Kastel, 1909-1911*, $650-800.

j. Porcelain, .5L, *Bayerisches 1. Pionier Bataillon, Ingolstadt, 1909-1911*, finial unscrews, $600-800.

a. Pottery, .5L, *Pionier Bataillon Nr. 7, Köln-Riehl, 1909-1911*, $600-800.

b. Porcelain, .5L, *Pionier Bataillon Nr. 11, Mainz, 1899-1901*, $500-700.

c. Porcelain, .5L, *Bayerisches Eisenbahn Batl., 1. Comp., München, 1903-1905*, $800-1000.

d. Porcelain, .5L, *Eisenbahn Regt. Nr. 1, Schöneberg-Berlin, 1901-1903*, $750-1000.

e. Pottery, .5L, *Betriebs Abteilung Eisenbahn Brigade, Schöneberg-Berlin, 1900-1902*, $1200-1500.

a. Porcelain, .5L, *Telegraphen Batl. Nr. 1, Berlin, 1906-1908,* $1300-1700.
b. Porcelain, .5L, *Telegraphen Batl. Nr. 2, Frankfurt, 1905-1907,* $1500-2000.
c. Porcelain, .5L, *Telegraphen Batl. Nr. 4, Karlsruhe, 1907-1909,* $1500-2000.
d. Stoneware, .5L, *Telegraphen Batl. Nr. 4, Funker Abteilung, Karlsruhe, 1911-1913,* $400-600.

Opposite page bottom:
f. Pottery, .5L, *Eisenbahn Regt. 1, 3. Comp., Berlin, 1899-1901,* $700-900.
g. Pottery, .5L, *Eisenbahn Regt. Nr. 3, 8. Comp., Berlin-Schöneberg, 1908-1910,* $1300-1700.
h. Pottery, .5L, *Eisenbahn Regt. Nr. 3, 4. Comp., Berlin, 1903-1905,* $900-1200.
i. Pottery, .5L, *Eisenbahn Regt. Nr. 2, 2. Comp., Berlin-Schöneberg, 1903-1905,* $700-900.
j. Porcelain, .5L, *Eisenbahn Regt. Nr. 1, 7. Comp., Berlin-Schöneberg, 1909-1911,* $1300-1700.

a. Pottery, .5L, *Dragoner Regt. Nr. 9, Metz, 1902-1905*, $600-800.

b. Porcelain, .5L, *Dragoner, Regt. Nr. 22, Mülhausen, 1904-1907*, $600-800.

c. Porcelain, .5L, *Bayerisches 1. Schweres Reiter Regt., München, 1910-1913,* finial unscrews to reveal photo of owner, $800-1000.

d. Porcelain, .5L, *Dragoner Regt. Nr. 21, Bruchsal, 1894-1896*, $400-500.

e. Porcelain, .5L, *Chevaleuger Regt. Nr. 6, Bayreuth, 1894-1897*, $500-650.

Opposite page top:

a. Porcelain, .5L, *Dragoner Regt. Nr. 13, Metz, 1904-1908*, $650-800.

b. Porcelain, .5L, *Dragoner Regt. Nr. 15, Hagenau, 1910-1913*, $650-800.

c. Porcelain, .5L, *Dragoner Regt. Nr. 21, Schwetzingen, 1910-1913*, $700-900.

d. Porcelain, .5L, *Dragoner Regt. Nr. 23, Darmstadt, 1907-1910*, $700-900.

Opposite page bottom:

e. Pottery, .5L, *Dragoner Regt. Nr. 7, Saarbrücken, 1904-1907*, $600-800.

f. Pottery, .5L, *Dragoner Regt. Nr. 5, Hofgeismar, 1910-1913*, $800-1000.

g. Pottery, 1.0L, *Dragoner Regt. Nr. 13, Metz, 1908-1911*, $800-1000.

h. Pottery, .5L, *Dragoner Regt. Nr. 15, Hagenau, 1907-1910*, $800-1000.

a.   Pottery, .5L, *Garde Kürassier Regt., Berlin, 1900-1903, $1000-1250.*
b.   Pottery, .5L, *Kürassier Regt. Nr. 4, Munster, 1909-1912, $1000-1250.*
c.   Pottery, 1.0L, *Kürassier Regt. Nr. 5, Riesenburg, 1909-1912, $1400-1800.*
d.   Porcelain, .5L, *Jäger Regt. Zu Pferde, Nr. 5, Mülhausen u. Husaren Regt. Nr. 3, Rathanow, 1906-1909, $1300-1700.*
e.   Pottery, .5L, *Jäger Regt. Zu Pferde, Nr. 11, Tarnowitz, 1913-1915, u. Husaren Regt. Nr. 12, Torgau, 1912-1913, $1500-2000.*

Opposite page top:
a.   Porcelain, .5L, *Husaren Regt. Nr. 12, Torgau, 1906-1909, $600-800.*
b.   Porcelain, .5L, *Husaren Regt. Nr. 15, Wandsbeck, 1904-1907, $700-900.*
c.   Porcelain, .5L, *Husaren Regt. Nr. 19, Grimma, 1906-1909, $900-1200.*
d.   Porcelain, .5L, *Husaren Regt. Nr. 13, Diedenhofen, 1910-1913, $800-1000.*
e.   Porcelain, .5L, *Ulanen Regt. Nr. 21, Chemnitz, 1908-1911, $800-1000.*

Opposite page bottom:
f.   Porcelain, .5L, *Bayerisches 1. Ulanen Regt., Bamberg, 1903-1906, $700-900.*
g.   Pottery, .5L, *Ulanen Regt. Nr. 5, Düsseldorf, 1906-1909, $650-800.*
h.   Pottery, .5L, *Ulanen Regt. Nr. 11, Saarburg, 1902-1905, $650-800.*
i.   Pottery, .5L, *Sächsisches Garde Reiter Regt., Dresden, 1901-1904, $1400-1800.*
j.   Pottery, .5L, *Regiment der Gardes du Corps, Potsdam, 1907-1910, $1100-1400.*

a.   Pottery, 1.0L, *S.M.S. Oldenburg u. S.M.S. Schlesien, 1910-1913,* $1200-1500.

b.   Pottery, 1.0L, *S.M.S. Pommern, 1912-1915,* $1400-1700.

c.   Pottery, 1.0L, *S.M.S. Kaiser Karl der Grosse, 1908-1909 u. S.M.S. Braunschweig, 1909-1911,* $1000-1300.

d.   Pottery, 1.0L, *S.M.S. Schleswig Holstein, 1910-1913,* $1100-1400.

e.   Pottery, 1.0L, *S.M.S. Westfalen, 1911-1914,* $1100-1400.

Opposite page top:

a.   Pottery, 1.0L, *S.M.S. Hohenzollern, 1907-1910,* $1100-1400.

b.   Pottery, 1.0L, *S.M.S. Hamburg, 1906-1909,* $900-1200.

c.   Pottery, 1.0L, *S.M.S. Frederich Karl, 1910-1913,* $1100-1400.

d.   Pottery, 1.0L, *S.M.S. Gneisenau, 1909-1912,* Neptune figural lid, $2200-2800.

e.   Porcelain, 1.0L, *S.M.S. Stuttgart, 1909-1912,* $1500-2000.

Opposite page bottom:

f.   Pottery, .5L, *S.M.S. Kaiser Barbarossa, 1905-1908,* $800-1000.

g.   Porcelain, .5L, *S.M.S. Drache, 1908-1911,* $900-1200.

h.   Porcelain, .5L, *S.M.S. Wettin, 1905-1908,* $900-1100.

i.   Porcelain, .5L, *Telegraphen Zug. II See Bataillon, Wilhelmshaven, 1910-1913,* $2400-3000.

j.   Porcelain, .5L *Maschinengewehr Zug. II See Bataillon, Wilhelmshaven, 1911-1914,* $2400-3000.

a. Stoneware, .5L, *Luftschiffer Abteilung, München, 1901-1903*, $3500-4500.

b. Pottery, .5L, *Luftschiffer Batl., 2. Comp., Berlin, 1901-1903*, $5000-7000.

c. Stoneware, .5L, *Luftschiffer u. Kraftfahr Bataillon, München Kraftfahr Komp. Reserve, 1912-1914*, $2400-3000.

d. Mettlach, .5L, *406, Bayerisches Luftschiffer Bataillon, München, 1893-1895*, $2500-3500.

Opposite page bottom:

e. Mettlach, .5L, 790(2140), PUG, *Garde Feld Artillerie Regt. Nr. 2*, c.1900, pewter lid, $550-700.

f. Mettlach, .5L, 825(2140), PUG, *Infanterie Regt. Nr. 141*, c.1900, pewter lid, $500-650.

g. Mettlach, .5L, 786(2140), PUG, *Eisenbahn Regt. Nr. 3*, c.1900, pewter lid, $500-650.

h. Mettlach, .5L, 775(2140), PUG, *Garde Kürassier*, c.1900, pewter lid, $600-800.

i. Mettlach, .5L, 894(2140), PUG, *Pionier Bataillon Nr. 10*, c.1900, pewter lid, $600-800.

a. Porcelain, .5L, *Bayerisches 15. Infanterie Regt., Neuburg, 1900-1902,* named to *Sanitätsgefreiter,* two medical scenes in side panels, $2200-2800.

b. Porcelain, .5L, *Bayerisches Train Bataillon Nr. 2, Sanitäts Comp., Würzburg, 1898-1900,* $1800-2200.

c. Porcelain, .5L, *Infanterie Regt. Nr. 134, Plauen, 1906 u. Militär Bäcker Abteilung des 2. Armeekorps Nr. 19, Riesa,* $1200-1500.

d. Porcelain, .5L, *Militärbäckerie, Ulm, 1907-1909,* $1000-1200.

Below are examples of U.S. Military Regimental steins purchased by American soldiers in Germany.

a. Pottery, .5L, relief, *Army of Occupation, 148. F.A., Army Artillery,* c.1919, no lid, $100-150.
b. Pottery, .5L, transfer, *First Division Circus, Montabaur Germany, July 11 & 12, 1919,* no lid, $60-90.
c. Pottery, .5L, *440 th. AAABN, On the Rhine in 1945,* no lid, $80-120.
d. Pottery, .5L, transfer, *110th Infantry Regiment, Ulm/Donau, 1951-1952,* pewter lid with relief combat infantry badge, army eagle thumblift, $150-250.

e. Porcelain, .5L, *Naval Air Facility, Naples, Italy,* 1950s, pewter lid, $80-120.
f. Porcelain, .5L, *Headquarters Twelfth Air Force, Germany, 1956-1959,* pewter lid, $100-150.
g. Porcelain, .5L, *A. Troop, 3rd Squadron, 7th Cavalry, Schweinfurt, 1965,* pewter lid, $100-150.
h. Porcelain, .5L, *209th Ge. Disp., Hanau, 1964,* pewter lid, $100-150.
i. Porcelain, .5L, *511th Airborne Infantry, Augsburg, 1956,* pewter lid, $100-150.

15. Military

15.1 History of Military Steins

The history of the military steins covered in this chapter begins on June 28, 1914, when Archduke Francis Ferdinand of Austria-Hungary and his wife were murdered in Bosnia, triggering events that led to World War I.

World War I steins, for the purposes of this chapter, are of two general types: commemorative (usually featuring an Iron Cross and mostly made in 1914 when the war was going well for Germany) and military steins for a specific unit, often dated with the word *Weihnachten* (Christmas). The World War I steins were generally much simpler in style than the previous Imperial Reservist steins. The production costs of those tall porcelain steins were just too high. The most common military steins are smaller stoneware steins with print-under-glaze decals, those being generally from the Höhr-Grenzhausen area factories. Considering the German defeat and the revolt against the Imperial system, it is not surprising that relatively few German wartime souvenirs were generated in the postwar era.

The army steins of the Reichswehr (German military 1919–1935) are also frequently found with a Christmas date and are occasionally marked with twelve-year service intervals. Single-date and undated versions also exist, and these were used for birthdays, anniversaries, weddings, or other occasions that occurred during the service period. These steins are usually made of gray saltglazed or ivory stoneware (pottery), and were produced mainly in the Westerwald region. They are mostly .25L or .5L, with print-under-glaze decorations, and pewter or nickel-plated lids. Some steins from this period were made to commemorate meetings of Imperial or World War I veterans' organizations. Such meetings were first held in about 1920 but did not continue past 1933 when they were declared illegal by the government.

With regard to steins, it is important to note that on March 16, 1935, the name *Reichswehr* (army) was officially changed to *Deutsche Wehrmacht* (Nazi army). The increase in national pride at this time resulted in greater production of military steins, usually of the smaller stoneware types. Considering the years between 1914 and 1945, the most prolific production of military steins took place from 1936 to 1939. Most of these steins were .5 liter in size and were made from stoneware. Those found with manufacturers' marks were usually made by Wick-Werke, Merkelbach, or Marzi & Remy, although the Mettlach factory also produced a few commemorative military steins during this period.

Then, beginning in September 1939, and while the war was expanding, stein production was severely curtailed. That there were any steins produced at all demonstrates that they were considered important morale boosters. Even fewer steins exist from the period of 1941 through 1944. One can only speculate, however, on how many were actually produced. Most soldiers who were with the invading forces have recalled that Nazi and other steins too large to pocket as souvenirs were methodically destroyed wherever they were encountered.

15.2 Collecting Military Steins

From 1918 through the early 1920s, and again from 1945 through the early 1960s, American soldiers purchased steins as souvenirs of their service. While the porcelain .5 liter steins of the 1950s are fairly common, earlier German military steins are somewhat harder to find.

Collecting military steins is often approached from the view of collecting history. Therefore, some collectors are interested in specific military units or types of units. Other collectors use a more general approach of collecting by style or type of decoration.

15.3 Evaluation Information

Price trends in the past ten years have been mostly level for military steins from World War I and the Reichswehr periods. During the past ten years price trends have been mostly upward for Third Reich steins. Many rare Third Reich steins have increased in value significantly. The more common Third Reich steins increased during the early 1990s, but became steady or fell slightly during the late 1990s.

a. Military, 1.0L, stoneware, *In Ost und West Treu, Stark Fest,* pewter lid, $250-350.

b. Military, 1.0L, stoneware, *Wachkommando Dillingen, Weihnachten 1915,* pewter lid, $500-700.

c. Military, 1.0L, stoneware, *Kriegs Gefangenen Lager* (prison camp), c.1916, pewter lid, $400-600.

d. Military, 1.0L, stoneware, *Einigkeit macht stark,* pewter lid dated 1914, $300-400.

e. Military, .5L, stoneware, relief soldiers, 1914 Iron Crosses on sides, pewter lid with relief eagle, $200-300.

f. Military, 1.0L, stoneware, handpainted, *Kriegs-Weihnachten, 1915,* Red Cross, relief pewter lid with Bavarian city crest, $1000-1500.

g. Military, 1.0L, stoneware, *Sturmangriff* (Storm Troopers), pewter lid with Iron Cross, 1914, $200-300.

a.   Military, .5L, stoneware, pewter lid with relief Iron Cross, 1914, $200-300.
b   Military, .5L, stoneware, *1914*, German & Austrian alliance, Iron Cross lid, $250-350.
c.   Military, .5L, stoneware, *1914*, pewter lid with relief Bavarian crest, $150-250.
d.   Military, .5L, stoneware, *1914,* Wilhelm II, pewter lid with eagles, $200-300.
e.   Military, .5L, stoneware, Bavarian, Iron Cross, *1914*, pewter lid with Iron Cross, $150-250.

.   Military, .5L, stoneware, Artillery Shell, 1914, pewter lid, $700-1000.
.   Military, 1.0L, stoneware, marked Martin Pauson, Artillery Shell, *Einigkeit Macht Stark*, 1915, pewter lid, $800-1100.
.   Military, .5L, stoneware, relief soldiers, c.1916, metal lid, $200-300.
.   Military, .5L, stoneware, *Einig und stark, 1914-15,* pewter lid, $200-300.
.   Military, .5L, stoneware, *Mitt Gott für Kaiser und Reich,* c.1916, inlaid lid, $500-700.

a. Military, .5L, pottery, *Hochgebirgs M.W. Komp. 19, Weihnachten, 1928,* pewter lid, $200-300.

b. Military, .5L, pottery, *Unteroffizier-Korps der 7. Komp. 3 (PR.) Inft. Regt.,* 1920s, metal lid with relief soldier, $300-400.

c. Military, .5L, pottery, *Polizeivorschule-Bamberg, Lehrabteilung 1, LPB (Polizie), Weihnachten 1929,* pewter lid, $300-400.

d. Military, .5L, stoneware, *Marine Kameradschaft, München, von 1890,* Fiftieth Anniversary Navy Veterans, 1940, Battleship Bismarck, pewter lid, $350-450.

e. Military, .5L, stoneware, *Auf Erinnerung an meine Dienstzeit im Stahlhelm,* WWI Veterans organization, probably c.1930, metal lid, $200-300.

f. Military, .5L, pottery, *Oberjäger - Vereinigung, Jäger - Batl. Inf. Regt. 15, 1.11.1926 - 31.10.1938,* served twelve years in the army, pewter lid with helmet finial, $450-600.

g. Military, .5L, pottery, *M.W.K., I.R. 13,* owner *Stabsgefreiter Sauter,* 1920s, pewter lid with helmet finial, $450-600.

h. Military, .5L, pottery, *Uffz. - Korps 4./R.R.I.,* 1920s, pewter lid with helmet finial, $400-550.

i. Military, .5L, pottery, *2. (Württ.)Komp. Kraftfahr - Abtlg. 5, Weihnachten 1927,* pewter lid, $500-650.

j. Military, .5L, stoneware, *Nachrichten-Abt. Weihnachten 1921,* pewter lid, $250-350.

a. Military, .5L, pottery, *Die Bestschiessende Kompanie 1930, 1931, 1932, 3./I.R. 19, Weihnachten 1932,* The Best Shooting Company for 1930 to 1932, pewter lid with relief helmet, $250-350.

b. Military, .5L, stoneware, *Streif Batl., 1919, Weihnachten,* patrol from very early post WWI army, functioned to prevent anti-government uprisings, pewter lid, $350-450.

c. Military, .5L, porcelain, *Erinnerung an meine Dienstzeit!, 1917-1929,* roster, Bavarian crest thumblift, pewter lid with helmet finial, $500-650.

d. Military, .5L, stoneware, *Der Stahlhelm Bund der Frontsoldaten, Gew. v.d. 3. Gruppe d. 4. Kameradschaft - Weihnachten 1929,* tenth meeting of Stahlhelm organization, the design is from a poster by Ludwig Hohlwein, has roster, pewter lid with helmet finial, $600-800.

e. Military, 1.0L, stoneware, *1. Komp., 7. (Bayerische) Kraftfahr Abteilung, 1933,* pewter lid, $400-550.

f. Third Reich, .5L, stoneware, *Nachrichten-Abteilung 27, Weihnachten 1936,* metal lid, $250-350.

g. Third Reich, .5L, stoneware, *Inf. Rgt. Nbg. Bamberg, 2. Kompanie,* pewter lid, $300-400.

h. Third Reich, .5L, stoneware, *15. (E.) Komp., I.R. 19, Freising,* pewter lid with relief helmet with swastika, $300-400.

i. Third Reich, .5L, stoneware, *11./U.K. 212, Kriegsweihnacht 1940,* pewter lid, $250-350.

j. Third Reich, .5L, pottery, *Arbeitsdienstzeit, Kitzingen, 1/284, 1934-35,* metal lid with relief worker, $200-300.

a.   Third Reich, .5L, porcelain, *16. Reit. Regt., Erfurt, 1933-1934,* pewter lid, $600-900.

b.   Third Reich, .5L, pottery, *1. Gren. Ausb. Kp. I/133, Kriegsweihnachten 1942,* pewter lid with relief helmet with swastika, $400-550.

c.   Third Reich, .5L, pottery, *M.G. Batl. 6, Coburg,* pewter lid with relief scene of *Veste Coburg,* $400-550.

d.   Third Reich, .5L, pottery, *List auf Sylt* (telegraph battalion), pewter lid with relief telegraph emblem, $700-900.

e.   Third Reich, .5L, stoneware, *Fliegerhorst Mannheim-Sandhofen,* 1940, pewter lid, $400-550.

f.   Third Reich, .5L, stoneware, relief, airplane with swastika on wing, metal lid, $400-550.

g.   Third Reich, .5L, stoneware, *Geb. Jäger Regt. 99, 12. (M.G.) Komp. Sonthofen, 1936-1938,* pewter lid with relief helmet with swastika, $500-750.

h.   Third Reich, .5L, pottery, *Inft. Regt. 95, Coburg,* owner's name on pewter lid with relief scene of Veste Coburg, $400-550.

i.   Third Reich, .5L, pottery, *3./Panzerregiment 7.,* pewter lid with relief helmet with swastika, $400-550.

j.   Third Reich, .5L, pottery, *1. Minensuchhalbflottille, M. 145, U-Messe 1934,* pewter lid with relief buoy, $800-1100.

16. Characters

A character stein is a stein with a shape designed to represent an object, person, or animal. So, like Occupationals and Regimentals, they belong to a style category as opposed to a materials category as described in most of the other sections.

16.1 History and Production

Although figural vessels date back to several centuries before the ancient Greeks, true character steins had to await the development of the hinged lid in the early 1500s. And, in fact, there are stoneware character steins that date from about that period, generally in the form of owls or seated bears, but they are quite rare.

One can only speculate as to the reasons for the scarcity of character steins that pre-date the late 1800s. One theory is that the odd shapes were too whimsical to be socially acceptable in earlier times. The other popular theory is that before the 1800s and the introduction of molds that could more easily accommodate such shapes, it required too much effort to produce these statuettes.

Some of the character steins that appeared around the 1850s were dull-finished bisque porcelain pieces that were made in slip molds. (See Subsection 2.3.) Among the most common are skulls of various designs, which were frequently purchased by medical students and members of student societies or fraternities. Many of these have been identified as products of E. Bohne Söhne of the Thuringen region, a factory that started in 1854. Much of the initial manufacture of character steins is attributable to this firm and other producers situated in Plaue.

Beginning in the 1870s, several other factories that produced character steins were founded, but they probably did not actually begin production of character steins until the 1880s. These include Merkelbach & Wick, Dümler & Breiden, Reinhold Merkelbach, Simon Peter Gerz, and Marzi & Remy. The Villeroy & Boch factory at Mettlach began producing character steins around 1892. Marks used by these factories are shown at the end of Section 2.

Porzellanmanufaktur Plaue (C.G. Schierholz & Söhn) used the commonly seen hash, or crosshatch, mark. It is often accompanied by the word *MUSTER-SCHUTZ*, which conveys the same meaning as a copyright mark. The crosshatch is most often seen in green, *MUSTERSCHUTZ* in blue.

The Plaue factory has long been associated with the manufacture of lithophanes, a subject that deserves a word here. Lithophanes, which are occasionally found in the bottom of porcelain steins, are panels that show a picture when put up to a source of light. The visibly darker and lighter parts of lithophanes result from thicker and thinner areas of porcelain.

Lithophanes were designed by first putting a layer of translucent beeswax on a pane of glass with a light underneath. The wax was carved until the desired scene was completed, then the wax was used to make the plaster mold for the base of the stein. On rare occasions, colored glazes were used to tint the outside of a lithophane in a stein, producing a subtly colored scene.

The material most frequently used to make character steins was porcelain. The next most common was stoneware, often also slip molded, but occasionally press-molded stoneware steins are found. These stoneware steins were mostly decorated with blue or purple saltglazes, or a kind of blackish combination. Brown and green saltglazes, which were also known in the late 1800s, are sometimes seen on stoneware character steins.

Various kinds of pottery, earthenware, and pewter round out the character stein materials that are occasionally encountered.

Many of the porcelain character steins were made in more than one coloration pattern. The most common duplication is a tan and brown stein that also exists in a full-color version and in blues. The blue and white versions are sometimes thinner and may have been produced with a slightly different porcelain recipe. Some of these are so delicate that it is easy to imagine that they were intended only as decorative items.

16.2 Collecting Characters

Unlike many occupational steins, particular character stein designs were often produced in such large quantities that a collector can specifically seek out and find a certain stein. This affects collecting strategies.

For one thing, it makes the condition of the more common steins more important. When an example is known to be available in better condition, the price of a less-perfect one often has to be considerably discounted in order to make a transaction.

In addition, a market price establishes itself for specific character steins when several examples are available, and this is not a market that lends itself to any kind of formula. The most important determinant of this market price is probably rarity, which cannot be determined by looking at a character stein. Even the absurd-looking steins, like the radishes, can be relatively common.

Although aesthetics can be judged by looking at a stein, great appeal is not always indicative of high market price. In fact, it sometimes seems that the most attractive character steins are often relatively common and thus lower in price.

16.3 Evaluation Information

Price trends in the past ten years have been mostly upward for character steins. Many rare character steins have increased in value significantly. The more common character steins have recently had some up and down trends, however, the overall trend has been up for the last ten years. Less than 20% of character steins have not increased in value during the 1990s.

a. Bismarck, .5L, porcelain, honey colored, Schierholz, c.1900, $500-700.
b. Bismarck in Retirement, .5L, porcelain, honey colored, Schierholz, c.1900, $900-1100.
c. Bismarck Radish, .5L, porcelain, white & green, Schierholz, c.1900, $500-650.
d. Frederich III, .5L, porcelain, honey colored, Schierholz, c.1900, $2200-2600.

a. Wilhelm I, .5L, porcelain, honey colored, Schierholz, c.1900, $1000-1400.
b. Wilhelm II, .5L, porcelain, honey colored, Schierholz, c.1900, $1400-1800.
c. Von Moltke, .5L, porcelain, honey colored, Schierholz, c.1900, $900-1200.
d. Uncle Sam, .5L, porcelain, honey colored, Schierholz, c.1900, $2000-2500.

. Soldier with Caterpillar Helmet, .5L, porcelain, honey colored, Schierholz, c.1900, $900-1200.
. Soldier with Spiked Helmet, .5L, porcelain, honey colored, Schierholz, c.1900, $900-1200.
. Soldier, .5L, porcelain, full color, Schierholz, early 1900s, $1400-1800.
. Trainmaster, .5L, porcelain, full color, Schierholz, early 1900s, $1500-2000.

a. School Teacher, .5L, porcelain, honey colored, Schierholz, c.1900, $1300-1700.

b. Father Jahn, .5L, porcelain, honey colored, Schierholz, c.1900, $1400-1800.

c. Clown, .5L, porcelain, full color, Schierholz, c.1900, $2200-2800.

d. Clown, .5L, porcelain, full color, c.1900, $1400-1800.

e. Pixie, .5L, porcelain, honey colored, Schierholz, c.1900, $800-1100.

f. Satan, .5L, porcelain, full color, Ernst Bohne Söhne, #4708, c.1900, $600-750.

g. Mephisto, .5L, porcelain, full color, Schierholz, c.1900, $2200-2800.

h. Black Man, .5L, porcelain, full color, Schierholz, c.1900, $2200-2800.

i. Indian Chief, .5L, porcelain, full color, Ernst Bohne Söhne, #5228, c.1900, $600-750.

a. Man with Bug on Forehead, .5L, pottery, full color, Reinhold Hanke, #1426, early 1900s, $200-300.
b. Man Smoking Pipe, .5L, pottery, full color, Reinhold Hanke, #1425, early 1900s, $150-250.
c. Alpine Woman, .5L, porcelain, full color, c.1900, $1200-1800.
d. Caroline, .5L, porcelain, honey colored, Schierholz, c.1900, $550-700.
e. Hops Lady, .5L, porcelain, honey colored, Schierholz, c.1900, $600-750.

f. Masquerade Lady, .5L, porcelain, honey colored, Schierholz, c.1900, $3000-4000.
g. Alpine Man, .5L, porcelain, honey colored, Schierholz, c.1900, $1000-1400.
h. Judge with Jester thumblift, .5L, porcelain, honey colored, Schierholz, c.1900, $1000-1400.
i. Burgermeister, .5L, porcelain, honey colored, Schierholz, c.1900, $800-1100.

a. Sea Captain, .5L, porcelain, honey colored, Schierholz, c.1900, $900-1200.
b. Turkish Man, .5L, porcelain, honey colored, Schierholz, c.1900, $900-1200.
c. Barmaid, .5L, porcelain, honey colored, Schierholz, c.1900, $1800-2400.
d. Bustle Lady, .5L, stoneware, blue saltglaze, late 1800s, $1100-1400.

e. Mushroom Man, .5L, porcelain, full color, Schierholz, c.1900, $1800-2400.
f. Mushroom Lady, .5L, porcelain, full color, Schierholz, c.1900, $2000-2500.
g. Radish Lady, .5L, porcelain, full color, Schierholz, c.1900, $2400-3000.
h. Dutch Boy, .5L, porcelain, blue & white, Schierholz, c.1900, $1200-1600.
i. Dutch Girl, .5L, porcelain, blue & white, Schierholz, c.1900, $1200-1600.

a. Bismarck Wearing Cap, .5L, porcelain, full color, c.1900, $1000-1300.
b. Bismarck Wearing Helmet, .5L, pottery, Reinhold Hanke, #584, c.1900, $450-600.
c. Frederich III, .5L, pottery, Merkelbach & Wick, c.1900, $450-600.
d. Von Moltke, .5L, pottery, Reinhold Hanke, #585, c.1900, $400-550.
e. Wilhelm I, .5L, stoneware, blue saltglaze, Marzi & Remy, #809, c.1900, $550-750.

f. Miner, .5L, pottery, full color, Reinhold Merkelbach, #736, c.1900, $700-900.
g. Nürnberg Gooseman, .5L, porcelain, weathered-bronze tones, #2477, c.1900, $600-800.
h. Man Holding Cat, .5L, pottery, full color, Diesinger, #765, early 1900s, $500-700.
.   Man with Funnel Hat, .5L, pottery, color accented, Reinhold Hanke, #622, c.1900, $300-450.
.   Society Student, .5L, porcelain, full color, c.1960, $200-300.

a. Men Under Umbrella, .5L, porcelain, full color, c.1900, $900-1200.

b. Sailor, .5L, pottery, full color, Reinhold Hanke, #1821, c.1900, $600-800.

c. Roly-Poly Soldier, .5L, pottery, full color, Reinhold Hanke, #1577, early 1900s, $500-700.

d. Clown, .5L, pottery, Reinhold Hanke, #987, early 1900s, $350-450.

e . Falstaff, .5L, pottery, full color, Reinhold Hanke, #1439, early 1900s, $300-400.

f. Fireman, .5L, stoneware, blue saltglaze, Marzi & Remy, #750, c.1900, $400-550.

g. Man, .5L, earthenware, full color, #1045, c.1900, $300-450.

h. Chinaman, .5L, pottery, full color, Merkelbach & Wick, early 1900s, $300-450.

i. Rich Man, .5L, stoneware, blue saltglaze, Merkelbach & Wick, #257a, early 1900s, $275-375.

a. Rich Man Wearing Beret, .5L, stoneware, blue saltglaze, Reinhold Hanke, #461, early 1900s, $250-350.
b. Barmaid, .5L, pottery, full color, Reinhold Hanke, #1571, early 1900s, $500-750.
c. Barmaid (Lisl), .5L, pottery, full color, J. Reinemann, c.1900, $450-600.
d. Iron Maiden, .5L, stoneware, blue saltglaze, Theodor Wieseler, c.1900, $350-500.
e. Rich Mother-in-Law, .5L, pottery, green accents, c.1900, $400-600.

f. Little Red Riding Hood, .25L, stoneware, full-color enamel, J. Reinemann, #55, early 1900s, $600-800.
g. Hanswurst the Clown, .5L, stoneware, full-color enamel, J. Reinemann, #50, c.1900, $600-800.
h. Jester Holding Horn, .25L, stoneware, full-color enamel, J. Reinemann, #56, c.1900, $600-800.
i. Black Man Holding HB Stein, .5L, pottery, full color, Reinhold Merkelbach, #737, c.1900, $400-600.
j. Black Student Dueler, .5L, earthenware, full color, #1005, early 1900s, $250-350.

a. Alpine Man, .5L, earthenware, full color, #1044, c.1900, $300-450.
b. Clown Pointing to Nose, .5L, pottery, full color, Diesinger, #747, early 1900s, $750-1000.
c. Clown with Hands in Pockets, .5L, pottery, full color, Diesinger, #749, early 1900s, $750-1000.
d. Jester, .5L, pottery, S.P. Gerz, #305, early 1900s, $250-350.
e. Rich Woman, .5L, pottery, Merkelbach & Wick, #257b, c.1900, $250-350.

f. Monk (Wearing Beret), .5L, stoneware, blue saltglaze, Reinhold Hanke, #462, c.1900, $200-300.
g. Monk, .5L, stoneware, blue saltglaze, c.1900, $150-250.
h. Monk, .5L, stoneware, blue saltglaze, Reinhold Hanke, #67, c.1900, $150-250.
i. Monk, .5L, pottery, full color, Reinhold Hanke, #462, early 1900s, $150-250.
j. Monk, .5L, stoneware, blue saltglaze, c.1900, $200-300.

a. Monk Holding Scroll, .5L, pottery, full color, Dümler & Breiden, #572, c.1900, $250-350.
b. Monk, .5L, porcelain, full color, c.1900, $200-300.
c. Tipsy Monk, .5L, porcelain, full color, Ernst Bohne Söhne, #5647, c.1900, $800-1100.
d. Nun, .5L, porcelain, black body, c.1900, $200-300.
e. Nun, .5L, stoneware, blue saltglaze, Merkelbach & Wick, #270, c.1900, $200-300.

f. Munich Child (HB body), 1.0L, stoneware, full color, Reinhold Hanke, #1285, early 1900s, $450-650.
g. Munich Child, .5L, porcelain, full color, J. Reinemann, c.1900, $400-600.
h. Munich Child (Barrel Body), .5L, porcelain, full color, Schierholz, c.1900, $750-1000.
i. Munich Child, .5L, porcelain, black robe, #46931, early 1900s, $250-350.
j. Munich Child, .5L, porcelain, full color, Martin Pauson, c.1900, $300-400.

a. Munich Child, .3L, pottery, full color, M. Girmscheid, #298, early 1900s, $250-350.
b. Munich Child, .5L, pottery, full color, Reinhold Merkelbach, #1, late 1800s, $300-450.
c. Munich Child (Holding Radish), .5L, pottery, Marzi & Remy, #314, early 1900s, $350-500.
d. Munich Child (Holding Chicken), .5L, pottery, full color, Reinhold Merkelbach, #323, early 1900s, $350-500.
e. Munich Child, .5L, pottery, full color, Merkelbach & Wick, c.1900, $300-450.

f. Skull on Book, .5L, porcelain, natural coloration, Ernst Bohne Söhne, #9136, c.1900, $650-850.
g. Skull (Caduceus Handle), .5L, porcelain, natural coloration, Ernst Bohne Söhne, #695, c.1900, $800-1000.
h. Skull, .5L, porcelain, natural coloration, Ernst Bohne Söhne, #8423, c.1900, $500-650.
i. Back-to-Back Skulls, .4L, porcelain, natural coloration, Ernst Bohne Söhne, c.1900, $800-1000.

a.   Skull, .5L, pottery, natural or coral coloration, Marzi & Remy, #1796, c.1900, $250-350.
b.   Happy Radish, .5L, porcelain, full color, Schierholz, c.1900, $350-475.
c.   Sad Radish, .5L, porcelain, full color, Schierholz, c.1900, $350-475.
d.   Cucumber, .5L, porcelain, full color, Schierholz, c.1900, $1200-1600.
e.   Mushroom with Dwarfs, .5L, porcelain, honey colored, Schierholz, c.1900, $2000-2500.

f.   Gentleman Boar Head, .5L, porcelain, full color with gray face, Schierholz, c.1900, $3500-4500.
g.   Stag Head, .5L, porcelain, full color, Schierholz, c.1900, $4500-6000.
h.   Monkey Head Eating Fruit, .5L, porcelain, full color, Ernst Bohne Söhne, #3949, c.1900, $3000-4000.
i.   Monkey Head (Orangutan), .5L, porcelain, full color, Ernst Bohne Söhne, #4781, c.1900, $1300-1800.

a. Bison Head, .5L, porclelain, full color, Ernst Bohne Söhne, #5827, c.1900, $1400-1800.
b. Gentleman Dog Head, .5L, porcelain, full color, Schierholz, c.1900, $2400-3000.
c. Gentleman Fox, .5L, porcelain, full color, Schierholz, c.1900, $2400-3000.
d. Gentleman Rabbit Head, .5L, porcelain, full color, Schierholz, c.1900, $2400-3000.

e. Sitting Alligator, .5L, porcelain, full color, Schierholz, c.1900, $900-1200.
f. Herrings (Fish), .5L, pottery, full color, Reinhold Merkelbach, #1152, c.1900, $300-450.
g. Fish, .5L, porcelain, full color, Schierholz, c.1900, $1000-1300.
h. Frog, .5L, porcelain, full color, Schierholz, c.1900, $1100-1400.
i. Frog, .25L, pottery, full color, M. Girmscheid, #825, early 1900s, $150-250.

a. Wraparound Alligator, .5L, porcelain, 3040, full color, Ernst Bohne Söhne, c.1900, $600-800.
b. Cat with Hangover, .5L, porcelain, honey colored, Schierholz, c.1900, $500-700.
c. Cat Holding Scroll, .5L, pottery, Merkelbach & Wick, c.1900, $450-600.
d. Cat on Book, .5L, porcelain, full color, Ernst Bohne Söhne, #514, c.1900, $2500-3500.
e. Cat with Seltzer Bottle, .5L, pottery, full color, Reinhold Merkelbach, #575, c.1900, $400-600.

f. Bulldog, .5L, pottery, full color, Reinhold Hanke, #1440, early 1900s, $350-500.
g. Poodle Dog Bowling, .5L, pottery, full color, Reinhold Merkelbach, #1452, early 1900s, $500-700.
h. Dapper Donkey, .5L, pottery, full color, Reinhold Hanke, #1454, early 1900s, $700-900.
i. Elephant, .5L, porcelain, full color, Schierholz, c.1900, $900-1200.
j. Elephant, .5L, pottery, full color, Reinhold Hanke, early 1900s, $600-800.

a. Fox, .5L, stoneware, blue saltglaze, Marzi & Remy, #806, c.1900, $350-450.
b. Fox, Student, .25L, pottery, full color, Diesinger, #739, early 1900s, $500-700.
c. Fox, Student, .5L, porcelain, full color, early 1900s, $500-700.
d. Seated Ram, .5L, porcelain, honey colored, Schierholz, c.1900, $500-700.
e. Drunken Monkey, .5L, porcelain, honey colored, Schierholz, c.1900, $500-700.

f. Monkey Resting on Stein, .5L, pottery, full color, Reinhold Merkelbach, #576, early 1900s, $300-450.
g. Monkey with Pipe & Stein, .5L, pottery, full color, M. Girmscheid, #828, early 1900s, $350-500.
h. Monkey with Top Hat, .5L, pottery, black accents, Reinhold Hanke, #1261, early 1900s, $250-350.
i. Military Monkey, .5L, pottery, full color, J.W. Remy, #769, early 1900s, $400-550.
j. Pig with Panel of Bowling Scene, .5L, pottery, Reinhold Merkelbach, #1116, early 1900s, $450-600.

a. Smoking Pig, .5L, porcelain, full color, Schierholz, c.1900, $500-650.
b. Singing Pig, .5L, porcelain, full color, Schierholz, c.1900, $500-650.
c. Gentleman Rooster, .5L, porcelain, full color, Schierholz, c.1900, $2200-2800.
d. Rooster, .5L, stoneware, Sarreguemines, c.1900, $700-1000.
e. Owl, .5L, pottery, M. Girmscheid, #740, early 1900s, $200-300.

f. Owl, .5L, stoneware, blue saltglaze, Hauber & Reuther, #64, 1890s, $500-700.
g. Owl (Bibite), .5L, stoneware, full color, Mettlach, #2036, c.1900, $800-1000.
h. Sitting Owl, .5L, porcelain, full color, Ernst Bohne Söhne, #1794, c.1900, $1600-2200.
i. Owl with Jester Cap, .5L, porcelain, full color, Schierholz, c.1900, $900-1200.

a. LAW High-Wheel Bicycle, .5L, porcelain, honey colored, Schierholz, c.1900, $400-550.
b. Bowling Ball, .5L, porcelain, brown wood tones, Schierholz, c.1900, $350-500.
c. Bowling Pin, .5L, porcelain, full color, c.1900, $300-400.
d. Bowling Pin, .5L, pottery, wood tones, Reinhold Hanke, #1134, early 1900s, $150-250.
e. Bowling Pin, .5L, pottery, full-color panels, Reinhold Merkelbach, #885, c.1900, $300-450.

f. Bowling Pins, 1.0L, pottery, green accents, M. Girmscheid, #1266, early 1900s, $250-350.
g. Bowling Pins, .5L, pottery, M. Girmscheid, #1222, early 1900s, $200-300.
h. High-Wheel Bicycle, .5L, stoneware, blue saltglaze, late 1800s, $1800-2400.
i. Football - Princeton Football Passer, .5L, porcelain, T. Maddocks Sons, full color, early 1900s, $400-500.

a. Artillery Shell, .5L, porcelain, early 1900s, $250-350.

b. Artillery Shell (1914), .5L, stoneware, blue glaze, $450-600.

c. Artillery Shell (1915), .5L, stoneware, blue glaze, #5309, $350-500.

d. Rook (Castle), .5L, stoneware, blue saltglaze, J. Reinemann, München, c.1900, $1300-1700.

e. Round Tower, .5L, pottery, full color, #1541, c.1900, $800-1200.

f. St. Elizabeth Church Tower (Nürnberg), .5L, stoneware, blue saltglaze, c.1900, $800-1100.

g. Frauenkirche Church Tower, .5L, stoneware, blue saltglaze, Theodor Wieseler, c.1900, $300-450.

h. Nürnberg Tower, .5L, pewter, Felsenstein & Mainzer, c.1900, $250-350.

i. Hot Air Balloon, .75L, pottery, full color, M. Girmscheid, #1232, early 1900s, $900-1200.

a. Barrel with Radish, .5L, stoneware, browns & beiges, Mettlach, #675, late 1800s, $100-150.
b. Barrel with Playing Cards, .5L, pottery, brown wood grain, Reinhold Hanke, #1778, 4 full-color playing cards on front, early 1900s, $300-450.
c. Perkeo on Barrel, .5L, porcelain, honey colored, Schierholz, c.1900, $650-850.
d. Munich Child on Barrel, .5L, porcelain, honey colored, Schierholz, c.1900, $750-900.
e. Beehive, .5L, pottery, Reinhold Merkelbach, #1384, early 1900s, $300-400.

f. Tree Trunk, 1.0L, stoneware, full color, Mettlach, #376, 1880s, $300-450.
g. Zugspitze Mountain, .5L, stoneware, full color, Martin Pauson, c.1900, $550-750.
h. Nürnberg Trichter (Funnel), .5L, porcelain, gray body, Schierholz, c.1900, $600-750.
i. Insulator, .5L, porcelain, blue and gold, early 1900s, $600-800.

17. Brewery

The obvious relationship between beer steins and beer brewers naturally leads to brewery steins. While beer-making implements can be found as decorations on steins made in the 1600s and 1700s, the motifs of specific brewers were generally used until the late 1800s.

Brewery steins can be found for many German and American breweries and occasionally for those from other countries. During the late 1800s and early 1900s, large quantities of brewery steins were produced as promotional tools for the breweries. Due to World War I and economic conditions of the period, few brewery steins were made between 1914 and the early 1920s. German brewery stein production rebounded from the late 1920s into the 1930s but ceased with the start of World War II.

The 1960s saw the start of the production of the modern German brewery steins, followed in the 1970s by the resurgence of American brewery steins. The growth of interest in collecting American brewery steins has been phenomenal, and particular designs frequently number in excess of 100,000 for some breweries.

German brewery steins are generally pottery or stoneware, and most designs are transfer decorations. Usually, these steins have pewter lids with relief or engraved-looking (actually impressed) designs matching the motif on the body. Sometimes undecorated glass steins with pewter lids depicting a brewery motif are found. They are generally worth much less than the pottery or stoneware steins.

American brewery steins are primarily pottery, stoneware, or glass. Pottery and stoneware are usually relief or transfer decorated. The glass steins are usually plain with decorated porcelain inlaid lids. Villeroy & Boch (Mettlach) made many American brewery steins. Some were etched, others were print-over-glaze, but most were PUG (print under glaze) or transfer decorations.

The lid is generally an integral part of a German brewery stein. The absence of the correct lid reduces the value to a small fraction of the lidded stein price. This will also generally be true of American brewery steins, except that many came with very simple steeple lids or with no lid at all. For those that were originally sold without a lid, the absence of a lid has an insignificant effect on value.

17.1 Collecting Brewery Steins

Brewery steins can be collected either according to geography or based on a specific brewery, which is a narrower approach.

Many collectors of antique German brewery steins concentrate on Munich breweries. The lack of steins representing other German cities makes it rather difficult to collect them specifically. It is possible to collect antique American brewery steins using the city approach, Chicago and St. Louis being two locations with many different examples.

Modern steins are generally easy to find, and in some cases, such as with Anheuser-Busch, many different steins have been made, so that a collection can easily be assembled from the steins of only one brewery. In recent years many of the collectors of the modern Anheuser-Busch steins have become interested in older brewery steins as well as other antique steins. Therefore, we are now seeing collections which include old as well as modern steins. Section 18 and the color photo section also cover this subject.

17.2 Evaluation Information

Price trends in the past ten years have been mostly upward for brewery steins. Most rare brewery steins have increased in value significantly. German brewery steins have recently had some up and down trends, however, the overall trend has been up for the last ten years. American brewery steins have increased in value at all price levels during the 1990s.

a. Glass, .5L, porcelain inlaid lid, *Old Times, Monarch Brewery (Chicago)*, 1920s, $100-200.
b. Glass, .5L, porcelain inlaid lid, *Pabst Blue Ribbon (Pabst Brewery Co.)*, 1920s, $100-200.
c. Glass, .5L, porcelain inlaid lid, *Primator, Garden City Brewery, Chicago, Ill.*, 1920s, $100-200.

d. Glass, .5L, porcelain inlaid lid, *Edelweiss, Hofbrau*, 1920s, $100-200.
e. Glass, .5L, porcelain inlaid lid, *Dober Brew, Mutual Brewing Co.*, 1920s, $200-300.
f. Glass, .5L, porcelain inlaid lid, *Michelob* (Anheuser-Busch, Inc.), 1920s, $200-300.
g. Glass, .5L, porcelain inlaid lid, *Michelob, Anheuser-Busch, Inc.*, dated 1933, $200-300.
h. Glass, .5L, porcelain inlaid lid, *Olympia, Pilsen Brewing Co. (Chicago)*, 1920s, $100-200.

a. Pottery, .5L, transfer, *Fred Sehring Brewing Co., Joliet, Ill.,* c.1900, no lid, $150-250.
b. Stoneware, .25L, transfer, Mettlach, #1909, *Everett Brewing Co., Everett, Wash.,* c.1900, no lid, $150-250.
c. Stoneware, .3L, transfer, Mettlach, #1909, *South Bend Brewing Association,* c.1900, no lid, $100-200.
d. Stoneware, .3L, transfer, marked Thuemler Mfg. Co., *Omaha Brewing Ass'n. Export Beer,* c.1900, no lid, $100-200.
e. Stoneware, .3L, transfer, Mettlach, #1526, *Rochester Brewing Co.,* c.1900, no lid, $100-200.

f. Stoneware, .4L, transfer, Mettlach, #2213, *Joseph Cramer, Eagle Brewery, Marshall, Mich.,* c.1900, no lid, $400-600.
g. Pottery, .25L, relief, *Rainier Brewery, Seattle, Wash.,* c.1900, no lid, $80-120.
h. Stoneware, .5L, relief, *Atlas Brewing Co., Chicago,* c.1900, no lid, $150-250.
i. Pottery, .3L, relief, *H. Weinhard (Brewery), Portland, Ore.,* c.1900, no lid, $100-200.
j. Stoneware, .4L, print over glaze, Mettlach, #1909, *Export Lager, Keeley Brewing Co., Chicago, Ill.,* c.1900, pewter lid, $200-300.

a. Stoneware, .5L, transfer, Mettlach, #2140, *E. Tosetti Brewing Co's., Chicago,* c.1900, pewter lid, $300-450.

b. Stoneware, .5L, transfer, Mettlach, #1909, *Bartholomay's Brewing Co., Rochester,* c.1900, inlaid lid, $250-350.

c. Stoneware, .5L, transfer, Mettlach, #1909, *Pilsner Export Beer,* c.1900, pewter lid, $350-500.

d. Stoneware, .5L, etched & transfer, Mettlach, #1998, *Martin Moehn Brewery, Burlington, Iowa,* late 1800s, inlaid lid, $2500-3500.

e. Pottery, .5L, relief, *Falstaff* (Brewery), 1950s, pewter lid, $50-100.

f. Pottery, .5L, transfer & relief, marked Reinhold Merkelbach, transfer, *John Kress Brewing Co., New York,* early 1900s, pewter lid, $300-400.

g. Pottery, .5L, transfer, *Louis Bergdall, Philadelphia, 1849-1893,* inlaid lid, $200-300.

h. Stoneware, .5L, transfer, *Lemps Special Brew, St. Louis,* early 1900s, pewter lid, $600-800.

i. Porcelain, .5L, transfer, *Faust* (tavern), early 1900s, inlaid lid, $300-500.

j. Pottery, .5L, relief, marked #997, *Porters Wiener Beer,* ceramic frog inside stein, early 1900s, pewter lid, $300-500.

a. Stoneware, 1.25L, impressed, *Hofbräuhaus, München,* early 1900s, relief pewter lid, $50-100.
b. Stoneware, .5L, transfer, *Hofbräuhaus, München,* early 1900s, relief pewter lid, $80-120.
c. Stoneware, .25L, impressed, *Hofbräuhaus, München,* early 1900s, relief pewter lid, $50-100.
d. Stoneware, 1.0L, impressed, *Hofbräuhaus, München,* late 1800s, relief pewter lid, $150-250.
e. Stoneware, 1.0L, impressed, *Hofbräuhaus, München,* early 1900s, relief pewter lid, $80-120.

f. Stoneware, 1.0L, transfer, *Hofbräuhaus, München,* design by Franz Ringer, early 1900s, relief pewter lid, $400-550.
g. Stoneware, .5L, transfer, *Hofbräuhaus, München,* early 1900s, relief pewter lid, $200-300.
h. Stoneware, .5L, impressed, *Hofbräuhaus, München,* early 1900s, relief pewter lid, $80-120.
i. Stoneware, .25L, impressed, *Hofbräuhaus, München,* early 1900s, relief pewter lid, $80-120.
j. Stoneware, 1.0L, impressed, *Unions-Bräu, München,* late 1800s, pewter lid, $300-500.

a.   Stoneware, .5L, transfer, *Hacker-Bräu, München*, early 1900s, relief pewter lid, $300-400.

b.   Stoneware, .5L, transfer, *Hacker-Bräu, München*, designed by Ludwig Hohlwein, c.1904, impressed pewter lid, $250-350.

c.   Pottery, .5L, transfer, *Hacker-Bräu, München*, early 1900s, impressed pewter lid, $250-350.

d.   Pottery, .5L, transfer, *Hacker-Bräu, München*, early 1900s, relief pewter lid, $250-350.

e.   Stoneware, 1.0L, transfer, Mettlach 1526, *Hacker-Bräu, München*, early 1900s, relief pewter lid, $700-1000.

f.   Stoneware, 1.0L, impressed, *Hacker-Bräu, München*, late 1800s, relief pewter lid, $300-500.

g.   Stoneware, 1.0L, impressed, *Hacker-Bräu, München*, late 1800s, relief pewter lid, $300-500.

h.   Stoneware, 1.0L, transfer, *Wagner-Bräu, München*, early 1900s, relief pewter lid, $400-600.

i.   Stoneware, 1.0L, impressed, *Wagner-Bräu, München*, early 1900s, relief pewter lid, $400-600.

j.   Stoneware, 1.0L, impressed, *Wagner-Bräu, München*, early 1900s, relief pewter lid, $350-550.

a. Pottery, .5L, transfer, *Pschorr-Bräu, München,* early 1900s, impressed pewter lid, $200-300.

b. Pottery, .5L, transfer, *Pschorr-Bräu, München,* early 1900s, impressed pewter lid, $200-300.

c. Stoneware, 1.0L, transfer, *Braeu Rosl, Pschorr-Bräu,* München, early 1900s, impressed pewter lid, $500-750.

d. Stoneware, 1.0L, transfer, *Pschorr-Bräu, München,* early 1900s, impressed pewter lid, $300-450.

e. Stoneware, 1.0L, impressed, *Pschorr-Bräu, München,* late 1800s, impressed pewter lid, $300-450.

f. Stoneware, .5L, transfer, *Pschorr-Bräu, München,* early 1900s, impressed pewter lid, $200-300.

g. Stoneware, 1.0L, impressed, *Pschorr-Bräu, München,* late 1800s, pewter lid, $400-600.

h. Stoneware, 1.0L, impressed & relief, *Pschorr-Bräu, München,* early 1900s, pewter lid, $300-450.

i. Stoneware, 1.0L, impressed, *Kochel-Bräu, München,* late 1800s, relief pewter lid, $400-600.

j. Stoneware, .5L, transfer, *Kochel-Bräu, München,* early 1900s, impressed pewter lid, $300-450.

a. Pottery, .5L, transfer, *Münchner Kindl-Brauerei,* early 1900s, relief pewter lid, $300-400.

b. Stoneware, 1.0L, transfer, *Münchner Kindl-Brauerei,* early 1900s, impressed pewter lid, $400-600.

c. Stoneware, 1.0L, impressed, *Münchner Kindl-Brauerei,* late 1800s, relief pewter lid, $350-500.

d. Stoneware, 1.0L, impressed, *Münchner Kindl-Brauerei,* late 1800s, relief pewter lid, $350-500.

e. Pottery, 1.0L, transfer, *Münchner Kindl-Brauerei,* early 1900s, relief pewter lid, $400-550.

f. Pottery, .5L, transfer, *Münchner Kindl-Brauerei,* early 1900s, relief pewter lid, $300-400.

g. Stoneware, 1.0L, impressed, *Münchner Kindl-Brauerei,* early 1900s, relief pewter lid, $400-600.

h. Stoneware, .5L, impressed, *Münchener Bürger-Bräu,* (Bürgerliches Brauhaus), early 1900s, relief pewter lid, $250-350.

i. Stoneware, .5L, transfer, *Münchener Bürger-Bräu,* (Bürgerliches Brauhaus), early 1900s, impressed pewter lid, $300-400.

j. Pottery, .5L, impressed, *Münchener Bürger-Bräu,* (Bürgerliches Brauhaus), early 1900s, relief pewter lid, $250-350.

a. Stoneware, .5L, impressed, *Münchener Bürger-Bräu,* (Bürgerliches Brauhaus), early 1900s, relief pewter lid, $250-350.
b. Pottery, .5L, transfer, *Münchener Bürger-Bräu,* (Bürgerliches Brauhaus), early 1900s, relief pewter lid, $250-350.
c. Stoneware, 1.0L, transfer, *Münchener Bürger-Bräu,* (Bürgerliches Brauhaus), early 1900s, relief pewter lid, $600-800.
d. Stoneware, 1.0L, impressed, *Münchener Bürger-Bräu,* (Bürgerliches Brauhaus), early 1900s, relief pewter lid, $350-450.
e. Stoneware, .5L, transfer, *Münchener Bürger-Bräu,* (Bürgerliches Brauhaus), early 1900s, relief pewter lid, $ 250-350.

f. Stoneware, .5L, transfer, *Spaten-Bräu, München,* early 1900s, pewter lid, $200-300.
g. Stoneware, .5L, transfer, *Spaten-Bräu, München,* early 1900s, pewter lid, $200-300.
h. Stoneware, .5L, transfer, *Spaten-Bräu, München,* early 1900s, relief pewter lid, $250-350.
i. Stoneware, 1.0L, transfer, *Spaten-Bräu, München,* early 1900s, pewter lid, $250-350.
j. Stoneware, 1.0L, transfer, *Spaten-Bräu, München,* early 1900s, relief pewter lid, $300-400.

a. Stoneware, 1.0L, transfer, *Lowen-Bräu, München,* early 1900s, impressed pewter lid, $100-200.

b. Stoneware, .5L, transfer, *Lowen-Bräu, München,* early 1900s, impressed pewter lid, $80-120.

c. Stoneware, 1.0L, impressed *Lowen-Bräu, München,* early 1900s, relief pewter lid, $100-200.

d. Stoneware, .5L, impressed, *Lowen-Bräu, München,* early 1900s, relief pewter lid, $100-200.

e. Stoneware, .5L, impressed, *Lowen-Bräu, München,* early 1900s, relief pewter lid, $100-200.

f. Stoneware, 1.0L, impressed, *Lowen-Bräu, München,* early 1900s, pewter lid, $100-200.

g. Stoneware, 1.0L, impressed, *Lowen-Bräu, München,* early 1900s, pewter lid, $150-250.

h. Stoneware, 1.0L, transfer, *Mathäser-Bräu, München,* early 1900s, relief pewter lid, $1000-1500.

i. Stoneware, 1.0L, impressed, *Mathäser-Bräu, München,* early 1900s, relief pewter lid, $350-550.

j. Stoneware, 1.0L, impressed, *Mathäser-Bräu, München,* late 1800s, impressed pewter lid, $350-550.

a. Stoneware, .5L, transfer, *Franziskaner Leist-Bräu, München,* early 1900s, impressed pewter lid, $200-300.
b. Stoneware, 1.0L, transfer, *Franziskaner Leist-Bräu, München,* early 1900s, impressed pewter lid, $400-600.
c. Stoneware, 1.0L, transfer, *Franziskaner Leist-Bräu, München,* early 1900s, impressed pewter lid, $300-500.
d. Stoneware, .4L, impressed, *Franziskaner Leist-Bräu, München,* early 1900s, impressed pewter lid, $250-350.
e. Stoneware, 1.0L, impressed, *Franziskaner Leist-Bräu, München,* late 1800s, impressed pewter lid, $350-500.

f. Stoneware, .5L, transfer, *Franziskaner Leist-Bräu, München,* early 1900s, impressed pewter lid, $250-350.
g. Stoneware, .5L, transfer, *Franziskaner Leist-Bräu, München,* early 1900s, impressed pewter lid, $250-350.
h. Pottery, .5L, transfer, *Zacherl-Bräu, München,* early 1900s, relief pewter lid, $350-500.
i. Stoneware, 1.0L, transfer, *Zacherl-Bräu, München,* early 1900s, relief pewter lid, $600-900.
j. Stoneware, 1.0L, impressed, *Zacherl-Bräu, München,* late 1800s, relief pewter lid, $500-800.

a.   Stoneware, .5L, transfer, *Paulaner-Bräu, München,* early 1900s, relief pewter lid, $200-300.

b.   Stoneware, .5L, transfer, *Paulaner-Bräu, München,* early 1900s, relief pewter lid, $250-350.

c.   Stoneware, 1.0L, impressed, *Paulaner-Bräu, München,* late 1800s, relief pewter lid, $300-450.

d.   Stoneware, 1.0L, transfer, *Paulaner-Bräu, München,* early 1900s, relief pewter lid, $300-450.

e.   Stoneware, 1.0L, impressed, *Paulaner-Bräu, München,* early 1900s, relief pewter lid, $300-450.

f.   Stoneware, .5L, transfer, *Schwabinger-Bräu, München,* early 1900s, relief pewter lid, $300-500.

g.   Stoneware, 1.0L, impressed, *Schwabinger-Bräu, München,* late 1800s, relief pewter lid, $400-600.

h.   Stoneware, 1.0L, impressed, *Schwabinger-Bräu, München,* late 1800s, relief pewter lid, $300-500.

i.   Stoneware, 1.0L, impressed, *Schwabinger-Bräu, München,* early 1900s, relief pewter lid, $300-500.

j.   Stoneware, .5L, transfer, *Salvatorbrauerei, München,* early 1900s, relief pewter lid, $300-500.

a. Stoneware, 1.0L, transfer, *Augustiner-Bräu, München,* late 1800s, relief pewter lid, $350-500.

b. Stoneware, 1.0L, transfer, *Augustiner-Bräu, München,* late 1800s, relief pewter lid, $350-500.

c. Stoneware, 1.0L, transfer, *Augustiner-Bräu, München,* late 1800s, relief pewter lid, $350-500.

d. Pottery, .5L, transfer, *Augustiner-Bräu, München,* early 1900s, relief pewter lid, $300-400.

e. Stoneware, 1.0L, transfer, *Kloster-Brauerei, München,* early 1900s, relief pewter lid, $800-1200.

f. Pottery, .5L, transfer, *Kloster-Brauerei, München,* early 1900s, relief, pewter lid, $350-500.

g. Stoneware, 1.0L, impressed, *Eberl-Bräu, München,* early 1900s, relief pewter lid, $300-400.

h. Stoneware, .5L, transfer, *Eberl-Bräu, München,* early 1900s, relief pewter lid, $350-500.

i. Stoneware, 1.0L, impressed, *Thomas-Bräu, München,* early 1900s, relief pewter lid, $300-400.

j. Pottery, .5L, transfer, *Thomas-Bräu, München,* early 1900s, relief pewter lid, $250-350.

a. Stoneware, .5L, transfer, *Leder-Bräu, Nürnberg,* early 1900s, relief pewter lid, $200-300.

b. Stoneware, .5L, transfer, *Brauhaus, Nürnberg,* early 1900s, relief pewter lid, $200-300.

c. Pottery, .5L, transfer, *Schwanenbräu, Herbsthausen,* early 1900s, relief pewter lid, $300-400.

d. Stoneware, .5L, transfer, *Brauerei z.d. 3 Kannen,* early 1900s, relief pewter lid, $250-350.

e. Pottery, .5L, transfer, *Brauerei, zum Storchen, Speyer,* early 1900s, pewter lid, $300-400.

f. Pottery, .5L, impressed, *Rizzi Bräu, Kulmbach,* early 1900s, impressed pewter lid, $200-300.

g. Pottery, .5L, impressed, *Rizzi Bräu, Kulmbach,* early 1900s, impressed pewter lid, $200-300.

h. Pottery, .5L, transfer, *Hofbräu, Würzburger,* dated 1905, impressed pewter lid, $200-300.

i. Pottery, .5L, transfer, *Schloss-Bräu, Friedenfels,* early 1900s, relief pewter lid, $250-350.

j. Pottery, .5L, transfer, *Kulmbacher Rizzibräu, Kulmbach,* early 1900s, impressed pewter lid, $200-300.

a. Stoneware, .5L, transfer, *Stadt-Brauerei, Spalt,* early 1900s, impressed pewter lid, $150-250.
b. Stoneware, .5L, transfer, *Hechtbrauerei, Biberach,* early 1900s, relief pewter lid, $200-300.
c. Stoneware, .5L, transfer, *Stadt-Brauerei, Roth,* early 1900s, impressed pewter lid, $150-250.
d. Stoneware, .5L, transfer, *Hofbräu, A.G., Bamberg,* early 1900s, impressed pewter lid, $200-300.
e. Stoneware, .5L, transfer, *Göppinger Radbier,* early 1900s, impressed pewter lid, $150-250.

f. Stoneware, 1.0L, impressed, *Brauerei-Bachbräu, Weilheim,* early 1900s, impressed pewter lid, $300-450.
g. Stoneware, 1.0L, transfer, *Hasenbräu, Augsburg,* early 1900s, impressed pewter lid, $200-300.
h. Stoneware, 1.0L, transfer, *Freiherrl Tucher Brauerei, Nürnberg,* early 1900s, relief pewter lid, $200-300.
i. Stoneware, 1.0L, transfer, *Stuttgarter Hofbräu,* early 1900s, impressed pewter lid, $200-300.
j. Pottery, 1.0L, transfer, *Heineken's aan de Zuiderzee, New York World's Fair 1939,* pewter lid, $400-600.

a. Stoneware, 1.0L, transfer, *St. Georgenbräu, Buttenheim,* early 1900s, relief pewter lid, $200-300.
b. Stoneware, 1.0L, transfer, *Gampert-Bräu, Weissenbrunn, Bayern,* 1920s, metal lid, $200-300.
c. Stoneware, 1.0L, transfer, *Humbser Bräu,* early 1900s, relief pewter lid, $150-250.
d. Stoneware, 1.0L, impressed, *Thüringer Hof, Leipzig,* early 1900s, relief pewter lid, $250-400.
e. Pottery, .5L, impressed, *Frankenbräu, Bamberg,* early 1900s, relief pewter lid, $200-300.

f. Stoneware, 3.0L, handpainted, *Schwanen-Brauerei, Giengen-Brz.,* late 1800s, two handles & two pewter lids, $1000-1400.

18. Modern Brewery

The most rapid-growing segment of stein collecting in the 1990s has been modern brewery steins. This popular advertising medium used by German and American breweries from the late 1800s through the 1920s is experiencing a revival.

18.1 History and Production

Since the mid-1970s, Anheuser-Busch has initiated the production of over 500 different steins, most of which display at least one of its symbols or trademarks. Ceramarte, a Brazilian manufacturer specializing in promotional products, is responsible for the majority of these steins. Gerz has produced a significant portion as well. Most Anheuser-Busch steins made after 1980 were produced in quantities of 5000 to 100,000.

Other breweries, including Coors, Miller, and Stroh, have followed the lead of Anheuser-Busch in marketing this new collectible and in using Ceramarte as the primary manufacturing source. The appeal of Anheuser-Busch steins and those from other breweries has led to greater interest in beer stein collecting.

18.2 Collecting Modern Brewery Steins

Unlike other areas of stein collecting, the modern brewery steins offer an increasing supply of new items to collect as well as a fairly steady availability of already-issued steins. Because of the large assortment that exists, most collectors focus on one or two breweries, and, in many cases, they will collect only certain types of modern brewery steins such as character/brewery steins or those that depict brewery logos. Production facilities and other decorations that relate directly to brewing also make popular focus areas for collectors. A valuable reference for Anheuser-Busch steins can be found listed in section 20.

18.3 Evaluation Information

Modern brewery steins is the most difficulty category to generalize about past price performance. There have been some steins that have had incredible price increases during the 1990s while others have actually decreased in value.

Anheuser-Busch steins have offered collectors the most opportunities to own steins that have performed better than any antique steins during the 1990s. Many of the Anheuser-Busch steins produced in the 1970s and sold for around $10 have increased during the 1990s to the $300 - $500 range. Most of these increased during the late 1980s and the 1990s. In the late 1990s, there have been decreases in some of the more expensive steins.

From 1980 on, the majority of steins produced increased only moderately in value. There have been a few exceptions that have increased in value 100% to 300%. Some of the steins with larger production quantities have decreased in value.

Opposite page top:

a. Anheuser-Busch, .5L, stoneware, Ceramarte, Budweiser, California, CS56, 1981, $30-60.
b. Anheuser-Busch, .5L, stoneware, Ceramarte, Budweiser, San Francisco, CS59, 1983, $75-150.
c. Anheuser-Busch, .5L, stoneware, Ceramarte, Budweiser, Texas, CS52, 1981, $30-60.
d. Anheuser-Busch, .5L, stoneware, Ceramarte, Budweiser, Chicago Skyline, CS40, 1980, $30-60.
e. Anheuser-Busch, .5L, stoneware, Ceramarte, Budweiser, Chicagoland, CS51, 1981, $30-60.

Opposite page second row:

f. Anheuser-Busch, 1.0L, stoneware, Chicago, Our Kind of Town, 1982, $50-100.
g. Anheuser-Busch, .5L, stoneware, Ceramarte, German Tavern Scene, CS4, 1976, $50-100.
h. Anheuser-Busch, .5L, stoneware, Ceramarte, German Tavern Scene, CS4, with reverse colors, 1976, $200-350.
i. Anheuser-Busch, .5L, stoneware, Ceramarte, Busch Gardens, c.1975, $75-150.
j. Anheuser-Busch, .5L, stoneware, Ceramarte, Busch Gardens, Williamsburg, c.1975, $75-150.

a. Anheuser-Busch, 1.0L, pottery, Rogers Ceramic Studio, 10 Years of Service, 1970s, $150-250.

b. Anheuser-Busch, 1.0L, stoneware, Gerz, 20th Century In Review Series, 1900-1919, CS311, 1997, $150-250.

c. Anheuser-Busch, 1.0L, stoneware, Gerz, 20th Century In Review Series, 1920-1939, CS335, 1998, $150-250.

Opposite page third row:

k. Anheuser-Busch, .5L, stoneware, Ceramarte, German Pilique miniature variation of CS5, 1975, $250-400.
l. Anheuser-Busch, .5L, stoneware, Ceramarte, Americana, CS17, one of six different designs, late 1970s, $300-500.
m. Anheuser-Busch, .5L, stoneware, Ceramarte, Bud Girl, CS21, late 1970s, $600-900.
n. Anheuser-Busch, 1.0L, stoneware, Ceramarte, Michelob, CS45, 1980, $50-100.
o. Anheuser-Busch, .5L, stoneware, Ceramarte, Blue Delft, CS11, one of six different designs, 1977, $200-400.
p. Anheuser-Busch, .5L, stoneware, Ceramarte, A & Eagle, Barrel, CS26, 1976, $100-200.

Opposite page bottom:

q. Anheuser-Busch, .5L, stoneware, Ceramarte, Hamburg (one of six cities), CS16, late 1970s, $200-300.
r. Anheuser-Busch, .5L, stoneware, Ceramarte, Heidelberg (one of six cities), CS16, late 1970s, $200-300.
s. Anheuser-Busch, .5L, stoneware, Ceramarte, Michelob, CS27, 1976, $100-200.
t. Anheuser-Busch, .5L, stoneware, Ceramarte, CS19, red cases, name impressed, 1980, $50-100.
u. Anheuser-Busch, .5L, stoneware, Ceramarte, CS19, red cases & barrels, name impressed, pre-1980, $75-150.

a. Anheuser-Busch, .5L, stoneware, Ceramarte, Bud Man, CS100, 1989, $50-100.
b. Anheuser-Busch, .5L, stoneware, Ceramarte, Bud Man, CS213, 1993, $50-100.
c. Anheuser-Busch, .5L, stoneware, Thewalt and Gerz, Bevo Fox, CS160, 1991, $150-250.
d. Anheuser-Busch, .5L, porcelain, Albert Stahl, Budweiser Frog, CS301, 1997, $175-275.

e. Anheuser-Busch, .5L, porcelain, Albert Stahl, Bud Ice Penguin, CS315, 1997, $100-200.
f. Anheuser-Busch, .5L, porcelain, Albert Stahl, Louie the Lizard, CS344, 1997, $100-200.
g. Anheuser-Busch, .5L, stoneware, Gerz, Mallard, GM7, 1994, $125-250.
h. Anheuser-Busch, .5L, stoneware, Gerz, Giant Panda, GM8, 1995, $125-250.

a. Anheuser-Busch, 1.0L, stoneware, Ceramarte, Opera Card Series, *Martha*, CS300, 1997, $100-175.
b. Anheuser-Busch, 1.0L, stoneware, Ceramarte, Opera Card Series, *The Hugenhots*, CS331, 1997, $100-175.
c. Anheuser-Busch, 1.0L, stoneware, Ceramarte, American Originals Series, Black & Tan, CS314, 1997, $125-225.
d. Anheuser-Busch, 1.0L, stoneware, Ceramarte, American Originals Series, Faust, CS330, 1997, $125-225.
e. Anheuser-Busch, .5L, stoneware, Gerz, The Dugout, GL1, 1993, $50-100.

f. Anheuser-Busch, .5L, stoneware, Gerz, Rosie the Riveter, GM9, 1995, $75-150.
g. Anheuser-Busch, .5L, stoneware, Gerz, Call of the Wild Series, Grizzly, GL12, 1997, $50-100.
h. Anheuser-Busch, .5L, stoneware, Gerz, Call of the Wild Series, Wolf, GL9, 1996, $50-100.
i. Anheuser-Busch, .5L, stoneware, Ceramarte, Upland Game Birds Series, Prairie Chicken, CS337, 1998, $75-150.
j. Anheuser-Busch, .5L, stoneware, Ceramarte, Upland Game Birds Series, Wild Turkey, CS327, 1998, $75-150.

a.   Anheuser-Busch, 1.0L, stoneware, Ceramarte, Civil War Series, General Grant, CS181, 1992, $100-200.
b.   Anheuser-Busch, 1.0L, stoneware, Ceramarte, Civil War Series, General Lee, CS188, 1993, $100-200.
c.   Anheuser-Busch, 1.0L, porcelain, Gerz, Norman Rockwell, Triple Self-Portrait, GM6, 1994, $75-150.
d.   Anheuser-Busch, 1.0L, porcelain, Gerz, John F. Kennedy, GM4, 1993, $100-200.
e.   Anheuser-Busch, 1.0L, stoneware, Ceramarte, 1998 World Cup, CS351, 1998, $100-200.

f.   Anheuser-Busch, .5L, stoneware, Ceramarte, Post Convention - Olympic, Michelob, CS54, 1982, $50-100.
g.   Anheuser-Busch, .5L, stoneware, Ceramarte, Post Convention - Olympic, Budweiser, CS53, 1982, $50-100.
h.   Anheuser-Busch, 1.5L, stoneware, Ceramarte, Post Convention - Olympic, all brands, CS55, 1982, $100-200.
i.   Anheuser-Busch, .5L, stoneware, Ceramarte, 1984 Budweiser Olympic Games, CS60, 1984, $25-50.
j.   Anheuser-Busch, 4.0L, stoneware, Gerz, 1996 Olympic Games, CS267, 1996, $600-900.

a. Anheuser-Busch, .5L, stoneware, Ceramarte, Budweiser, Summer Olympics, CS92, 1988, $20-40.

b. Anheuser-Busch, .5L, stoneware, Ceramarte, Budweiser, Winter Olympics, CS85, 1988, $20-40.

c. Anheuser-Busch, .5L, stoneware, Ceramarte, 1992 U.S. Olympic Summer Team, CS163, $20-40.

d. Anheuser-Busch, .5L, stoneware, Ceramarte, 1992 U.S. Olympic Winter Team, CS162, $20-40.

e. Anheuser-Busch, .5L, stoneware, Ceramarte, 1996 U.S. Olympic Team Gymnastics, CS262, $20-40.

f. Anheuser-Busch, .5L, stoneware, Ceramarte, 1996 U.S. Olympic Team Track & Field, CS246, $20-40.

g. Anheuser-Busch, .5L, stoneware, Ceramarte, 1996 Centennial Olympic Games, CS266, $15-30.

h. Anheuser-Busch, .5L, stoneware, Ceramarte, 1996 Official Centennial Olympic Games, CS259, $20-40.

i. Anheuser-Busch, .5L, stoneware, Gerz, Nebraska, Traditions, SO50512, 1991, $15-30.
j. Anheuser-Busch, .5L, stoneware, Gerz, Nebraska, Wildlife, N4117, 1993, $15-30.
k. Anheuser-Busch, .5L, stoneware, Gerz, Kansas, Good To Know You, SO53618, 1991, $15-30.
l. Anheuser-Busch, .5L, stoneware, Gerz, Wake Up To Missouri, SO54149, 1991, $15-30.
m. Anheuser-Busch, .5L, stoneware, Gerz, Oklahoma, Better Sooner Than Later, SO53689, 1991, $15-30.
n. Anheuser-Busch, .5L, stoneware, Gerz, San Antonio, Fiesta, SO52190, 1991, $15-30.

a. Anheuser-Busch, .5L, stoneware, Staffel Stoneware and Ceramarte, Horseshoe Series, CS68, CS77, CS78, CS76, CS94, 1986-1988, $100-200.

b. Anheuser-Busch, .5L, stoneware, Ceramarte, Clydesdales Series (first five), CS74, CS90, CS99, CS131, CS161, 1987-1992, $75-150.

c. Anheuser-Busch, .5L, stoneware, Gerz, Post Convention Heritage Series, CS87, CS102, CS114, CS141, CS174, 1988-1991, $100-200.

d. Anheuser-Busch, .5L, stoneware, Ceramarte, History of Brewing Series (also known as the Limited Edition Series), CS64, CS65, CS71, CS75, CS98, 1985-1989, $100-200.

e. Anheuser-Busch, .5L, stoneware, Ceramarte, A & Eagle Trademark Series, with tin container, CS201, CS218, CS238, CS255, 1992-1995, $100-200.

a. Anheuser-Busch, .5L, stoneware, Ceramarte, Historical Landmark Series, CS67, CS73, CS83, CS84, 1986-1988, $100-200.
b. Anheuser-Busch, .5L, stoneware, Gerz, Wild Mustang, GL15, 1998, $50-100.
c. Anheuser-Busch, .5L, stoneware, Gerz, Winchester Model 94, GM10, 1994, $75-125.
d. Anheuser-Busch, .5L, stoneware, Gerz, Winchester, GL2, 1994, $50-100.

e. Anheuser-Busch, .5L, ceramic, made in Italy, Bud Girl Commemorative Set, AN1, 1973, $1200-1800.
f. Anheuser-Busch, .5L, porcelain, Rastal, Porcelain Heritage Series, Berninghaus, CS105, 1990, $50-100.
g. Anheuser-Busch, .5L, porcelain, Rastal, Porcelain Heritage Series, After The Hunt, CS155, 1991, $50-100.
h. Anheuser-Busch, .5L, porcelain, Gerz, Porcelain Heritage Series, Cherub, CS182, 1992, $50-100.

i. Anheuser-Busch, .5L, stoneware, Ceramarte, St. Patrick's Day Series (first six), CS166, CS109, CS193, CS210, CS242, CS269, 1991-1996, $175-150.

a. Anheuser-Busch, .5L, stoneware, Gerz, Birds of Prey Series, CS164, CS183, CS212, CS264, 1991-1995, $800-1000.
b. Anheuser-Busch, .5L, stoneware, Gerz, Saturday Evening Post Christmas Collection, GM1, GM13, GM3, 1992-1994, $250-400.

c. Anheuser-Busch, .5L, stoneware, Gerz, Founders Series, CS216, CS229, CS265, CS286, 1993-1996, $300-450.
d. Anheuser-Busch, .5L, stoneware, Gerz, Sports Legends Series, CS142, CS171, CS206, 1991-1993, $100-200.

e. Anheuser-Busch, .5L, stoneware, Gerz, Classic Series, CS93, CS104, CS113, CS130, 1988-1991, $150-250.
f. Anheuser-Busch, .5L, stoneware, Gerz, Saturday Evening Post Christmas I, II & III, GL5, GL6, GL13, 1995-1997, $125-225.

a. Anheuser-Busch, .5L, stoneware, Ceramarte, Archives Series, CS169, CS190, CS222, CS252, 1992-1995, $150-250.

b. Anheuser-Busch, .5L, stoneware, Ceramarte, Busch Gardens Extinction is Forever Series, no #, BG1, BG2, 1985-1992, $125-225.

c. Anheuser-Busch, .5L, stoneware, Gerz, First Hunt Series, GM2, GM5, GM16, GM17, 1993-1996, $300-450.

d. Anheuser-Busch, .5L, stoneware, Ceramarte, Discover America Series, CS107, CS129, CS138, 1990-1992, $75-125.

e. Anheuser-Busch, .5L, stoneware, Ceramarte, Endangered Species Series, CS106, CS126, CS135, CS173, CS199, CS226, CS253, CS283, 1989-1996, $500-700.

f. Anheuser-Busch, .5L, stoneware, Ceramarte, Budweiser Field & Stream Set, with wood display shelf, CS95, 1988, $175-275.

a. Anheuser-Busch, .5L, stoneware, Ceramarte, Budweiser Holiday Series, CS19, CS50, CS57, CS58, CS62, CS63, CS66, CS70, CS88, CS89, CS112, CS133, CS167, CS192SE, CS211SE, CS263SE, CS273SE, CS313SE, CS343, 1980-1998. CS19, $50-100; CS50, $100-200; CS57 to CS167, $10-20 each; CS192SE to CS313SE $40-80 each; CS343, $10-20.

b. Anheuser-Busch, .5L, stoneware, Ceramarte, Oktoberfest Series, SO54077, CS185, CS291, CS202, 1991-1996, $50-100.

a. Miller, 1.0L, stoneware, Alwe, Plank Road Brewery, 1989, $30-60.
b. Miller, .5L, stoneware, Ceramarte, Great American Achievements, 1986-1990, $50-100.

c. Miller, .75L, stoneware, Thewalt, Frederick Miller, 1989, $10-25.
d. Miller, .75L, stoneware, Thewalt, Delivery Wagon, 1990, $10-25.
e. Coors, .5L, porcelain, four steins from Winterfest Series, early 1990s, $40-80.

f. Miller, .5L, porcelain, Christmas Series, early 1990s, $40-80.

a. Coors, .5L, porcelain, CUI, Ltd. Editions, Coors Rodeo, early 1990s, $40-80.

b. Coors, 1.0L, porcelain, Legacy, 19_1, $15-30.
c. Coors, 1.0L, porcelain, Legacy, 1992, $15-30.
d. Webco, 1.0L, stoneware, Ceramarte, Schultz, 1972, $50-100.
e. Webco, .5L, stoneware, Ceramarte, Dooley, 1972, $50-100.
f. Webco, .5L, stoneware, Gerz, Countess, 1982, $50-100.
g. Webco, .5L, stoneware, Gerz, Old Man, 1990, $50-100.

h. Webco, .5L, stoneware, Ceramarte, Officer Suds, 1982, $50-100.
i. Webco, .5L, stoneware, Gerz, Farmer Magee, 1982, $50-100.
j. Webco, .5L, stoneware, Gerz, Oliver Wendell Foams, 1993, $50-100.
k. Webco, .5L, stoneware, Gerz, Bubbles La Brew, 1989, $50-100.

19. Modern Era

Beer stein production has undergone many changes since 1945. Prior to World War I, the beer stein industry in Germany was, perhaps, the most noteworthy segment of the ceramic industry in that country. From the beginning of World War I through the end of World War II, various economic and physical (wartime) influences significantly reduced the production and manufacturing capacity of the German ceramic manufacturers.

During the first ten years following the end of World War II, beer stein production in Germany gradually revived. While most steins produced during the 1950s were reproductions of earlier designs using old molds, two notable types of new steins were introduced: Regimental and souvenir. The former are similar to pre-1914 Imperial Regimental steins. These are frequently referred to as *reproductions*, because they are fairly accurate copies. See Section 14. The souvenir steins were produced for sale to U.S. military personnel and were designed with military unit information applicable to the buyer. Examples of these can be found in Section 15.

During the 1960s and 1970s, the number of beer stein producers decreased. Now, only a few firms are responsible for well over 50% of the German beer stein production.

Historically, nearly all stein production took place in Germany and nearby areas. However, in the mid-1970s, Ceramarte of Brazil began producing steins and, during the 1980s, became the largest producer of beer steins in the world, specializing in promotional products for companies and organizations. Examples of the various types of steins produced by Ceramarte can be found in this section, Section 18, and the color section.

In recent years, about one-third of the steins produced by German manufacturers were exported. In addition, tourists from America and other countries bought a significant percentage of the steins sold inside Germany. Other European countries account for most of the export sales not made to the United States, although sales to Japan have been on the rise in recent years.

19.1 Production

Most steins being made today are produced using the same techniques that were developed about 100 years ago. In many cases, the same molds are being used. Some companies, such as Thewalt, use a mark to identify designs made from an old (original) mold. The glazes (colors) that are used on beer steins have undergone extensive development over the years. The accompanying color section shows nearly all of the existing color styles, many of which were developed during the 1980s.

While some German manufacturers were slow to modernize, others such as Thewalt and Villeroy & Boch have adopted modern manufacturing techniques. While most steins are made using all of the same procedures as steins that were made at the turn of the century, modern equipment is frequently utilized for such mundane, labor-intensive tasks as mixing, moving or carrying, cleaning, wrapping, and packaging.

Villeroy & Boch (Mettlach) became famous for their etched steins. During the 1980s, this company produced many steins that closely resemble the original c.1900 etched steins. Different and secret techniques are used to make these modern steins. Both Thewalt and Gerz also produced etched-type steins during the 1980s. Porcelain steins with transfer or handpainted decorations are produced in the same manner as c.1900 steins. Glass steins are also made in the same way and in many of the same styles as earlier steins.

Faience steins have been produced (or reproduced) in recent years, primarily as items for gift stores. Sometimes production quality is good enough to confuse novice collectors. Generally, the quality of the newer faience steins is not the same as their 200-year-old counterparts, but they have important merit of their own.

Pewter relief steins are currently made in the same manner as their c.1900 counterparts. Except for natural aging (patina), it can be difficult to distinguish the new pewter steins from the old.

19.2 Limited Editions

Production of limited edition collectible steins increased in the 1980s. First introduced by Gerz in 1974, limited edition steins have become popular as a result of the overall growth of the beer stein collecting hobby. Limited editions are commonly issued in quantities such as 1000, 2500, 4000, 5000, or 10,000. Occasionally, however, much lower or higher quantities are made available.

19.3 Evaluation Information

Price trends for steins produced over the last 50 years can be more difficult to establish than for older steins. First, we need to consider that many of the steins are still being made and therefore can be purchased new in a retail store. Secondly, increases in production costs have led to much higher retail prices for new steins.

Generally, limited editions have performed considerably better than other modern steins. While very few general interest steins have performed as well as some of the Anheuser-Busch steins (see Section 18), there have been some that have increased in value substantially.

Some of the factories involved in stein production from 1950 to the present:	
Factory	**Current Status**
Beyer GmbH	closed 1995
Ceramarte (Brazil)	producing
W. Corzelius	producing
Domex	producing
Dümler & Breiden	closed 1957
Eckhardt & Engler	closed c.1971
Gerz GmbH	closed 1999
M. Girmscheid	producing, but not steins
W. Goebel	producing, but not steins
Kurt Hammer	producing
Reinhold Hanke	producing, but not steins
Elisabeth Liegl	producing
Lindner Porzellan	producing
Marzi & Remy	closed
Rastal	producing
J.W. Remy	closed 1960s
Sahm	producing
Schierholz & Söhn	producing
Albert Stahl & Co.	producing
A.J. Thewalt	producing
Villeroy & Boch	producing
Westerwald Team	producing
Wick Werke	closed 1984
Würfel & Müller (King)	producing
Zoeller & Born	producing

Opposite page bottom:

f. Stoneware, .5L, incised, Villeroy & Boch, Snow White, Fairy Tale Series, Brothers Grimm, Limited Edition 10,000, 1980, inlaid lid, $120-180.

g. Stoneware, .5L, incised, Villeroy & Boch, Hansel & Gretel, Fairy Tale Series, Brothers Grimm, Limited Edition 10,000, 1980, inlaid lid, $120-180.

h. Stoneware, .5L, incised, Villeroy & Boch, Pied Piper, Fairy Tale Series, Limited Edition 10,000, 1981, inlaid lid, $120-180.

i. Stoneware, .5L, incised, Villeroy & Boch, The Red Knight, Russian Fairy Tale Series, Limited Edition 10,000, 1986, inlaid lid, $120-180.

j. Stoneware, .5L, incised, Villeroy & Boch, Mercedes, Centennial Car Series, Limited Edition 10,000, 1987, inlaid lid, $120-180.

a. Stoneware, 1.0L, cameo, Villeroy & Boch, Spring, Four Seasons Series, Limited Edition 10,000, 1978, inlaid lid, $200-300.

b. Stoneware, 1.0L, cameo, Villeroy & Boch, Summer, Four Seasons Series, Limited Edition 10,000, 1979, inlaid lid, $200-300.

c. Stoneware, 1.0L, cameo, Villeroy & Boch, Fall, Four Seasons Series, Limited Edition 10,000, 1980, inlaid lid, $200-300.

d. Stoneware, 1.0L, cameo, Villeroy & Boch, Winter, Four Seasons Series, Limited Edition 10,000, 1981, inlaid lid, $200-300.

e. Stoneware, .5L, incised, Villeroy & Boch, Wiliam Tell, 1981, inlaid lid, $100-150.

Identification of new Regimental steins is usually not difficult, although some new steins are very similiar to the originals. Many things can indicate a Regimental stein is not an original, including:

1. Porcelain steins with a manufacturer's marks on the bottom are almost always new (1 in 1000 old Regimentals are marked). A common new mark is a crown in blue or gold.

2. A lithophane of a semi-nude woman indicates a new stein.

3. A stamped rather than cast pewter lid would indicate a modern stein.

4. Information about the unit (Regiment) that is not correct, such as putting Munich in Prussia, would indicate a new stein.

5. A sharply tapered body is frequently an indication of a new stein.

6. Trying to determine age using transfer vs. hand-painting is unreliable.

Opposite page and above:

New Regimental steins (reproductions), .5L, porcelain, made by various manufacturers, generally unmarked, transfer decorations, 1960s through 1990s, pewter lids, current retail store prices for new steins, $100-150, current price in secondary (resale) market, $50-$200.

Right:

New Regimental steins (reproductions), .5L, pottery, unknown manufacturers, transfer decorations, 1970s, pewter lids, current price in secondary (resale) market, $125-$250.

This page:
Faience, .75L to 1.5L, transfer decorations, 1960s through 1990s, pewter mounts resemble 18th century pewter, price in secondary (resale) market, $100-$250.

Stoneware, .5L, primarily from A. Thewalt and Gerz, 1980s and early 1990s, pewter lids, original retail store prices, $60-120.

Stoneware, .5L, primarily from A. Thewalt and Gerz, 1980s and early 1990s, pewter lids, original retail store prices, $60-120.

a.   Stoneware, .5L, Cermarte, 1970s, pewter lid, price in secondary (resale) market, $150-$300.

b.   Stoneware, 1.0L, Cermarte, 1970s, pewter lid, price in secondary (resale) market, $200-$400.

c.   Stoneware, .5L, Duck Stamps, by C.U.I., 1985, 1990, 1991, 1992, pewter lids, price in secondary (resale) market, $30-60 each.

d.   Stoneware, .5L, Ducks Unlimited, Waterfowl of North America Series, by C.U.I., made in China, 1990s, pewter lids, price in secondary (resale) market, $100-$200.

The steins on the following four pages are currently being produced in Germany. The values listed are the approximate retail prices at stores in the United States.

a. Stoneware, 1.0L, New York City Commemorative Stein, Famous Cities of the World Series, Limited Edition of 9000, inlaid lid, $230-250.

b. Stoneware, .25L, Fantasy Castle Stein, Limited Edition of 5000, inlaid lid, $100-120.

c. Stoneware, 1.0L, Black Forest Commemorative Stein, Germany's Most Beautiful, Citadels, Castles & Buildings Series, Limited Edition of 9000, inlaid lid, $250-275.

d. Stoneware, .5L, Fire Station Stein, Limited Edition of 5000, pewter lid, $180-200.

e. Stoneware, .5L, Munich Panorama Stein, Limited Edition of 9000, inlaid lid, $200-225.

f. Stoneware, .25L, Rheinland Stein, Limited Edition of 5000, pewter lid, $95-110.

g. Stoneware, .5L, Bavarian Kings Crest Stein, Royal Series, Limited Edition of 999, gold-plated lid & footring, $400-450.

h. Stoneware, .5L, Royal Bavarian Crest Stein of 1835, Masterwork Series, Limited Edition of 500, gold-plated lid & footring, $500-550.

i. Stoneware, .5L, British Empire Stein, Masterworks Series, Limited Edition of 500, gold-plated lid & footring, $500-550.

j. Stoneware, .5L, France Imperial Crest Stein, Masterworks Series, Limited Edition of 500, gold-plated lid & footring, $500-550.

a.   Stoneware, .5L, Deutschland Stein, Limited Edition of 10,000, pewter lid with wood finial, $100-120.

b.   Stoneware, .5L, Bayern Stein, Limited Edition of 10,000, pewter lid, $110-130.

c.   Stoneware, .75L, Berlin Wall Stein, Limited Edition of 5000, pewter lid with stone finial, $170-200.

d.   Stoneware, .5L, Neuschwanstein Stein, pewter lid, $100-120.

e.   Stoneware, .5L, Niagara Falls Stein, pewter lid, $85-100.

f.   Stoneware, 1.0L, Deutschland Eagle Crest Stein, pewter lid, $110-125.

g.   Stoneware, .6L, Nürnberg Stein, from an old mold, pewter lid, $60-75.

h.   Stoneware, .5L, Full Speed Ahead Stein, Limited Edition of 5000, pewter lid, $80-90.

i.   Stoneware, 1.0L, Fearless Firefighter Stein, Limited Edition of 3500, pewter lid, $200-225.

j.   Stoneware, .5L, End of the Trail Stein, Limited Edition of 3500, bronze inlaid lid, $200-225.

a. Stoneware, 1.5L, The Sleeping Hunters Stein, Limited Edition of 1000, stoneware lid, $300-350.
b. Stoneware, .5L, Wedding Stein, pewter relief, Limited Edition of 5000, pewter lid, $160-190.
c. Stoneware, .5L, Peter Dümler Royalty Stein, pewter relief, Limited Edition of 5000, pewter lid, $160-190.
d. Stoneware, .5L, Archangel Michael Stein, pewter relief, Limited Edition of 5000, pewter lid, $160-190.
e. Stoneware, 2.0L, Firefighter Stein, pewter lid, $200-225.

f. Stoneware, .75L, Rhein Stein, pewter lid, $80-100.
g. Stoneware, .5L, Hunters Stein, pewter lid, $50-60.
h. Stoneware, .5L, Dancers Stein, pewter lid, $50-60.
i. Stoneware, .5L, Barrel Stein, pewter lid, $50-60.
j. Stoneware, 1.0L, Falstaff Stein, pewter lid, $85-100.
k. Stoneware, .5L, Bayern Stein, pewter lid, $80-100.

a. Stoneware, .5L, Timber Wolf Winter Stein, body made in China, pewter lid made in Germany, $50-60.
b. Stoneware, .5L, Bald Eagle Spring Stein, body made in China, pewter lid made in Germany, $50-60.
c. Stoneware, .5L, Loon Summer Stein, body made in China, pewter lid made in Germany, $50-60.
d. Stoneware, .5L, White Tail Deer Autumn Stein, body made in China, pewter lid made in Germany, $50-60.

e. Stoneware, .5L, Buffalo Hunt Stein, body made in China, pewter lid made in Germany, $100-120.
f. Stoneware, .5L, Pocketknife Stein, pewter lid, $50-60.
g. Stoneware, .5L, Coca-Cola® Collector Stein, pewter lid, $60-75.
h. Stoneware, .5L, Soccerball Stein, stoneware made in China, pewter made in Germany, $50-60.
i. Stoneware, .5L, Basketball Stein, stoneware made in China, pewter made in Germany, $50-60.

20. Bibliography and References

General

Bernay, J. et. al., *Das Grosse Lexikon vom Bier und seinen Brauereien*, Stuttgart, Scripta Verlag, 1983.

Chaffers, Wm., *Marks & Monograms on European and Oriental Pottery and Porcelain*, Los Angeles, Borden Publishing Company, undated.

Dexel, W., *Deutsches Handwerksgut - Eine Kultur - und Formengeschichte des Hausgerats*, Berlin, 1939.

Erling, F., et. al., *Bier-Trinkgefasse*, Bad Homburg, Limpert-Verlag, 1978.

Hansen, H.J., *Das pompose Zeitalter zwischen Biedermeier und Jugendstil*, Oldenburg, Gerhard Stallung Verlag, 1970.

Harrell, J.L., *Regimental Steins*, Frederick, MD, The Old Soldier Press, 1979.

Kirsner, G., and J. Gruhl, *The Beer Stein Book*, Coral Springs, FL, Glentiques, Ltd., 1990.

Kirsner, G., *German Military Steins*, Coral Springs, FL, Glentiques, Ltd., 1996.

Kirsner, G., and J. Gruhl(ed.), *The Mettlach Book*, Third Edition, Coral Springs, FL, Glentiques, Ltd., 1994.

Kohlhausen, H., *Geschichte des deutschen Kunstwerks*, München, 1955.

Manusov, E., *Encyclopedia of Character Steins*, Des Moines, IA, Wallace Homestead Book Co., 1976.

Manusov, E., and M. Wald, *Character Steins, A Collector's Guide*, Cranbury, NJ, Cornwall Books, 1987.

Monson-Fitzjohn, G.J., *Drinking Vessels of Bygone Days*, London, 1927.

Münchner Stadtmuseum, *125 Jahre Bayerischer Kunstgewerbeverein*, München, 1976.

Oshkosh, *Antique Steins at the Paine Art Center*, 1969.

Schiedlausky, G., *Essen und Trinken*, München, 1956.

Scholz, R., *Humpen und Krüge-Trinkgefasse 16.-20. Jahrhundert*, Keyser, München, 1978.

Uhlig, O.O., *Bierkrug-Deckel*, Rosenheimer, 1982.

Glass

Dexel, T., *Gebrauchsglas*, Braunschweig, 1977.

Frankfurt a.M. Museums fur Kunsthandwerk, *Europaisches und aussereuropaisches Glas*, Frankfurt a.M., 1973.

Fuchs, F.L., *Die Glaskunst im Wandel der Jahrtausende*, Darmstadt, 1956.

Kalnein, W.G., *Das Wein Gefass*, Frankfurt a.M., Ariel Verlag, 1978.

Kampfer, F., *Viertausend Jahre Glas*, Dresden, 1966.

Klesse, B., and G. R. von Bock, *Kunstgewerbemuseum der Stadt Köln: Glas*, Köln, 1973.

Lipp, F.C., *Bemalte Glaser*, München, 1974.

Saldern, A. von, *German Enameled Glass*, New York, 1965.

Schade, G., *Deutsches Glas,* Leipzig, 1968.

Schlosser, J., *Das alte Glas*, Braunschweig, 1977.

Schmidt, R., *Das Glas*, Berlin/Leipzig, 1922.

Unusual Materials

Brunner, H., *Altes Tafelsilber*, München, 1964.

Doucet, F.W., *Silber*, München, 1973.

Fritz, J.M., "Goldschmiedearbeiten des 14.-18. Jhrs. im Rhein," in *Bonner Jahrbuch*, 164, pg. 407, 1964.

Neuwirth, W., *Markenlexikon fur Kunstgewerbe, Edle und unedle Metalle, vol. 1, 1875-1900*, Wien, 1978.

Philippovich, E.v., *Elfenbein*, Braunschweig, 1966.

Rohde, A., *Bernstein, ein deutscher Werkstoff*, Berlin, 1937.

Theuerkauff, C., *Elfenbeinarbeiten aus dem Barock*, Hamburg & Berlin, 1967.

Weinholz, G., *Gefasse und Gerate aus Bernstein*, Dresden, Staatliche Kunstsammlungen Dresden, undated.

Pewter

Aichele, Frieder, *Zinn, Battenberg Antiquitäten-Kataloge*, München, Battenburg Verlag, 1977.

Dietz, A., *Das Frankfurter Zinngiessergewerbe und seine Blutezeit im 18. Jh.,* Frankfurt a.M., Historischen Museums in Frankfurt a.M., 1903.

Dolz, *Zinn*, München, 1974.

Drier, F.-A., "Die mittelalterlichen Baluster-zinnkannen Norddeutschlands," in *Zeitschrift fur Kunstwissenschaft*, 13, pp. 27-50, 1959.

Haedeke, H.-U., *Zinn*, Leipzig, Zentren der Zinngiesserkunst von der Antike bis zum Jugendstil, 1973.

Hintze, E., *Die deutschen Zinngiesser und Ihre Marken*, 7 vols., Leipzig, Karl W. Hiersemann, 1928.

Mory, L., *Schones Zinn,* 5. Aufl., München, 1975.

Ohm, A. and M. Bauer, *Steinzeug und Zinn, Catalog of the Museums fur Kunsthandwerk*, Frankfurt a.M., 1977.

Wagner, E., *Jugend-Zinn*, München, 1977.

Wuhr, H., *Altes Zinn*, Darmstadt, 1957.

Faience and Porcelain

Badischen Landesmuseum, *Durlacher Fayencen*, Karlsruhe, 1975.

Bauer, M., *Europaische Fayencen*, Frankfurt a.M., Museum fur Kunsthandwerk, 1977.

Bayer, Hans-Wolfgang, *Mufflebrand und Scharfes Feuer, 250 Jahre Künersberger Fayencen*, Weissenhorn (Bayern), Anton H. Konrad, 1995.

Behse, A., *Deutsches Fayencemarken-Brevier*, Braunschweig, 1955.

Behse, A., *Porzellanmarken-Brevier*, Braunschweig, 1965.

Bosch, H., *German Faience Jugs and Tankards of the 17th and 18th Centuries*, Mainz a.R., Verlag Philipp von Zabern, 1983.

Bosch, H., *Die Nürnberger Hausmaler*, München, Klinkhardt & Biermann, 1984.

Danckert, L., *Handbuch des Europaischen Porzellans*, München, 1954.

Dewiel, L., *Deutsche Fayencen*, München, 1977.

Ducret, S., *Deutsches Porzellan und deutsche Fayencen*, Baden-Baden, 1962.

Ducret, S., *Meissner Porzellan bemalt in Augsburg*, Brunswick, 1972.

Erdner, H. and G.K. Nagel, *Die Fayencefabrik zu Schrezheim, 1752-1865,* Jagst, Schwabenverlag Ellwangen, 1972.

Fregnac, C., *Europaische Fayencen*, Fribourg, 1976.

Fuchs, E. and P. Heiland, *Die deutsche Fayence-Kultur*, München, 1925.

Graesse, J.G. and E. Jaennicke, *Führer fur Sammler von Porzellan und Fayence*, Brunswick, 1967.

Hauger, O., *Durlacher Fayencen*, Karlsruhe, Verlag G. Braun, 1951.

Hofmann, F.H., *Das Porzellan der europaischen Manufakturen im 18. Jahrhundert*, Berlin, 1932.

Huseler, K., *Deutsche Fayencen, Ein Handbuch der Fabriken, ihrer Meister und Werke*, 3 vols., Stuttgart, 1956-1958.

Jedding, H., *Europaisches Porzellan*, vol. 1, München, 1971.

Klein, Adalbert, *Deutsche Fayencen*, Braunschweig, Klinkhardt & Biermann, 1975.

Klein, Adalbert, *Fayencen Europas*, Braunschweig, Klinkhardt & Biermann, 1980.

Langer, H., *Österreichische Fayencen*, München, Weltkunst Verlag, 1988.

Nagel, Gert, *Fayencen, Battenberg Antiquitäten-Kataloge*, München, Battenburg-Verlag, 1977.

Pazaurek, G.E., *Deutsche Fayence- und Porzellan-Hausmaler*, 2 vols., Leipzig, 1925.

Riesebieter, O., *Die deutsche Fayencen des 17. und 18. Jahrhunderts*, Leipzig, 1921.

Schnorr von Carolsfeld, L., *Porzellan der europaischen Fabriken*, Braunschweig, 1956.

Schwarze, W., *Alte Deutsche Fayence-Krüge*, Wuppertal, Schwarze Verlag, 1980.

Spies, G., *Braunschweiger Fayencen*, Braunschweig, Klinkhardt & Biermann, 1971.

Stohr, A., *Deutsche Fayencen und deutsches Steingut*, Berlin, 1920.

Ceramic

Anheuser-Busch, *The Official Collector's Guide to Anheuser-Busch Steins, Volume III*, Anheuser-Busch Inc., 1998.

Albrecht, R., *Die Topferkunst in Creussen*, Rothenburg o.T., 1909.

Arens, F., "Die ursprungliche Verwendung Gotischer Stein- und Tonmodel," in *Mainzer Zeitschrift*, 66, p. 106, 1971.

Bock, G. R., von "Steinzeug - Nachahmung, Nachbildung oder Falschung," in *Keramos*, 49, 1970.

Bock, G. R., von, *Meister der deutschen Keramik 1900-1950*, Kunstgewerbemuseum Köln.

Borrmann, R., *Moderne Keramik*, Leipzig, undated.

Cohausen, A. von, "Einige technische Bemerkungen uber die groberen Thonwaaren auf der Pariser Austellung 1879," in *Mittheilungen des Gewerbevereins fur Nassau*, 1879.

Cox, W.E., *The Book of Pottery and Porcelain*, New York, 1959.

Dexel, W., *Keramik, Stoff und Form*, Braunschweig/ Berlin, 1958.

Dexel, W., *Das Hausgerat Mitteleuropas; Wesen und Wandel der Formen in Zwei Jahrtausend*, Braunschweig/Berlin, 1962.

Dry-v.Zezschwitz, B., *R. Merkelbach: Grenzhausen und München, Spezialpreisliste, 1905*, München, Dr. Graham Dry, 1981.

Dry-v.Zezschwitz, B., *Rosskopf & Gerz*, München, Verlag Dry, 1982.

Eber, H., *Creussner Topferkunst*, München, 1913.

Endres, Irmgard and Werner, *Regensburger Steinzeug, Krüge und Kannen*, 8352 Grafenau, Morsak Verlag, 1991.

Engelmeier, P., "Westerwalder Steinzeugkruge mit dem Monogram GR", in *Keramos*, 44, pp. 3-11, 1969.

Falke, O.v., *Das rheinische Steinzeug*, 2 vols., Berlin, 1908.

Finke, U.C., *Westerwälder Steinzuegkrüge der Spätrenaissance*, Höhr-Grenzhausen, Kannenbäckerstadt, 1988.

Fischer, W., *Die Saltglasur*, Coburg, 1927.

Funcke, W.F., *Die Entwicklung des rheinischen Topfergewerbes seit dem 15. Jahrhundert*, Gladbach, Universitat Köln, 1927.

Graesse, J.G., *Führer fur Sammler von Porzellan, Fayence, Steinzeug, Steingut, usw.*, Braunschweig, 1974.

Groschopf, G., *Die suddeutsche Hafnerkeramik, in Jahrbuch 1937 d. Bayerischen Landesvereins fur Heimatsschutz*, 1937.

Grundriss, *Der Keramik*, Stuttgart, Paul Neff, 1879.

Haedecke, H.-U., "Zur Soziologie der Topfer im Rheinland," in *Keramos*, 37, pp. 63-68, 1967.

Hillier, B., *Pottery and Porcelain 1700-1914, The Social History of Decorative Arts*, London, 1968.

Honey, W.B., *European Ceramic Art*, 2 vols., London, 1949.

Honey, W.B., *European Ceramic Art from the End of the Middle Ages to about 1815*, London, 1952.

Horschik, J., "Sachisches und Thuringisches Steinzeug," in *9. Int. Hafnerei-Symposium*, Frechen, 1977.

Horschik, J., *Steinzeug*, Dresden, Verlag der Kunst, 1978.

Hughes, G.B., *Victorian Pottery and Porcelain*, London, 1959.

Jaennicke, F., *Deutsches Steinzeug*, 1978.

Jaennicke, F., *Geschichte der Keramik*, Leipzig, 1900.

Just, R., "Creussen un sachsische Steinzeug mit Emailfarbenbemalung," in *Keramik-Freunde der Schweiz*, 52, pp. 18-24, Zurich, 1960.

Klinge, E., *Creussner Steinzeug*, Coburg, Neue Presse, 1977.

Klinge, E., *Deutsches Steinzeug der Renaissance und Barockzeit*, Dusseldorf, Hetjens-Museum, 1979.

Kohnemann, M., *Auflagen auf Raerener Steinzeug*, Raeren, Töpfereimuseums, 1982.

Kroll, J., *Creussner Steinzeug*, Braunschweig, Klinkhardt & Biermann, 1980.

Liebscher-Willert, *Technologie der Keramik*, Dresden, 1955.

Lüthgen, G.E., *Deutsches Steinzeug*, München, Verlag Dr. Graham Dry, 1981.

Mettlach, Dreitausend Jahre Topferkunst: Ein Rundgang durch das Keramische Museum von Villeroy & Boch, 1937.

Ohm, A. and M. Bauer, *Steinzeug und Zinn*, Frankfurt a.M., Museum fur Kunsthandwerk, Frankfurt Besitz, 1977.

Pazaurek, *Steingut, Formgebung und Geschichte*, Stuttgart, 1927.

Pelka, O., *Keramik der Neuzeit*, Leipzig, 1924.

Reinheckel, G., *German and Austrian Ceramics*, Tokyo, 1978.

Reinhold, Harald, *Hanke, Reinhold und August Westerwälder Steinzeug, Historismus-Jugendstil*, Höhr-Grenzhausen, Keramikmuseum-Westerwald, 1986.

Rijksmuseum Amsterdam, *Villeroy & Boch 1748-1930, Two Centuries of Ceramic Products*, Amsterdam, 1977.

Rolfes, D., *Keramikmuseum Westerwald - Deutsche Sammlung fur historische und zeitgenossische Keramik*, Höhr-Grenzhausen, Keramikmuseum Westerwald, 1982.

Seng, A., *Dumler & Breiden - 100 Jahre Keramik*, Höhr-Grenzhausen, 1983.

Stieber, P., "Deutsches Hafnergeschirr," in *Keysers Kunst- und Antiquitatenbuch III*, München, 1973.

Stoehr, A., *Deutsche Fayencen und deutsches Steingut*, Berlin, 1920.

Strauss, K., "Die Topferkunst in Hessen," in *Studien zur Deutschen Kunstgeschichte*, vol. 228, Strassburg, 1925.

Strauss, Konrad and Frieder Aichele, *Steinzeug, Battenberg Antiquitäten Kataloge*, Augsburg, Battenberg Verlag, 1992.

Thieler, E.R., *Making Steins in an Old Monastery*, Brochure by E.R. Thieler Co., 1909.

Thieler, E.R., *Mettlach Wares Catalog*, 1909.

Zobeltiz, H. von, "Villeroy & Boch," in *Velhagen und Klassing's Monatsheften XIII, Bd. 1*, pp. 193-207, 1899.

Appendices

A. Price Adjustments for Condition

Many factors contribute to the value of a specific stein. But unlike some assets that have other productive uses, steins have value only as something beautiful to collect for enjoyment or speculative purposes. For this reason, the value of any antique stein is simply that which one person will pay another in order to own it.

The price, or value, for every stein shown in this book has been set at the average U.S. retail price for a stein in good condition. Deviations from these prices can occur for any number of reasons, reasons that are important to many collectors. An explanation of these is contained herein.

A.1 Normal Variations

The stein market is relatively stable, and the prices for certain types of steins generally move up in an orderly fashion. Of course, even for identical steins in good condition, one can expect to see fluctuations in day-to-day sale prices. What causes these fluctuations? Large variations can occur when the buyer or seller, or both, lack a good understanding or reference for the current price of a particular stein.

Aside from the deviations due to abnormal circumstances, what amount of diversity in price should one expect? Informed variations exist when the buyer and the seller know the market price of a stein but have decided on a different price due to personal preferences, time constraints, or speculation. Take, for example, the range of prices for Mettlach steins. For

steins under $200, such variations might be as great as +/-20%. For more valuable steins, the range decreases to about +/-10%.

The variations for other types of steins are similar. Pewter, occupational, faience, early stoneware, and etched ceramic steins will have deviations slightly greater than Mettlachs. Relief pottery, glass, porcelain, very rare steins, or steins of unusual materials will generally have somewhat greater fluctuations. Character and Regimental steins tend to have variations of about the same magnitude as Mettlach steins.

There are *real* costs and *time* costs involved in finding different sellers or buyers for the same stein; and, in many cases, these are the reasons for the price fluctuations. Stein prices in Germany may vary somewhat from those in this book, some being higher and some lower. Occasionally, the foreign price may be different enough to stimulate substantial shipments of steins in or out of the United States. For the most part, these temporary differences are caused by currency fluctuations and not by sudden changes in tastes or supplies.

A.2 Original Quality of Body

A stein's color is generally produced using glazes or enamels that are quite resistant to fading. Thus, when a stein has noticeably less-attractive coloring, it is generally not due to original color variations or subsequent natural fading but to repairs or the use of improper cleaning materials, such as abrasives or caustic cleaners (vinegar, turpentine, and ammonia). Most transfer-decorated porcelains or stonewares will be affected by caustic cleaners, although the majority of other types of steins will not. In any event, if the aesthetic appeal of the stein is affected, the value will decrease accordingly.

Blotching or sloppy decorations can occasionally be seen on a stein. Of course, blotching near the handle or away from the detail on the front of the stein will have less of an effect on the price than imperfections that are immediately noticeable.

Firing lines are primarily a concern with etched Mettlach steins, and are due to slightly different shrinkage levels between the dyed clays and the body clays. Reductions in price rarely exceed 5% or 10% unless there is a heavy concentration of firing lines in an important part of the decoration.

Occasionally, a transfer-decorated stein will show a tear, gap, or distortion in the decoration, or a handpainted stein will show some similar flaws, all of which must be evaluated with respect to the effect on the overall appearance of the stein. Price adjustments in excess of 15% are occasionally necessary in order to make a fair valuation.

A.3 Body Damage and Repairs

There is a tremendous variation in the price reductions that generally compensate for damage to a stein. However, there are several generalizations to consider:

1) Damage is more tolerable, even acceptable, on a very old stein. For example, cracks and chips would be the norm on a c.1600 stoneware stein, but cracks and chips on a modern stein would necessitate tremendous discounting in order to stimulate a sale.

2) The more visible the damage, the greater the effect on price. Chips or cracks on a glass stein are more visible and thus more important than those on stoneware. Damage to the front (opposite the handle) discounts the price more than damage to the back or to the inside.

3) Paradoxically, damage to a more fragile stein reduces its value more than similar damage to a stein made from sturdier materials. For example, chips and cracks on glass or porcelain cause greater price reductions than similar damage on a ceramic or pewter stein.

4) Damage to a common stein is more detrimental than damage to a rare or one-of-a-kind stein. If collectors know they can obtain a better example of a stein,

they will wait to do so unless the discount is significant.

This last point is often important when considering Mettlach steins, and a study of the price reductions for damage was made for *The Mettlach Book*. The findings are roughly summarized here. Repaired chips up to 1" in size reduce value by 15% to 35%. Larger repaired chips and broken pieces can require reductions of 50% or more. Repaired hairline cracks reduce value by 25% to 50%.

Sometimes the value of a repaired piece is less than the cost of high-quality repairs, which can run between $25 and $200, depending upon the extent of damage and the amount of detailed work involved. New handles or sections of a stein can cost $100 or more. Besides being aware that the stein may not be worth repairing, there are several other cautionary tips to consider. Repairs are less acceptable for older pieces because damage to them is more permissible. That is to say, do not repair a very old stein unless it cannot be displayed in the damaged state. It is also a fact that some stein parts, such as handles or inlays, are easier to make than to repair. Thus, you must insist that the original part be used in repairs unless it is missing or beyond all usefulness. Also, be aware that very few people are capable of making high-quality repairs or replacement parts.

A.4 Original Mountings

The quality or type of the original lid can be an important factor in determining the price of a stein. The value shown in this book is applicable only to a stein that has the same lid as illustrated.

A Mettlach stein could almost always have been originally ordered with either a plain or a fancy pewter lid, a lid with a ceramic insert, or no lid. One ordered without a lid was undoubtedly sent to a special pewterer (often in Munich) who created a spectacular pewter lid at additional expense. These fancy pewter lids that Mettlach provided (possibly attached by a local contractor rather than by Villeroy & Boch) were usually more expensive than the lids with a ceramic inlay. The original cost of a lid, however, does not relate directly to current desirability. In fact, today's collectors prize an inlaid lid, especially on a smaller-sized etched Mettlach stein. A stein that has a less desirable pewter lid will be worth about 10% to 35% less.

Other ceramic stein manufacturers either concentrated on using heavy pewter lids (as did Hauber & Reuther) or generally used ceramic inlaid lids (J.W. Remy, Gerz, Marzi & Remy, and most others). There is usually little or no discount for a stein found with a different type of high-quality lid.

There is, however, a particular kind of low-quality pewter lid that will always be measurably less desirable. This type of lid has been made since the early 1900s out of a lighter-weight pewter alloy, generally containing lead that has been stamped into a low, steepled lid. It often has a design that is not sharp and a shape that is somewhat conical to accommodate the stamping process.

Occasionally, an older stein is found with an out-of-period lid that seems to be original after examining the strapping around the handle (as described in Section 2). Examples include a stein from the 1600s with a lid typical of the 1700s or, more commonly, a stein from the 1700s with an 1800s lid. It should be noted that this type of lid may be an old replacement. During almost all European wars, people were asked to turn in any metal objects they possessed, including items like pewter lids. If such a lid was later replaced, it would, of course, be of a more modern type. It also seems likely that a lid may have been intentionally changed to make a stein more stylish. Although such examples might have mystery or romance, collectors and museums are generally looking for archetypal steins that do not have a confusing appearance. Therefore, the price for this type of stein must often be somewhat discounted in order for it to pass through the market.

The same is usually true of a stein that has a lid of atypical material. For example, a Mettlach stein with a silver-plated, copper, or brass lid will generally be worth somewhere around 30% to 50% less than one with a typical lid. Upgraded materials, such as sterling instead of the usual pewter, will generally increase the value of a stein except if the lid seems suspicious or incongruous (such as silver on pewter or faceted glass on pottery).

A.5 Damaged, Replaced, or Missing Mountings

Section 2 contains some important information about the mountings on steins, and about ways to detect a replaced lid. Additional information about the mountings, from the standpoint of pricing, is worth noting here.

It is commonplace to find a very nice stein that, unfortunately, does not have its lid. Also, unfortunately, stein lids were not made in a set of standard sizes. Surprisingly, a variation of plus or minus 1/8 inch is often enough to cause a replacement lid to fit improperly. Also, the tang and the shaft must be the appropriate length or a difficult splicing is required. Thus, particularly for an older stein, a missing lid will cause a substantial price reduction. A badly damaged old stein or unattractive c.1900 stein with a nice lid is often purchased and made into a mug because the lid is perfect for some other special piece needing a replacement. Intentionally seeking such matches has some of the pleasures, as well as the displeasures, of gambling.

The picture sections of this book clearly show the types of steins that generally have footrings. These include faience and, sometimes, glass steins. Missing footrings, of course, have much less visual impact than do missing lids, so the price reduction is much less. Yet, while it would seem to be easier to find replacements because only the diameter must match, there are precious few good footrings available, even from repairmen who are constantly trying to stock up on parts. Therefore, if you are considering purchasing a stein without its footring, do not count on being able to find a replacement.

Although pewter is easily damaged and can show dings and tears, it is also relatively easy to repair. The following are some of the more common types of damage:

1) Hinges occasionally bind up. Often they can be cleaned with water (do not use oil). If that doesn't work, have a repairman deal with it rather than forcing the hinge.

2) A hinge with a missing tooth or ring will only nominally influence value, usually by less than 10%.

3) Tears, dents, and missing thumblifts can be repaired for about $30 to $60 and, once fixed, should not reduce the value of the stein by more than about 10% to 15%.

4) The cost of repairing the strap is also in the 10% to 15% range. Recall that repairs to the strap often signify that the lid has been replaced, which can mean a price reduction from as little as 10% to as much as 25% or 35%. If the lid is not appropriate to the stein, the reduction can be 50% or more.

Some collectors and museums feel that pewter and silver items must be kept polished for proper care and display. Others would rather see the dark patina, especially on pewter. Non-abrasive polishing should have no effect on price, but be forewarned that a few collectors will shy away from a polished pewter stein. On the other hand, a diseased pewter stein, such as one that is pitted, powdered, or scaled, can be devalued by 10% or even more if the pewter is heavily damaged.

B. Important Information for Collectors

B.1 Sources of Steins

The first important collections of steins seem to have been started in the middle 1800s by museums vying for examples of fine Renaissance art. Private collectors became an important force in stein collecting in the late 1800s, and some astonishingly high prices were paid in those days for the best examples of Renaissance steins.

Of course, stein collections of a sort existed long before steins were being collected as antiques. In kitchens and in taverns and inns, narrow shelves along the upper parts of the walls, so-called plate rails, held collections of steins. In homes, the number of steins was a measure of hospitality; in taverns it was a measure of prosperity, signifying the number of regular customers. To increase this measure, and probably for aesthetic reasons as well, there were often more steins displayed than were really necessary. Such decorative tastes were brought to the United States by the early English settlers, the Pennsylvania Dutch, and the many waves of European immigrants.

Great numbers of German stoneware steins were brought to Canada and the Northeastern United States in the 1700s. Important stoneware shipments were also made in the late 1800s and led some U.S. manufacturers of that time to begin their own production of stoneware and porcelain steins. Beginning in the late 1800s, Mettlach and other German factories actively advertised their steins in the U.S. Significant quantities of steins also began flowing into the United States in the 1940s. These came back with soldiers, tourists, and as of the late 1950s, with antique importers. With all of the political and economic turmoil in Europe, the quantity of steins which have made their way to the U.S. have become an important fraction of the world supply.

In both Europe and the U.S., the more desirable steins, once scattered throughout the countryside, have continued to become more concentrated in collections. Increasingly, the places to find good steins include a small number of U.S. and German dealers, auctions, and fellow collectors upgrading or disposing of their collections.

If the intent of a collector is to buy a stein only occasionally and with little consideration for the type or characteristics of the stein, then shopping at antique shops and antiques shows could yield the desired results. However, if a specific objective is important, such as acquiring a nicely planned collection, it would be advantageous to develop contacts with knowledgeable and trustworthy dealers and collectors.

B.2 Collection Strategies

In varying degrees, most collectors combine the enjoyment and the investment aspects of stein collecting. First, consider the investment angle.

During the 1960s and early 1970s, steins proved to be a very good investment both in comparison to other antiques and to other investment alternatives. Their performance in the middle and late 1970s and 1980s, was not as strong, with some other antiques increasing in value more rapidly. In the 1990s, most stein prices have remained steady or increased moderately, indicating steins to be strong, if unspectacular, performers.

It is difficult to predict a future price trend with p recision, but based upon past performance, it is likely that steins will be a fairly good investment on a long-term basis. A general and rapid appreciation in prices over any short period of time is unlikely, but there will always be a few spectacular performers. Those steins that seem to a collector (after looking over all the steins in this book) to be priced disproportionately low, are also likely to be good investments.

Also with respect to the future, the steady performance of most steins over recent years seems to indicate a very solid price base. It is the collectors who have created the demand for and prices of steins, not the investors. The absence of investment capital artificially forcing up the price of steins, beyond the price collectors would be willing to pay, has kept stein prices firm even as other investment opportunities changed drastically. It is possible that old and new collectors could plunge into a bidding war with museums, and the resultant prices would continue upward.

As for the enjoyment of collecting steins, consider the possibilities. Since steins come in many sizes and types, and cover a wide range of prices, different approaches to collecting are possible. Collections always contain certain elements of similarity and certain elements of diversity. Most frequently, the materials are similar and the decorations vary.

Most collectors enjoy putting together sets or pairs, particularly of the scarcer or more aesthetically pleasing items. The artistic arrangement of a collection can also greatly enhance its appeal to the collector, and the use of plaques, bowls, and other items, together with steins, provides an additional dimension that ought to be considered.

A collection should contain what the individual collector likes, and not what seems to be rare, in vogue, or expensive. If you like a stein, there will always be a proper place for it to be displayed in your collection.

B.3 Buying Steins

If you purchase steins at prices near those in this book, you will be receiving a fair value for your money. These are prices that other collectors are willing to pay for the same pieces. Of course, this assumes that any defects that might exist have been detected and the price properly discounted.

Recognizing repaired defects has gotten to be increasingly difficult. In the last few years the techniques, materials, and experience developed by a few repairmen have resulted in some excellent repairs being performed on some steins. Many steins have been sold by dealers, and by collectors, with repairs or damages that were not indicated to the buyer. Some sellers do not know of the repairs, or do not feel obligated to point out repairs or damages to prospective buyers.

Learning to detect repairs and damage, and to distinguish them from factory flaws, takes time and requires the advice and coaching of experienced collectors or dealers. In the meantime, you will have to rely on the reputation of the individual dealer or collector from whom you make your purchase.

Do not assume that an advertisement of steins for sale, even one carried in a respectable publication such as an antiques periodical, can be relied upon for accuracy. While many dealers and collectors are honest, a lack of knowledge by some, and a tendency for the dishonest dealers to gravitate toward advertising, has left knowledgeable buyers with a cautious suspicion toward advertisements. Many advertisers do deliver what is promised, but be certain you can return the stein if you are not satisfied, and do not expect the publication to be of any help should a problem arise.

Auctions are a uniquely different way to buy. If you have a very good idea what you are doing, and you have time and patience, you might do very well. If you are not well informed or are not patient, beware! Simple rules to remember for auction buyers are:

1) some auctioneers know very little or nothing about steins and even less about repairs;

2) auctions that sell *as is* (no description or condition) naturally tend to attract merchandise with defects that sellers would rather not describe;

3) at many auctions, some items will not be sold until their prices reach a level above the price that the consignor (owner) is willing to accept, and this reserve price may be more than the stein is worth; not all items at auction are protected this way but many are; and

4) if a buyer's premium exists, usually 10% or 15%, remember to add that to your total cost before you make your bids. Should you decide to buy steins at an auction, try to arrive in plenty of time to thoroughly examine the steins at the preview. Take copious notes on conditions, qualities, and maximum bids you will make, even for items only remotely of interest to you. If possible, try to frequent only those auctioneers who knowledgeably indicate damage.

5) Stein specialty auctions have come into existence since 1982, having been pioneered by Gary Kirsner Auctions. These auctions offer collectors an opportunity to see and bid on hundreds of different steins. The best of these auctions offer accurate descriptions, in catalogs, with photos and estimates. Guarantees and return privileges are usually superior to those offered at most general line auctions. Bargains are possible, but not common on better quality steins. The selection is usually much better than can be found hunting in stores, shows and general line auctions.

B.4 Protecting Your Collection

First, there are some common-sense procedures to follow to avoid damaging your own steins. Hot beverages should be kept out of steins, and no hot water or dishwashers should be used to clean steins. Just use lukewarm water, mild soap, and a soft brush. Displaying steins in sunlit windows, or storing them in extremely hot or cold locations, can cause stress lines to develop in the bodies of the steins. Wrapping steins in newspaper and storing them in damp basements can discolor the pewter. When choosing a place to display steins, try to find an area free from flying objects, swinging brooms, or vacuum cleaner handles. Instruct curious friends in the proper way to hold or examine steins; warn them especially not to allow the inlaid or heavy pewter lids to flop closed.

Steins often break when transported. Wrap and box them carefully, then wrap and re-box the first box, and insure all packages that are being shipped.

Finally, valuable collections in homes should be fully covered by insurance policies; to protect larger collections, security systems should also be considered. Stein dealers can provide you with accurate insurance appraisals of your pieces for nominal fees.

B.5 Selling

Steins have always had a fairly high degree of liquidity relative to other antiques. Collectors throughout the country are always looking for desirable items to add to their collections. Many antique dealers around the country are also quite anxious to purchase a nice stein or two, in order to dress up their inventory.

Still, it is important to select the proper method, among the many available, for selling your stein or your collection. There are several avenues open for selling a small number of steins with a fairly low total dollar value.

1) *Direct to a collector*: This is an excellent idea, if you know a collector who wants the stein(s) that you want to sell.

2) *To a local antique dealer*: This is a fairly easy and appropriate method if a local dealer is willing to pay a fair price for your steins. Keep in mind he has to resell them at a profit. Depending on his location, he may be able to sell them quickly, or he may have to wait a long time before buyers come along. These factors will contribute to the price he can afford to pay. Many dealers would rather take expensive steins on consignment; if they sell, then you will get a percentage of the sale price.

3) *Through a general auction*: Many auctioneers are anxious to have high-quality steins to sell. Expect to pay about a 20% commission, perhaps higher. If a buyer's premium is charged, consider this part of the commission, because the buyer will keep this in mind and bid lower. Rarely do steins sell at retail prices in general auctions; generally, they will bring less than the retail price.

4) *Through a stein auction*: stein specialty auctions will reach the desired buyers. Retail prices will be obtained on most steins, depending on the abilities of the particular auction company chosen. Commissions are generally about 20% to 25%, including the buyer's premium.

5) *Advertise in an antique publication*: Fairly good results can be achieved sometimes, but there is no guarantee that the right person will see your advertisement, and most steins are difficult to describe accurately.

6) *Respond to an advertisement from a collector or a dealer in an antique publication*: Responding to a want advertisement from a collector may result in a sale, but he will have to want the stein(s) you are selling in order to pay a fair price. A dealer who specializes in steins will generally pay fair wholesale price. He will usually buy for resale at a fairly small margin because his turnover is probably more rapid than the average dealer. He will know steins very well, and therefore will not have to make allowances to cover risks due to his ignorance.

Should you have a large collection to sell, realizing a high percentage of the retail price could be of significant importance. A 10% difference in the total price could amount to a large sum of money. Therefore, a number of things must be considered. Do you want to sell everything in one group to one buyer? Do you want to sell immediately, or over a short or perhaps long period of time? Are you willing to work hard at selling your collection: communicating widely, wrapping packages, mailing the steins, and so on? To sell a large collection at retail prices, you would have to be prepared to undertake the expenses and do the work of being the dealer, advertiser, traveler, wrapper, and shipper. While this is possible, it is not practical for everyone. Some collectors have done so successfully, but most who have tried eventually became frustrated and impatient, and ultimately would have fared better with another approach.

A dealer specializing in steins, who is thus familiar with the market, can generally realize a retail price on a greater number of steins from a large collection, and with greater ease than can a collector selling for the first time. Depending upon the quality of the collection, that is to say its desirability, diversification, and condition, a collector can expect to sell a collection to a stein dealer at a discount in the vicinity of 30% from the retail prices. This can, of course, vary greatly depending upon the collection and general business factors.

Just as for the small collection, auctions offer a convenient method for disposing of a large collection. Auctions vary in a number of ways, but certain factors do not vary substantially. It will cost about 20% to 25% to sell a collection at auction. This commission is a percentage of the selling price, not the retail price. Some steins may sell at auction above a fair retail price, but on average, a large collection will not sell at auction above a fair retail price.

This section should provide the seller with the means to calculate the range of prices that are likely to be realized in the sale of steins. Selling steins can require a substantial investment of time and resources. It will be worthwhile for a seller to take the time to work through the mathematics of each alternative, to allow for a good bottom line comparison among the alternative methods of selling the steins.

Glossary

Allegory, the representation of incidents, scenes, or characters in a way that evokes a dual interest, providing both aesthetic enjoyment and a deeper intellectual interpretation.

Apostlekrug, a stout-shaped stein with the Apostles in relief around its body.

Art Nouveau, literally modern style, the bold and flat sinuous motifs abstractly based upon seaweed and other plant forms; this style was popular from 1895 to 1915 and was a rebellion against the derivative style of *Historicism*; see *periods.*

Baluster shape, bulbous in the middle with a thinned neck and pedestal base; a popular shape for early earthenware vessels.

Baroque, an ornate, florid, flamboyant style popular from 1600–1770; see *periods.*

Beaker, a cup-like drinking vessel, sometimes with a handle but never with a lid; contrast with *mug, pokal, and stein.*

Biedermeier, a peasant style of folk art that was important from 1810–1850; a provincial, rustic, sturdy functionalism favored by the new middle class; *see periods.*

Blockzinn, see *pewter purities.*

Britannia metal, alloy of tin and antimony.

Cameo, a type of stein design with low relief made from a translucent, porcelain-like material that allows contrasting background colors to show through the thinnest areas; compare with *relief.*

Character stein, or *figural stein*, a stein with a shape designed to represent a person, animal, or object, often a personified object.

Chinoiseries, style of design popular in the 1700s depicting Chinese genre scenes and Chinese landscapes; see *periods.*

Chip-carving, or *Kerbschnitt,* a pattern of vertical creases, sometimes hand-cut, sometimes simulated with a mold.

Clay glaze, see *glaze.*

Clay slip, or *colored slip*, see *slip.*

Cold painting, a non-durable method of stein decorating that does not require firing; uses varnishes or gold leaf.

Crack, an open break; contrast with *hairline.*

Double firing, the process of firing biscuit (unglazed) pottery, then glazing, decorating and refiring.

Earthenware, porous ceramic material fired to only about 800°C (1500°F); sometimes made impervious to liquids by the addition of a lead glaze, as in Hafner ware and folk pottery; see *stoneware.*

Edelzinn, Engelmarke, and *Englischzinn,* see *pewter purities.*

Enamel, painted decoration, usually on glass.

Engobe, see *slip, colored.*

Engraved, use of abrasive material to cut lines, ornaments, or script into a hard surface.

Etched, a type of stein decoration with uniformly colored design areas distinctively incised with black outlining.

Faience, a porous earthenware glazed with a white tin oxide (stanniferous); originally a porcelain substitute first made in Faenza, Italy.

Feinzinn, see *pewter purities.*

Finial, a figural representation positioned at the top of a stein; usually a person, animal, acorn or hops.

Footring, a pewter collar applied around the base of some steins to protect them from chipping and wear; see *pewter mountings.*

Four F, or **4F**, a symbol of the German gymnastic or athletic society; the Fs are flipped in a pattern that puts all their corners together making a cross shape; 4F stands for *Frisch, Fromm, Froh, Frei*, meaning alert, devout, joyful, free.

Form number, or **mold number**, usually an incised number in the base of a stein used to identify the mold from which it was made, thus providing a catalog number.

Gambrinus, legendary king of Flanders who supposedly discovered beer; the subject of many stein decorations.

Glaze, a hard, impervious coating fired on to ceramic materials, it can be clear or colored, transparent or opaque, matte or glossy; **clay glazes** are like **slips** and were used on very early ceramics, other glazes are all forms of glass made from powdered glass, geldspar, borax, salts, or metal oxides; **lead glaze** is found on Hafner ware and folk pottery; **leopard glaze** is a strong brown-speckled saltglaze found especially on Frechen wares; **saltglazes** are produced by pouring large quantities of salt into the furnace at its peak firing temperature; the sodium chloride reacts with water (hydrogen oxide) to produce a glassy coating (sodium oxide) and hydrochloric acid vapors; **tin glaze**, as commonly used on faience, is made from tin oxide.

Greenware, formed pottery that is air dried but unfired and, thus, still raw clay.

Hafner ware, lead-glazed earthenwares, including steins, made by potters best known for their oven tiles.

Hairline, a closed break that sometimes shows as a thin black line in ceramic materials; contrast with **crack**.

Handpainted, a type of ware that is either glazed and fired or just cold painted with a design.

Hausmalers, or **studio painters**, after the Thirty Years' War (in the mid-1600s), houses were often rebuilt to include artists' studios; the artists who occupied them decorated mostly porcelain or faience wares, working as independent craftsmen in their own home studios.

Hinge, a device, usually pewter, that enables the lid to swivel open on a stein.

Historicism, the style of art that dominated the Continent from about 1840 to 1910; it sought a return to the Renaissance as exhibited through powerful sculptural forms, complicated outlines and friezes, and deep reliefs or contrasting shadows; it originated with the archeological findings of numerous awe-inspiring Renaissance artifacts, and, in response, art schools began instructing pupils by having them copy the forms and ornaments of these artifacts; see **periods**.

Incised, refers to the lines in unfired ceramic material that were created by using a stamp, press, or mold; sometimes used synonymously with **etched**.

Inlay, the name of a type of lid for steins that have an insert, usually ceramic, porcelain, or glass, set into the pewter or silver flange of the lid; or **inlay** can be a decorative technique in which one material has been inlaid into another so as to help form the design, such as pewter inlaid wood; contrast with **overlay**.

Ivory stoneware, or *yellow stoneware*, a fine, light-colored clay fired as stoneware and used to make many steins from about 1850 to the present; frequently referred to as **pottery**.

Kayser-Zinn, not a measure of the quality of the pewter but rather indicative of manufacture by the J.P. Kayser Company in Krefeld-Bockum between the end of the 1800s and the beginning of the 1900s, many pieces are in the Art Nouveau style.

Krug, literally a jug, but often used to indicate a large, or master, stein.

Liter, or **L**, the metric measure of capacity, slightly more than a quart (1.057 quarts = 1 liter).

Lithophane, a porcelain panel with a relief decoration that is visible when light passes through it; often found in the bottom of porcelain steins; lithophane molds were taken from beeswax carvings made over lighted panels.

Luster, a metal oxide decoration fired onto a stein; including occasional platinum accents on early Mettlach steins, metal alkali sheens all over some glass steins, and many other types.

Mettlach, village on the bank of the Saar River in West Germany where Villeroy & Boch has one of their ceramics factories; commonly used as the name of the steins from that factory.

Mosaic, a type of stein on which colored glazes are painted into ridged sections that protrude from the stoneware or pottery.

Muffle-fired, a lower temperature third firing achieved by protecting the ceramic materials from the main heat of the kiln by placing them behind muffling fire bricks, or chamotte capsules; this process made an almost unlimited range of glaze colors available.

Mug, a cup, usually cylindrical, with a handle; a *lidded mug* is a mug with a set-on lid (not hinged), often used in spas for mineral water; contrast with **beaker** and **stein.**

Munich Child, *Munich Maid*, or *Munich Monk*, a common theme on steins, the symbol of the city of Munich, supposedly showing a monk's robe on the first child born in Munich after the massacre in the 10th Century.

Musterschutz, literally means *copyright protection*, but occasionally used almost as if it were a factory name; most frequently found on porcelain character steins made by Schierholz.

Occupational stein, a stein with a decoration or shape that depicts or symbolizes an occupation, probably the occupation of the original owner of the stein.

Orivit, a pewter and silver alloy mostly used around 1900.

Overglaze, a special glass and flux mixture that provides a clear glossy coating that provides extra sheen and vividness to ceramic materials.

Overlay, *filigree*, or *latticework*, an ornamental openwork of intricate design, usually made from pewter, applied to the outside of a stein.

Pate-sur-pate, marbleized porcelain, usually green and white.

Patina, an oxidation layer on metals; often indicates evidence of age.

Periods, or *styles*, the names of the different types of fashionable art, see **Art Nouveau**, **Baroque**, **Biedermeier**, **Chinoiseries**, **Historicism**, **Renaissance**, and **Rococo** for the most important stein styles.

Pewter, a very workable metallic alloy containing as much as 90% tin, with the remainder made up of lead, copper, zinc, nickel, bismuth, or antimony; see the following two entries.

Pewter mountings, includes the **footring** and all the pewterwork that is used to attach the lid to the handle of a stein; the attaching pewterwork has its own set of terminology that is important in describing damage and repairs; the *strap* encircles the handle, and a usually triangular *strap support* runs somewhat down the outside of the handle; the *shank* goes from the strap to the *hinge*; a *hinge pin* will show on most steins made after about 1860; it will not show on earlier steins; an odd number of *rings* or *teeth* make up the hinge; the *tang* proceeds from the hinge to the *lid rim*; the *thumblift* can be over the hinge or fastened to the rim; if there is an **inlay,** a pewter *flange* will hold it in place; the top of some all-pewter lids may contain an ornate pewter *finial*.

Pewter purities, have been carefully marked since the Middle Ages when lead and other impurities were suspected of being health threats; *Bergzinn, Blockzinn, Feinzinn,* and *Klar und Lauter Zinn* are pewters that are quite pure and known to contain very small quantities of copper or brass (copper and tin alloy); often they had to contain no recycled pewter; *Engelmarke* or *Angel-marked* is Feinzinn from the 1700s or 1800s that is marked with an angel and sword and scales (or trumpet and palm frond); *Englischzinn* or English Pewter is Feinzinn certified to also be lead-free; *Rosenmarke* or *Rose-marked* is a touchmark for Englisch Zinn; Probezinn contains lead but no more than 1/5 or a 4-tin-to-1-lead ratio, *Nürnberger Probe* is 10-to-1, *Kolnische Probe* is 6-to-1, *Frankfurter Probe* is 4-to-1; *Edelzinn* is from the 1800s and contains too much lead to allow the item to be used as a utensil; *Geringes Zinn, Mankgut,* or *Low Pewter* may contain as much as 50% lead and is occasionally found in thumblifts or applied relief on steins; see also **Britannia metal** and *Orivit*.

Pokal, or *brimmer*, a large ceremonial handleless beaker with a separate set-on lid and, usually, a pedestal base.

Porcelain, a vitrified, fine white clay, quartz, and feldspar mixture that has a hard surface; hard porcelain is fired to about 1450°C (2650°F) while soft porcelain is fired to about 1200°C (2200°F); compare with **stoneware** and **pottery**.

Porcellaine, another name for faience, which was originally intended as a porcelain substitute.

Pottery, or *Steingut*, a rather imprecise term for a usually light-colored porous ceramic with a hardness dependent upon the temperature of the firing, from 960°C (1800°F) to 1300°C (2350°F); generally used to include all tan-colored ceramic materials.

Print over glaze, a transfer decoration fired over the glaze.

Print under glaze, *PUG*, *transfer-printed*, or *transfer-decorated*, the name for a process of decoration that takes handpainted, silk-screened, or printed decals and transfers those decals to a smooth surface, then fires them in place.

Probe, a mark occasionally found on trial or test pieces; *Probe* can also refer to the lead content of pewter; see **pewter purities**.

Prunts, *bosses*, or *Nuppen*, glass drops, sometimes with an impressed design, found attached to the sides of glass vessels as decoration.

Pug mill, a device somewhat like a blender, but very large and previously horse driven, used for refining and mixing clay recipes.

Regimental stein, *reservist's stein*, or *military stein*, a stein that was purchased as a souvenir of service in the military; most often refers to those purchased by reservists upon discharge from the Imperial German Armies in the years 1890 to 1914.

Relief, the name of a type of ware that has figures or designs of opaque material, usually tan or white, that stand out substantially from the smooth or textured background; compare with **cameo**.

Renaissance, the style of art and the name of the time period from about 1300 to 1600 that was characterized by a revival of the Classical influence and vigorous aesthetic and intellectual activities; see **periods**.

Reservist's stein, see **Regimental stein**.

Rib, a wooden scraper or forming die, used for smoothing sides and forming the bands and moldings of steins on a potter's wheel.

Rococo, the last, less colorful but more figurative, phase of the Baroque period, from about 1735–1770; see **periods**.

Rorken, or *sampler*, a shape of stein that has a pedestal base then becomes slightly wider with height.

Saltglaze, formed when salt is added to the kiln to form a glassy mist that coats all the wares; should not be confused with painted metal oxide glazes such as cobalt oxide blues and manganese oxide violets that are merely glazes that can withstand the intense stoneware firing temperatures; see **glazes**.

Slip, a watered-down clay or porcelain recipe that is sufficiently liquid for use in coating, gluing, or casting pieces of ceramic material; *clay slip, colored slip,* or *engobe* are terms employed to describe slips that have been combined with coloring agents to facilitate use primarily as decorative coatings or paints, such as clay glazes; see **glazes, clay.**

Slurry, a recipe consisting of clays, water, and other additives that have been filtered, mixed, and poured into backs, or settling tanks.

Smoother, either a wooden paddle for smoothing the sides of wet, freshly turned pottery, or the person who smooths out turning marks with a wet cloth.

Stack marks, firing variations on the bottom of stoneware or pottery steins that show how they were stacked in the kiln, occasionally circles or parts of two or three circles are seen on some very old steins.

Stein, literally meaning *stone*, is a shortened form of *Steinzeugkrug* or *stoneware tankard*; generally expanded to mean any drinking vessel with a handle and an attached lid; a *lidless stein* did have, or was intended to have, a lid that is now missing; contrast with **mug**, **beaker** and **pokal**.

Stoneware, a vitrified ceramic material, usually a silicate clay, that is very hard, rather heavy, and impervious to liquids and most stains; achieved at firing temperatures between 1200°C (2200°F) and 1300°C (2350°F); *early stoneware*, or *Fruhsteinzeug,* did not quite reach those temperatures or was made from clays needing higher temperatures to vitrify, and was common from the 1300s to the early 1500s; color is usually gray or tan, but terra cotta and other colors were also made; see **earthenware**, **pottery**, and **porcelain**.

Tankard, technically synonymous with **stein**, but since this was the British term, some reserve its use for the typically British silver or pewter steins.

Threading, a low, fine, wire-like relief decoration, with colors usually painted between the raised lines; the reverse of etching.

Thumblift, a figural representation positioned at the rear of the lid of the stein, generally above the hinge, usually a person, animal, acorn, hops, crest or allegorical character.

Touchmark, a small stamp, usually found on pewter, that may indicate the name or symbol of the master pewterer, his city, or the pewter's purity.

Transfer-decorated or **transfer-printed**, see **print under glaze**.

Waldglas, or *forest glass,* made from sand and wood ashes and generally having a grayish-green color with small impurities and air bubbles.

Walzenkrug, *cylindrical tankard,* or *straight-up tankard,* a cylindrical stein about twice as high as it is wide; the most common shape in the 1700s.

White gold, a name that was used for porcelain, porcelain clays, or for the valuable stoneware clays with low vitrification temperatures and minimal warping and cracking potential.

Wiremark, concentric whorls on the base of some older stoneware or faience steins that indicates the "hump" was cut off the potter's wheel by pulling a wire across the base of the turning piece, as opposed to being cut off with smooth knives.

Zigzag decor, or *Knibistechnik,* decorative ribbons of tight, wide, incised zigzags made by wadding a wooden chisel across the surface of unfired clay.

Index

A.J. Thewalt, 148, 241, 353, 354
Advertisements,
    buying from, 373
    selling by, 374
Albert Stahl & Co., 354
Allegory, see *Motifs, allegorical*
Alloys, 15, see also *Pewter, Brittania metal*
Altenburg, 26
Amber, 110
Anheuser-Busch, 323, 339
Annaberg, 26
Ansbach, 45
Antimony, see *Recipe, Brittania metal*
Antwerp World's Fair (1885), 225
Apprentice, see *Labor, apprentice*
Art Nouveau, 14, 185, 227
Auctions,
    buying from, 373
    selling in, 374
Austria, 70

Baluster, 25, see also *Steins, shapes illustrated*
Baroque, 9, 12, 79, 126
Bas-relief, see *Relief*
Bavaria, 8, 9
BAVARIA, 226
Beakers, 9, 109
Beer, 8, 9, 12, 110
Beyer GmbH, 354
Biedermeier, 12, 44, 69, 80, 225, see also *Steins, shapes illustrated*
Birnkrug, 44
Bisque, see *Glaze, bisque*
Black Death, 8
Black salt, 26
Blotching, see *Factory flaws*
Boch-Buschmann, 225
Bohemia, 9, 70
Bohne (E. Söhne), 303

Böttager, Johann, 43, 125
Brass, 110
Brazil, see *Ceramarte*
Bremen, 7
Brewery steins, 323
    quantities produced, 323
Brittania metal, 70
Bubonic plague, see *Black Death*
Bunzlau, 26
Buyer's premium, see *Auctions, buying from*
Buying, see *Collecting, strategies*

Cameo, 226
    difference from relief, 226
Casting, 15, 70, 109
    mountings, see *Mountings, cast*
Castle trademark, 227
Catalogs, 18, 147, 241, see also *Auctions, buying from*
Ceramarte, 339, 353, 354
Ceramics, see *Earthenware, Hafner ware, porcelain, pottery, stoneware*
    hand-thrown, 18
    production of, 18
    slip-molded, 18
Character steins, 12, 14, 18, 273, 303, 304
    color variations, 304
Chicago, 323
Chinoiseries, see *Motifs, Oriental*
Chip-carving, 26
Chromolith, see *Mettlach, etched*
    theories, 226
Clay, 12, 18
    faience, 45
    mining, 26
    porcelain, 126
    pottery, 148
    Rhenish, 147
    stoneware, 25
Cleaning, 17, 373, see also *Patina*

Cloisters, 8
Coconuts, 110
Cold-painting, see *Painting, cold-*
Collecting,
    as an investment, 369
Cologne, see Köln
Coors, 339
Copyright, see MUSTERSCHUTZT
Corzelius (W.), 354
Covered container law, 7, 8, 15
    Origin of, 7
Creussen, 26
Crosshatch mark, 303
Crystal, see *Recipe, crystal*
Cylindrical, see *Walzenkrug*

Damage, 370, 371, see also *Faience, damage*
    caused by cleaning, 369, 370
    diseased pewter, 70
    impact on price, 27, 370, 371
    prevention, 373
Dates, see *Marks, dates*
Daubenkrug, 110
Dealers, 372, 373
DEC, 227
Decals, 80, 148, 273
    silk-screened, 80, 273
Decolorizers, see *Metal oxides, as decolorizers*
Decoration number, 227
Defregger, 148
Delft, 226, see also *Mettlach, Delft*
Deutsche Wehrmacht, see *Nazi Army*
Diamond-cut, 79
Displaying steins, see *Damage, prevention*
Domex, 354
Duingen, 26
Dümler & Breiden, 147, 148, 303, 354
Dümler, Peter, 147
Dutch Trade, 43
Dutch East Indies Trade Co., 110

E. Bohne Söhne, 303
Earthenware, 9, 18, 25, 304
Eckhardt & Engler, 148, 354
Elisabeth Liegl, 354
Empire, 225
Enamled, 69, 79, 80, 81
Enghalskrug, 44
England, 9, 126
Englishzinn, see *Pewter, purity*
Engraved, 9, 69, 79, 80, 109, see also *Diamond-cut,*
    wrigglework, zigzag
Etched, 14, 80, 226, 241, 323, 353
    techniques, 241
Exports, 353

Factory flaws, 370
Faenza, Italy, 43

Faience, 9, 12, 14, 43-47, 227, 354
    damage, 46
    factories, 44
    identifying reproductions, 45
Feinzinn, see *Pewter, purity*
File marks, see *Replacement parts, identifying*
Finials, 274
Firing,
    duration, 8
    temperature, 8, 18, 25, 45, 126, 148
Firing lines, see *Factory flaws*
Folk art, 12, 69, 79, see also *Biedermeier, motifs*
Footrings, 15, 17, 45, 371, see also *Mountings*
Form number, 227
Franco-Prussian War, 273
Frankfurt, 43
Frechen, 26, 27
Freiberg, 26
Frieze bands, 227
Furnace, 8, 25, 80

Genuine, see *Pewter, purity*
Geringen, see *Pewter, purity*
German flowers, 79, 126
German Imperial Armies, 273
Germany,
    map of, 13
GERMANY, see *Marks*
Gerz (Simon Peter), 147, 241, 303, 339, 354
Geschützt, 227
GESCHÜTZT, 19
Gilded, see *Gold*
Girmscheid (Matthias), 241, 354
Glass, 8, 9, 12, 14, 69, 79-81, 273, 323, 354
    acid etched, 12
    coloring agents, 81
    colors, 9, 80, see also *Waldglas*
    flashed, 81
    jewels, 80
    molded, 80
    overlaid, 12, 81
    pewter overlaid, 12
    stained, 81
Glasshouse, 80
Glaze, 8, 12, 45, 227, 274, 353
    bisque, 26, 303
    cobalt, see *Stoneware, cobalt-glazed*
    colors, 26
    glass based, 148
    lead based, 25, 148
    on lithophanes, 303
    porcelain, 126
    salt, see *Saltglaze*
Goebel (W.), 354
Gold, 69, 79, 109, see also *Glass, coloring agents*
    decoration, 125, 126
GR (Georgius Rex), 26
Greek art, 12

Guilds, 8, 9, 44
Gutenberg, Johann, 267

Hafner ware, 18, 25
Hamburg, 8
Hanau, 43
Handles, 70
    attachment, 18, 27, 45, 227
    illustrated, 27
    pewter, 69, 80
Handpainted, 147, 148, 273
    identifying, 148
Hanke (Reinhold), 147, 148, 354
Hash mark, 303
Hauber & Reuther (HR), 148, 241
Hausmaler, 44, 45, 126
Hesse, 27
Hinges, 9, 15, 17, 110, 371, see also *Wood, hinge*
    origin of, 7
    pin, 17
Historicism, 69, 80, 81, 147, 185
Höhr-Grenzhausen, 27, 147, 148, 185, 241, 297
Horn, 9, 110
HR, see *Hauber & Reuther*
Hump, see *Ceramics, hand-thrown*
Hungary, 70

Incising, see *Engraved*
Inlaid clays, see *Etched, techniques*
Inlays,
    porcelain, see *Lids, porcelain inlaid*
    repairs to, 371
Ivory, 9, 109, 110

J.W. Remy, 147, 241, 354, 370
Japan, 353

Kaiser Wilhelm II, 273
Kaolin, 125, 126, see also *Clay, porcelain and pottery*
KAYSERZINN (KZ), 70
Kiln, see *Furnace*
KL (klar und lauter), see *Pewter, purity*
Köln, 26, 147, 148, also called Cologne
Kulmbach, 69
Kurt Hammer, 354

Labels, paper, 19
Labor,
    apprentice, 44
Lathework, 15, 110
Lautere, see *Pewter, purity*
Lead, 15, see also *Recipe, pewter*
Lids, 9, 15, 25, 45, 70, 80, 274, see also *Mountings*
    atypical, 371
    ceramic inlaid, 370
    cut glass inlaid, 80
    impact on price, 323, 370
    origin of, 7

out of period, 371
    porcelain inlaid, 12, 80
    silver, 44, 79
    steepled pewter, 80, 126, 323, 371
Liegl (Elisabeth), 354
Limited editions, 14, 354
Lindner Porzellan, 354
Lithophane, 12, 274, 303
Lost-wax process, 15
Low, see *Pewter, purity*

Made in Germany, 19
Map, see *Germany, map of*
Marking Law (1891), 19
Marking rule, (1884), see *Silver, marking rule*
Marks, 17, 18, 26, 227, 353
    dates, 17, 227
    faience, 46-48
    illustrated, 19-24
    pewter, 70
    porcelain, see *Crosshatch mark, hash mark, marks illustrated*
Marzi & Remy, 147, 241, 297, 354, 370
Mass-production, 12, see also *Molds*
Master stein, 9, see also *Steins, shapes illustrated*
Matthias Girmscheid, 241, 354
Meissen, 43, 125
Melon, 26, see also *Steins, shapes illustrated*
Merkelbach (Reinhold), 148, 241, 303
Merkelbach & Wick, 147, 241, 297, 303
Metal oxides, 9
    as coloring agents, 81
    as decolorizers, 81
Mettlach, 12, 225, 241, 372, see also *Villeroy & Boch*
    brewery steins, 323
    delft, 226
    etched, 226, 323
    faience, 226, 227
    marks, illustrated, 227, see also *Marks illustrated*
    print under glaze, 226, 323
    Rookwood, 226, 227
    secret formulas & techniques, 226
Mettlach Book, 370
Middle Ages, 110
Military,
    steins, 297
    glossary, see *Regimental, terminology*
Milk glass, 79
Miller Brewery, 339
Mining, see *Clay, mining*
Molds, 12, 70, 147, 226, 353
    clay, 70
    iron, 70
    metal, 70
    number, 19
    plaster, 12, 18, 70, 303
    stoneware, 70
Monasteries, as breweries, 12

Mosaic, 227
Motifs, 9, 110, see also *German flowers*
    allegorical, 12
    folk art, 12, 69, see also *Biedermeier*
    influences on, 12, see also *Greek art, Roman art, Renaissance art*
    Oriental, 43, 79, 125
Mountings, 370
    attachment, 15
    cast, 45
    illustrated, 17
    pewter, 15, 17, 79
    replacing, 371
    silver, 79, 125
    silver gilded, 125, see also *Gold*
Muffle painting, muffle bricks, muffle firing, 45, 126
Mugs, 371
    defined, 7
Munich, 323, 370
Museums,14, 27, 44, 69, 126, 371, 372
Muskau, 26
MUSTERSCHUTZ, 19, 303

Napoleon, 275
Nazi Army, 297
Neo-Classical, see *Historicism*
Neo-Renaissance, see *Historicism*
Numbers,
    incised, see *Marks*
    painted, see *Marks*
Nürnberg, 69, 110

Occupational steins, 267
Overlaid,
    glass, see *Glass, overlaid*
    pewter, see *Glass, pewter overlaid*

Painting,
    cold-, 45, 79
    durability of, 12
Patina, 17, 45, 354, 371, see also *Replacements parts, identifying*
Pewter, 7, 8, 12, 15, 17, 69-70, 273, 304, 354, see also *Patina*
    contents of, 15
    diseased, 371
    expense of, 15
    genuine, 70
    low, 70, 371
    purity, 70
    repairs, 371
Pewter Guild, see *Guilds*
    records, 17
Piercework, 80, see also *Glass, pewter overlaid*
Plaster, see *Molds, plaster*
Plate rails, 372
Plaue, 303
Pokal, 9, see also *Steins, shapes illustrated*

Polishing, 70, 371
    gilding to avoid, 109
Pontil, 80
Porcelain, 12, 14, 18, 125, 126, 273, 303, 304, 353, 372
    Chinese, 9, 43
    substitutes, see *Faience, milk glass*
Porcellaine, see *Faience*
Porzellanmanufaktur Plaue, 303
Post World War II, 353, see also *Limited editions, Ceramarte*
Potters' Guild, see *Guilds*
Pottery, 12, 14, 18, 147, 148, 273, 303, 304, 323
Price, 27, 81, 274, 304, 369, 370, 371
    reduction for damage, 370, 371
    retail, 369, 374
    trends, 372
    variations, 369
Print over glaze, 323
Print under glaze, 126, 226, 274, 297, 323, see also *Transfer-decorated*
Probe, Probezinn, Proved, see *Pewter, purity*
Prunts, 79
Public health laws, see *Covered container law*
Punty, see *Pontil*

Raeren, 26
Rastal, 354
Recipe, 18
    Brittania metal, 70
    crystal, 81
    faience, 45
    glass, 80
    pewter, 70
    porcelain, 126
    pottery, 148
Regimental steins, 273-275
    terminology (glossary), 275
Reichsprobe, see *Pewter, purity*
Reichswehr Army, 297
Reinhold Hanke, 147, 148, 354
Reinhold Merkelbach, 148, 241, 303
Relief, 12, 69, 109, 110, 125, 147, 226, 323
Remy (J.W.), 147, 241, 354, 370
Renaissance, 79, 80, 81, 126, 147
    art, 12, 79
Repairs, 370
    identifying, 17, 373
Replacement parts, 371
    identifying, 45
Reproductions, 14, 27, 45, 70, 81, 353
Reserves, see *Auctions, buying from*
Reservist, see *Regimental*
Reverse painting, see *Chromolith, theories*
Rhineland, 25
Ribs, see *Ceramics, hand-thrown*
Rigaree, 80
Ringer, Franz, 148
Roman art, 12

Roman Catholic Church, 8, 9
Rorken, 70, see also *Steins, shapes illustrated*
Rosters, 274

Sachs, Hans, 267
Sahm, 354
Saltglaze, 8, 12, 26, 303
Saxony, 69
Scandinavia, 9, 69, 110
Schierholz & Söhn, 303, 354
Schlesien, 70
Schrezheim, 45
Scraper, see *Ceramics, hand-thrown*
Seams, see *Molds*
Selling steins, 374
Sick, 70
Siegburg, 26, 147
Simon Peter Gerz, 147, 241, 303, 339, 354
Silicic acid, see *Recipe, glass*
Silk-screened, see *Decals, silk-screened*
Silver, 8, 9, 12, 69, 109, 125
    and copper alloys, 109
    lids, see *Lids, silver*
    marking rule, 109
    purity, 109
Slip molding, 18, 303
Slurry, see *Ceramics, hand-thrown*
Spinmarks, see *Lathework*
Stahl (Albert & Co.), 354
Stained glass, 81
Steinau, 27
Steingut, 18, 148, see also *Pottery*
Steins,
    brewery, see *Brewery steins*
    buying, see *Collecting strategies*
    caring for, 70, 81, 373
    see *Chip-carving, motifs, prunts, rigaree, zigzag*
    defined, 7
    factories, 43, 44, 303, 354
    materials, 9, 12, 15, 18, 79, see also *Earthenware,
    faience, glass, gold, Hafner ware, horn, ivory, pewter,
    porcelain, pottery, silver, stoneware, wood*
    military, see *Military steins*
    occupational, see *Occupational steins*
    post World War II, see *Post World War II steins*
    regional characteristics, 9
    Renaissance, 372
    Selling, see *Selling steins*
    shapes, 9, 12, 25, 26, 44, 45, 70, 79-81, 109, 110,
    126, 147, see also *Baluster, Birnkrug, Character
    steins, Enghalskrug, Melon, Walzenkrug*
    shapes, illustrated, 10, 11
Steinzeug, see *Stoneware*
Steinzeugkrug, see *Steins, defined*
Steinzeugwerke, 241, see also *Reinhold Merkelbach,
    Simon Peter Gerz, Marzi & Remy*
St. Louis, 323

St. Louis Silver Co., 110
Stone, 110
Stoneware, 8, 9, 12, 14, 18, 25-27, 69, 125, 147, 148, 273,
    297, 303, 304, 323, 339, 372
    cobalt-glazed, 147
    identifying reproductions, 27
Storage, see *Damage, preventing*
Strap, 370, see also *Mountings*
Stroh, 339
Switzerland, 69, 70
Symbols, see *Marks*

Tankard, see *Steins, defined*
Temperature,
    firing, see *Firing, temperature*
    melting metals, 15
Thewalt (A.J.), 148, 241, 353, 354
Thumblifts, 16, 17, 274, 371, see also *Mountings*
    shapes, 16, 110
    shapes, illustrated, 16
Thumbpieces, see *Thumblifts*
Thüringen, 69, 303
Tin, 15, see also *Recipe, pewter*
Touchmarks, see *Marks, pewter*
Transfer-decorated, 126, 148, 227, 273, 297, 323, 370
Transporting, see *Damage, preventing*
Tschirnhaus, Ehrenfried (Walter), von, 43, 125

Veterans' organization, 297
Villeroy & Boch (V&B), 225, 226, 241, 303, 323, 353,
    see also *Mettlach*
    marks, see *Marks, illustrated*
Vitrification, 8, see also Clay

W. Corzelius, 354
W. Goebel, 354
Waldenburg, 26
Waldglas, 9
Walzenkrug, 44, 69, 80, 109, 125
WEST GERMANY, see *Marks*
Westerwald, 12, 25, 26, 27, 297
Westerwald Team, 354
White gold, 26, 43, see also *Clay, stoneware*
Wick-Werke, 297, 354
Wood, 8, 9, 69, 109, 110, see also *Daubenkrug*
    hinge, 9, 110
    pewter inlaid, see *Daubenkrug*
World War I, 297, 353
    impact on stein production, 14
Wrigglework, 69
Würfel & Müller (King), 354

X, see *Pewter, purity*

Zigzag, 26, 69
Zoeller & Born, 354

Glentiques, Ltd.
P.O. Box 8807
Coral Springs, FL 33075

Phone: 954 - 344 - 9856
FAX: 954 - 344 - 4421

We sell books about beer steins.

Please ask for our current brochure.

Gary Kirsner Auctions
P.O. Box 8807
Coral Springs, FL 33075

Phone: 954 - 344 - 9856
FAX: 954 - 344 - 4421

Beer Stein Auctions, six times each year.

Please ask for our auction brochure.